WINGATE JUNIOR COLLEGE

Ewing Galloway

THE ACROPOLIS.

A DAY IN OLD ATHENS

A PICTURE OF ATHENIAN LIFE

BY

WILLIAM STEARNS DAVIS

PROFESSOR OF ANCIENT HISTORY IN THE
UNIVERSITY OF MINNESOTA

———o◦◙◦o———

1947

ALLYN AND BACON

BOSTON   NEW YORK   CHICAGO
ATLANTA   SAN FRANCISCO   DALLAS

WINGATE JUNIOR COLLEGE

2790

COPYRIGHT, 1914, BY

WILLIAM STEARNS DAVIS.

IEP

Norwood Press
J. S. Cushing Co. — Berwick & Smith Co.
Norwood, Mass., U.S.A.

PREFACE.

THIS little book tries to describe what an intelligent person would see and hear in ancient Athens, if by some legerdemain he were translated to the fourth century B.C. and conducted about the city under competent guidance. Rare happenings have been omitted and sometimes, to avoid long explanations, *probable* matters have been stated as if they were ascertained facts; but these instances are few, and it is hoped no reader will be led into serious error.

The year 360 B.C. has been selected for the hypothetical time of this visit, not because of any special virtue in that date, but because Athens was then architecturally almost perfect, her civic and her social life seemed at their best, the democratic constitution held its vigor, and there were few outward signs of the general decadence which was to set in after the triumph of Macedon.

I have endeavored to state no facts and to make no allusions, that will not be fairly obvious to a reader who has merely an elementary knowledge of Greek annals, such information, for instance, as may be gained through a good secondary school history of ancient times. This naturally has led to comments and descriptions which more advanced students may find superfluous.

The writer has been under a heavy debt to the numerous and excellent works on Greek "Private Antiquities" and "Public Life" written in English, French, or German, as well as to the various great Classical Encyclopædias and Dictionaries, and to many treatises and monographs upon the topography of Athens and upon the numerous phases of Attic culture. It is proper to say, however, that the material from such secondary sources has been merely supplementary to a careful examination of the ancient Greek writers, with the objects of this book kept especially in view. A sojourn in modern Athens, also, has given me an impression of the influence of the Attic landscape upon the conditions of old Athenian life, an impression that I have tried to convey in this small volume.

I am deeply grateful to my sister, Mrs. Fannie Davis Gifford, for helpful criticism of this book while in manuscript; to my wife, for preparing the drawings from Greek vase-paintings which appear as illustrations; and to my friend and colleague, Professor Charles A. Savage, for a kind and careful reading of the proofs. Thanks also are due to Henry Holt and Company for permission to quote material from their edition of Von Falke's "Greece and Rome."

W. S. D.

UNIVERSITY OF MINNESOTA,
MINNEAPOLIS, MINNESOTA.
May, 1914.

CONTENTS.

v

Contents

Contents

Chapter XIII. The Armed Forces of Athens.

Chapter XIV. The Peiræus and the Shipping.

Contents

Chapter XV. An Athenian Court Trial.

Chapter XVI. The Ecclesia of Athens.

Chapter XVII. The Afternoon at the Gymnasia.

Chapter XX. The Temples and Gods of Athens.

Chapter XXI. The Great Festivals of Athens.

MAPS, PLANS, AND ILLUSTRATIONS.

A Day in Old Athens

A DAY IN OLD ATHENS.

CHAPTER I.

THE PHYSICAL SETTING OF ATHENS.

1. The Importance of Athens in Greek History. — To three ancient nations the men of the twentieth century owe an incalculable debt. To the Jews we owe most of our notions of religion; to the Romans we owe traditions and examples in law, administration, and the general management of human affairs which still keep their influence and value; and finally, to the Greeks we owe nearly all our ideas as to the fundamentals of art, literature, and philosophy, in fact, of almost the whole of our intellectual life. These Greeks, however, our histories promptly teach us, did not form a single united nation. They lived in many "city-states" of more or less importance, and some of the largest of these contributed very little directly to our civilization. Sparta, for example, has left us some noble lessons in simple living and devoted patriotism, but hardly a single great poet, and certainly never a philosopher or a sculptor. When we examine closely, we see that the civilized life of Greece, during the centuries when she was accomplishing the most, was peculiarly centered at Athens. Without Athens, Greek history would lose three quarters of its significance, and modern life and thought would become infinitely the poorer.

2. Why the Social Life of Athens is so Significant. — Because, then, the contributions of Athens to our own life are so important, because they touch (as a Greek would say) upon almost every side of "the true, the beautiful, and the good," it is obvious that the outward conditions under which this Athenian genius developed deserve our respectful attention. For assuredly such personages as Sophocles, Plato, and Phidias were not isolated creatures, who developed their genius apart from, or in spite of, the life about them, but rather were the ripe products of a society, which in its excellences and weaknesses presents some of the most interesting pictures and examples in the world. To understand the Athenian civilization and genius it is not enough to know the outward history of the times, the wars, the laws, and the lawmakers. We must see Athens as the average man saw it and lived in it from day to day, and *then* perhaps we can partially understand how it was that during the brief but wonderful era of Athenian freedom and prosperity,[1] Athens was able to produce so many men of commanding genius as to win for her a place in the history of civilization which she can never lose.

3. The Small Size and Sterility of Attica. — Attica was a very small country according to modern notions, and Ath the only large city therein. The land barely covered s 700 square miles, with 40 square miles more, if on cludes the dependent island of Salamis. It was th ar smaller than the smallest of our American "states" (de Island = 1250 square miles), and was not so large a any American counties. It was really a triangle of roc hill-scarred land thrust out into the Ægean Sea, as if ere a sort of continuation of the more level district of eotia. Yet small as it was, the hills inclosing it to th st, the seas pressing it from the northeast and south ve it a unity and isolation all its own. Attica was not an island;

[1] That era may be assumed to begin with the battle of Marathon (490 B.C.), and it certainly ended in 322 B.C., when Athens passed decisively under the power of Macedonia; although since the battle of Chæroneia (338 B.C.) she had done little more than keep her liberty on sufferance.

but it could be invaded only by sea, or by forcing the
resistance which could be offered at the steep mountain
passes towards Bœotia or Megara. Attica was thus distinctly separated from the rest of Greece. Legends told
how, when the half-savage Dorians had forced themselves
southward over the mainland, they had never penetrated

SKETCH MAP OF
ATTICA

SCALE OF MILES

into Attica; and the Athenians later prided themselves
upon being no colonists from afar, but upon being "earth-
sprung,"—natives of the soil which they and their twenty-
times grandfathers had held before them.

This triangle of Attica had its peculiar shortcomings and
virtues. It was for the most part stony and unfertile.
Only a shallow layer of good soil covered a part of its hard
foundation rock, which often in turn lay bare on the sur-

face. The Athenian farmer had a sturdy struggle to win a
scanty crop, and about the only products he could ever raise
in abundance for export were olives (which seemed to thrive
on scanty soil and scanty rainfall) and honey, the work of
the mountain bees.

4. The Physical Beauty of Attica. — Yet Attica had advantages which more than counterbalanced this grudging of
fertility. All Greece, to be sure, was favored by the natural beauty of its atmosphere, seas, and mountains, but Attica
was perhaps the most favored portion of all. Around her
coasts, rocky often and broken by pebbly beaches and little
craggy peninsulas, surged the deep blue Ægean, the most
glorious expanse of ocean in the world. Far away spread the
azure water,[1] — often foam-crested and sometimes alive with
the dolphins leaping at their play, — reaching towards a
shimmering sky line where rose "the isles of Greece,"
masses of green foliage, or else of tawny rock, scattered
afar, to adapt the words of Homer, "like shields laid on
the face of the glancing deep."

Above the sea spread the noble arch of the heavens, — the
atmosphere often dazzlingly bright, and carrying its glamour
and sparkle almost into the hearts of men. The Athenians
were proud of the air about their land. Their poets gladly
sung its praises, as, for example, Euripides,[2] when he tells
how his fellow countrymen enjoy being —

> Ever through air clear shining brightly
> As on wings uplifted, pacing lightly.

5. The Mountains of Attica. — The third great element,
besides the sea and the atmosphere of Athens, was the
mountains. One after another the bold hills reared them-

---

[1] The peculiar blueness of the water near Attica is probably caused by
the clear rocky bottom of the sea, as well as by the intensity of the sunlight.   [2] *Medea:* 829.

selves, cutting short all the plainlands and making the
farmsteads often a matter of slopes and terraces. Against
the radiant heavens these mountains stood out boldly,
clearly ; revealing all the little gashes and seams left from
that long-forgotten day when they were flung forth from the
bowels of the earth. None of these mountains was very
high : Hymettus, the greatest, was only about 3500 feet;
but rising as they often did from a close proximity to the
sea, and not from a dwarfing table-land, even the lower hills
uplifted themselves with proud majesty.

These hills were of innumerable tints according to their
rocks, the hue of the neighboring sea, and the hour of the
day. In spring they would be clothed in verdant green,
which would vanish before the summer heats, leaving them
rosy brown or gray. But whatever the fundamental tone,
it was always brilliant; for the Athenians lived in a land
where blue sky, blue sea, and the massive rock blent together into such a galaxy of shifting color, that, in comparison, the lighting of almost any northern or western
landscape would seem feeble and tame. The Athenians
absorbed natural beauty with their native air.

6. The Sunlight in Athens. — The Athenian loved sunshine, and Helios the Sun God was gracious to his prayers.
In the Athens of to-day it is reckoned that the year averages
179 days in which the sun is not concealed by clouds one
instant; and 157 days more when the sun is not hidden
more than half an hour.[1] Ancient Athens was surely not
more cloudy. Nevertheless, despite this constant sunshine
and a southern latitude, Athens was striken relatively seldom with semitropical heat. The sea was a good friend,

[1] The reason for these many clear days is probably because when the
moist west and southwest winds come in contact with the dry, heated
air of the Attic plain, they are at once volatilized and dispersed, not
condensed (as in northern lands) ; therefore the day resolves itself into
brilliant sunshine.

bringing tempering breezes.   In the short winter there might
be a little frost, a little snow, and a fair supply of rain.   For
the rest of the year, one golden day was wont to succeed another, with the sun and the sea breeze in ever friendly rivalry.

The climate saved the Athenians from being obliged to
wage a stern warfare with nature as did the northern peoples.
Their life and civilization could be one developed essentially
" in the open air " ; while, on the other hand, the bracing
sea breeze saved them from that enervating lethargy which
has ruined so many southern folk.   The scanty soil
forced them to struggle hard to win a living ; unless they
yielded to the constant beckoning of the ocean, and
sought food, adventure, wealth, and a great empire across
the seas.

7. The Topography of the City of Athens. — So much for
the land of Attica in general ; but what of the setting of the
city of Athens itself?   The city lay in a plain, somewhat
in the south central part of Attica, and about four miles
back from the sea.   A number of mountains came together
to form an irregular rectangle with the Saronic Gulf upon
the south.   To the east of Athens stretched the long gnarled
ridge of Hymettus, the wildest and grayest mountain in
Attica, the home of bees and goatherds, and (if there be
faith in pious legend) of innumerable nymphs and satyrs.
To the west ran the lower, browner mountains, Ægaleos,
across which a road (the " Sacred Way ") wound through an
easy pass towards Eleusis, the only sizable town in Attica,
outside of Athens and its harbors.   To the rear of the plain
rose a noble pyramid, less jagged than Hymettus, more
lordly than Ægaleos ; its summits were fretted with a white
which turned to clear rose color under the sunset.   This
was Pentelicus, from the veins whereof came the lustrous
marble for the master sculptor.   Closer at hand, nearer the
center of the plain, rose a small and very isolated hill, —

Lycabettus, whose peaked summit looked down upon the roofs
of Athens.   And last, but never least, about one mile southwest of Lycabettus, upreared a natural monument of much
greater fame, — not a hill, but a colossal rock.   Its shape
was that of an irregular oval; it was about 1000 feet long,
500 feet wide, and its level summit stood 350 feet above the

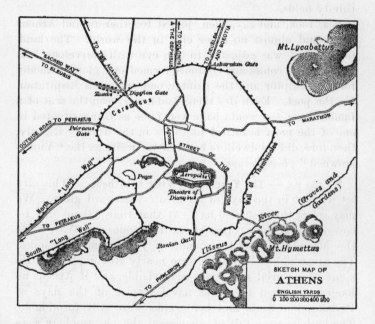

plain.   This steep, tawny rock, flung by the Titans, one might
dream, into the midst of the Attic plain, formed one of the
most famous sites in the world, for it was the Acropolis of
Athens.   Its full significance, however, must be explained
later.   From the Acropolis and a few lesser hills close by,
the land sloped gently down towards the harbors and the
Saronic Bay.

These were the great features of the outward setting of

Athens. One might add to them the long belt of dark green olive groves winding down the westward side of the plain, where the Cephisus (which alone among Attic rivulets did not run dry in summer) ran down to the sea. There was also a shorter olive belt west of the city, where the weaker Ilissus crept, before it lost itself amid the thirsty fields.

Sea, rock, and sky, then, joined together around Athens as around almost no other city in the world. The landscape itself was adjusted to the eye with marvelous harmony. The colors and contours formed one glorious model for the sculptor and the painter, one perpetual inspiration for the poet. Even if Athens had never been the seat of a famous race, she would have won fame as being situated in one of the most beautiful localities in the world. Rightly, therefore, did its dwellers boast of their city as the "Violet-crowned" (*Iostephanos*).

8. 360 B.C. — The Year of the Visit to Athens. — This city let us visit in the days of its greatest outward glory. We may select the year 360 B.C. At that time Athens had recovered from the ravages of the Peloponnesian War, while the Macedonian peril had not as yet become menacing. The great public buildings were nearly all completed. No signs of material decadence were visible, and if Athens no longer possessed the wide naval empire of the days of Pericles, her fleets and her armies were still formidable. The harbors were full of commerce; the philosophers were teaching their pupils in the groves and porticoes; the democratic constitution was entirely intact. With intelligent vision we will enter the city and look about us.

CHAPTER II.

THE FIRST SIGHTS IN ATHENS.

9. The Morning Crowds bound for Athens. — It is very early in the morning. The sun has just pushed above the long ridge of Hymettus, sending a slanting red bar of light across the Attic plain, and touching the opposite slopes of Ægaleos with livid fire. Already, however, life is stirring outside the city. Long since, little market boats have rowed across the narrow strait from Salamis, bringing the island farmers' produce, and other farmers from the plain and the mountain slopes have started for market. In the ruddy light the marble temples on the lofty Acropolis rising ahead of these hurrying rustics are standing out clearly; the spear and helmet of the great brazen statue of the Athena Promachos are flashing from the noble citadel, as a kind of day beacon, beckoning onward toward the city. From the Peiræus, the harbor town, a confused hum of mariners lading and unlading the vessels is even now rising, but we cannot turn ourselves thither. Our route is to follow the farmers bound for market.

The most direct road from the Peiræus to Athens is hidden indeed, for it leads between the towering ramparts of the "Long Walls," two mighty barriers which run parallel almost four miles from the inland city to the harbor, giving a guarded passage in wartime and making Athens safe against starvation from any land blockade; but there is an outside road leading also to Athens from the western farmsteads, and this we can conveniently follow. Upon this

9

route the crowd which one meets is certainly not aristocratic, but it is none the less Athenian.   Here goes a drover,
clad in skins, his legs wound with woolen bands in lieu of
stockings ; before him and his wolf-like dog shambles a flock
of black sheep or less man-
ageable goats, bleating and
baaing as they are pro-
pelled toward market.
After him there may come
an unkempt, long-bearded
farmer flogging on a pack
ass or a mule attached to
a clumsy cart with solid
wheels, and laden with all
kinds of market produce.
The roadway, be it said, is
not good, and all carters
have their troubles; therefore, there is a deal of gesticulating and profane in-

PEASANT GOING TO MARKET.

vocation of Hermes and all other gods of traffic ; for, early
as it is, the market place is already filling, and every delay
promises a loss.   There are still other companies bound
toward the city : countrymen bearing cages of poultry ;
others engaged in the uncertain calling of driving pigs ;
swarthy Oriental sailors, with rings in their ears, bearing
bales of Phœnician goods from the Peiræus ; respectable
country gentlemen, walking gravely in their best white
mantles and striving to avoid the mud and contamination ;
and perhaps also a small company of soldiers, just back
from foreign service, passes, clattering shields and spear
staves.

   10. The Gate and the Street Scenes. — The crowds grow
denser as everybody approaches the frequented " Peiræus

Gate," for nearly all of Attica which lies within easy reach of Athens has business in the Market Place every morning. On passing the gate a fairly straight way leads through the city to the market, but progress for the multitude becomes slow. If it is one of the main thoroughfares, it is now very likely to be almost blocked with people. There are few late risers at Athens; the Council of Five Hundred,[1] the huge Jury Courts, and the Public Assembly (if it has met to-day [2]) are appointed to gather at sunrise. The plays in the theater, which, however, are given only on certain festivals, begin likewise at sunrise. The philosophers say that "the man who would accomplish great things must be up while yet it is dark." Athenians, therefore, are always awake and stirring at an hour when men of later ages and more cold and foggy climes will be painfully yawning ere getting out of bed.

AT THE STREET FOUNTAIN.

The Market Place attracts the great masses, but by no means all; hither and thither bevies of sturdy slave girls, carrying graceful pitchers on their heads, are hurrying towards the fountains which gush cool water at most of the street corners. Theirs is a highly necessary task, for few or no houses

---

[1] The "Boule," the great standing committee of the Athenian people to aid the magistrates in the government.

[2] In which case, of course, the regular courts and the Council would hardly meet.

have their own water supply; and around each fountain
one can see half a dozen by no means slatternly maidens, splashing and flirting the water one at another,
while they wait their turn with the pitchers, and laugh
and exchange banter with the passing farmers' lads.
Many in the street crowds are rosy-cheeked schoolboys,
walking decorously, if they are lads of good breeding, and
blushing modestly when they are greeted by their fathers'
acquaintances. They do not loiter on the way. Close
behind, carrying their writing tablets, follow the faithful
'pedagogues,' the body-servants appointed to conduct them
to school, give them informal instruction, and, if need be,
correct their faults in no painless manner. Besides the
water maids and the schoolboys, from the innumerable
house doors now opening the respective masters are step-
ping forth — followed by one, two, or several serving varlets,
as many as their wealth affords. All these join in the crowd
entering from the country. "Athenian democracy" always
implies a goodly amount of hustling and pushing. No
wonder the ways are a busy sight!

11. The Streets and House Fronts of Athens. — Progress
is slower near the Market Place because of the extreme
narrowness of the streets. They are only fifteen feet wide
or even less, — intolerable alleys a later age would call
them, — and dirty to boot. Sometimes they are muddy,
more often extremely dusty. Worse still, they are con-
taminated by great accumulations of filth; for the city is
without an efficient sewer system or regular scavengers.
Even as the crowd elbows along, a house door will frequently
open, an ill-favored slave boy show his head, and with the
yell, "Out of the way!" slap a bucket of dirty water into
the street. There are many things to offend the nose as
well as the eyes of men of a later race. It is fortunate indeed that the Athenians are otherwise a healthy folk, or

they would seem liable to perpetual pestilence; even so, great plagues have in past years harried the city.[1]

The first entrance to Athens will thus bring to a stranger, full of the city's fame and expectant of meeting objects of beauty at every turn, almost instant disappointment. The narrow, dirty, ill-paved streets are also very crooked. One can readily be lost in a labyrinth of filthy little lanes the moment one quits the few main thoroughfares. High over head, to be sure, the red crags of the Acropolis may be towering, crowned with the red, gold, and white tinted marble of the temples, but all around seems only monotonous squalor. The houses seem one continuous series of blank walls; mostly of one, occasionally of two stories, and with flat roofs. These walls are usually spread over with some dirty gray or perhaps yellow stucco. For most houses, the only break in the street walls are the simple doors, all jealously barred and admitting no glance within. There are usually no street windows, if the house is only one story high. If it has two stories, a few narrow slits above the way may hint that here are the apartments for the slaves or women. There are no street numbers. There are often no street names. "So-and-so lives in such-and-such a quarter, near the Temple of Heracles;" that will enable you to find a householder, after a few tactful questions from the neighbors; and after all, Athens is a relatively small city [2] (as great cities are reckoned), very

[1] The most fearful thereof was the great plague of 430 B.C. (during the Peloponnesian War), which nearly ruined Athens.

[2] Every guess at the population of Athens rests on mere conjecture; yet, using the scanty data which we possess, it seems possible that *the population of all Attica* at the height of its prosperity was about *200,000 free persons* (including the *metics* — resident foreigners without citizenship); and a rather smaller number of slaves — say 150,000 or less. Of this total of some 350,000, probably something under one half resided in the city of Athens during times of peace, the rest in the outlying farms and villages. *Athens may be imagined as a city of about 150,000* — possibly a

closely built, and her regular denizens do not feel the need of a directory.

So the crowd elbows its way onward: now thinning, now gaining, but the main stream always working towards the Market Place.

12. The Simplicity of Athenian Life. — It is clear we are entering a city where nine tenths of what the twentieth century will consider the "essential conveniences" of life are entirely lacking; where men are trying to be civilized — or, as the Greeks would say, to lay hold upon "the true, the beautiful, and the good," without even the absolute minimum of those things which people of a later age will believe separate a "civilized man" from a "barbarian." The gulf between old Athens and, for instance, new Chicago, is greater than is readily supposed.[1] It is easy enough to say that the Athenians lacked such things as railways, telephones, gas, grapefruit, and cocktails. All such matters we realize were not known by our fathers and grandfathers, and we are not yet so removed from *them* that we cannot transport ourselves in imagination back to the world of say 1820 A.D.; but the Athenians are far behind even our grandfathers. When we investigate, we will find conditions like these — houses absolutely without plumbing, beds without sheets, rooms as hot or as cold as the outer air, only far more drafty. We must cross rivers without bridges; we must fasten on our clothes (or rather our "two pieces of cloth") with two pins instead of with a row of buttons; we must wear sandals without stockings (or go barefoot); must warm ourselves over a pot of ashes; judge plays or lawsuits on a cold winter morning sitting in the open air; we must

trifle more. During serious wars there would be of course a general removal into the city.

[1] See the very significant comment on the physical limitations of the old Athenian life in Zimmern's *The Greek Commonwealth*, p. 209.

study poetry with very little aid from books, geography without real maps, and politics without newspapers; and lastly," we must learn how to be civilized without being comfortable ! " [1]

Or, to reverse the case : we must understand that an Athenian would have pronounced our boasted "civilization" hopelessly artificial, and our life so dependent on outward material props and factors as to be scarcely worth the living. He would declare himself well able to live happily under conditions where the average American or Englishman would be cold, semi-starved, and miserable. He would declare that *his* woe or happiness was retained far under his own control than we retain ours, and that worthy of contemptuous pity rather than of a because we have refined our civilization to that the least accident, *e.g.* the suspension of for a few days, can reduce a modern city to ness.

Probably neither the twentieth century the fourth century B.C. in its contempt, truth upon its side.[2] The difference in must still stand. Preëminently Athen "City of the Simple Life." Bearing may follow the multitude and enter the use the name that stamps it as a tion, — the Agora.

[1] Zimmern, *ibid.*

[2] The mere matter of *climate* wo serious factor. The Athenian woul nitely more complex along the m *kalos-k'agathos* — *i.e.* a "noble a land where the thermometer even lower) from time to tim

CHAPTER III.

THE AGORA AND ITS DENIZENS.

13. The Buildings around the Agora. — Full market time![1]
...he great plaza of the Agora is buzzing with life.   The con-
... between the dingy, dirty streets and this magnificent
...laza is startling.   The Athenians manifestly care
...merely private display, rather they frown upon
...alth, patriotism, and best artistic energy seem
...pon their civic establishments and buildings.
...s a square of spacious dimensions, planted
...vith graceful bay trees.   Its greatest length
...south.   Ignoring for the time the teeming
...umanity, let our eyes be directed merely
... buildings.   The place is almost com-
...hem, although not all are of equal ele-
...Some are temples of more or less size,
..."Paternal Apollo" near the south-
...Metroön," the fane of Cybele "the
...s," upon the south.   Others are
...mewhat behind the Metroön rise
...Council House, where the Five
... the policy of Athens; and
..."Round House," with a
...eath which the sacred
...ing, and where the pre-
...nd certain high officials

take their meals, and a good deal of state business is transacted. The majority of these buildings upon the Agora,
however, are covered promenades, porticoes, or stoæ.

The stoæ are combinations of rain shelters, shops, picture galleries, and public offices. Turn under the pillars of
the "Royal Stoa" upon the west, and you are among a
whispering, nudging, intent crowd of listeners, pushing
against the barriers of a low court. Long rows of jurors
are sitting on their benches; the "King Archon" is on the
president's stand, and some poor
wight is being arraigned on a
charge of "Impiety".[1]; while
on the walls behind stand graved
the ancient laws of Draco and
Solon.

Cross the square, and on the
opposite side is one of the most
magnificent of the porticoes, the
"Painted Porch" (*Stoa Poikilē*),
a long covered walk, a delightful
refuge alike from sun and rain.
Almost the entire length of the
inner walls (for it has columns
only on the side of the Agora)

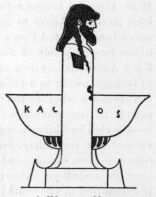

A WAYSIDE HERM.

is covered with vivid frescoes. Here Polygnotus and other
master painters have spread out the whole legendary story
of the capture of Troy and of the defeat of the Amazons;
likewise the more historical tale of the battle of Marathon.
Yet another promenade, the "Stoa of Zeus," is sacred to
Zeus, Giver of Freedom. The walls are not frescoed, but
hung with the shields of valiant Athenian warriors.

In the open spaces of the plaza itself are various altars,
e.g. to the "Twelve Gods," and innumerable statues of local

[1] The so-called " King Archon " had special cognizance of most cases
involving religious questions; and his court was in this stoa.

worthies, as of Harmodius and Aristogeiton, the tyrant-slayers; while across the center, cutting the Market Place from east to west, runs a line of stone posts, each surmounted with a rude bearded head of Hermes, the trader's god; and each with its base plastered many times over with all kinds of official and private placards and notices.

14. The Life in the Agora. — So much for the physical setting of the Agora: of far greater interest surely are the people. The whole square is abounding with noisy activity. If an Athenian has no actual business to transact, he will at least go to the Agora to get the morning news. Two turns under the " Painted Porch " will tell him the last rumor as to the foreign policy of Thebes: whether it is true that old King Agesilaus has died at Sparta; whether corn is likely to be high, owing to a failure of crops in the Euxine (Black Sea) region; whether the " Great King " of Persia is prospering in his campaign against Egypt. The crowd is mostly clad in white, though often the cloaks of the humbler visitors are very dirty, but there is a sprinkling of gay colors, — blue, orange, and pink. Everybody is talking at once in melodious Attic; everybody (since they are all true children of the south) is gesticulating at once. To the babel of human voices is added the wheezing whistle of donkeys, the squealing of pigs, the cackle of poultry. Besides, from many of the little factories and workshops on or near the Agora a great din is rising. The clamor is prodigious. Criers are stalking up and down the square, one bawling out that Andocides has lost a valuable ring and will pay well to recover it; another that Pheidon has a desirable horse that he will sell cheap. One must stand still for some moments and let eye and ear accustom themselves to such utter confusion.

15. The Booths and Shops in the Agora. — At length out of the chaos there seems to emerge a certain order.

The major part of the square is covered with little booths of boards and wicker work, very frail and able to be folded up, probably every night. There are little lanes winding amid these booths; and each manner of huckster has its own especial "circle" or section of the market. "Go to the wine," "to the fish," "to the myrtles" (*i.e.* the flowers), are common directions for finding difficult parts of the Agora. Trade is mostly on a small scale, — the stock of each vender is distinctly limited in its range, and Athens is without "department stores." Behind each low counter, laden with its wares, stands the proprietor, who keeps up a din from leathern lungs: "Buy my oil!" "Buy charcoal!" "Buy sausage!" etc., until he is temporarily silenced while dealing with a customer.

A CARPENTER.

In one "circle" may be found onions and garlic (a favorite food of the poor); a little further on are the dealers in wine, fruit, and garden produce. Lentils and peas can be had either raw, or cooked and ready to eat on the spot. An important center is the bread market. The huge cylindrical loaves are handed out by shrewd old women with proverbially long tongues. Whosoever upsets one of their delicately balanced piles of loaves is certain of an artistic tongue lashing. Elsewhere there is a pottery market, a clothes market, and, nearer the edge of the Agora, are "circles," where objects of real value are sold, like jewelry, chariots, good furniture. In certain sections, too, may be seen strong-voiced individuals, with little trays swung by straps before them, pacing to and fro, and calling out, not foods, but medicines, infallible cure-alls for every human distemper. Many are the unwary fools who patronize them.

16. The Flower and the Fish Venders. — Two circles attract especial attention, the Myrtles and the Fish. Flowers and foliage, especially when made up into garlands, are absolutely indispensable to the average Greek. Has he a great family festival, *e.g.* the birth of a son, then every guest should wear a crown of olives; is it a wedding, then one of flowers.[1] Oak-leaves do the honors for Zeus; laurel for Apollo; myrtle for Aphrodite (and is not the Love-Goddess the favorite?). To have a social gathering without garlands, in short, is impossible. The flower girls of Athens are beautiful, impudent, and not at all prudish. Around their booths press bold-tongued youths, and not too discreet sires; and the girls can call everybody familiarly by name. Very possibly along with the sale of the garlands they make arrangements (if the banquet is to be of the less respectable kind) to be present in the evening themselves, perhaps in the capacity of flute girls.

More reputable, though not less noisy, is the fish market. Athenians boast themselves of being no hearty "meat eaters" like their Bœotian neighbors, but of preferring the more delicate fish. No dinner party is successful without a seasonable course of fish. The arrival of a fresh cargo from the harbor is announced by the clanging of a bell, which is likely to leave all the other booths deserted, while a crowd elbows around the fishmonger. He above all others com-

---

[1] The Greeks lacked many of our common flowers. Their ordinary flowers were white violets, narcissus, lilies, crocuses, blue hyacinths, and roses ("the Flower of Zeus"). The usual garland was made of myrtle or ivy, and then entwined with various flowers.

mands the greatest flow of billingsgate, and is especially
notorious for his arrogant treatment of his customers, and
for exacting the uttermost farthing. The "Fish" and the
"Myrtles" can be sure of a brisk trade on days when all
the other booth keepers around the Agora stand idle.

All this trade, of course, cannot find room in the booths
of the open Agora. Many hucksters sit on their haunches
on the level ground with their few wares spread before
them. Many more have little stands between the pillars of
the stoæ; and upon the various streets that converge on
the market there is a fringe of shops, but these are usually
of the more substantial sort. Here are the barbers' shops,
the physicians' offices (if the good leech is more than an
itinerant quack), and all sorts of little factories, such as
smithies, where the cutler's apprentices in the rear of the
shop forge the knives which the proprietor sells over the
counter, the slave repositories, and finally wine establishments of no high repute, where wine may not merely be
bought by the skin (as in the main Agora), but by the pot-
ful to be drunk on the premises.

17. The Morning Visitors to the Agora. — The first tour of
inspection completed, several facts become clear to the visitor. One is the extraordinarily large proportion of *men*
among the moving multitudes. Except for the bread
women and the flower girls, hardly one female is to be
found among the sellers. Among the purchasers there is
not a single reputable lady. No Athenian gentlewoman
dreams of frequenting the Agora. Even a poor man's wife
prefers to let her spouse do the family marketing. As for
the "men folk," the average gentleman will go daily indeed
to the Agora, but if he is really pretentious, it will be merely
to gossip and to meet his friends; a trusted servant will
attend to the regular purchasing. Only when an important
dinner party is on hand will the master take pains to order

for himself. If he does purchase in person, he will never
carry anything himself. The slaves can attend to that; and
only the slaveless (the poorest of all) must take away their
modest rations of boiled lentils, peas, beans, onions, and
garlic, usually in baskets, though yonder now is a soldier
who is bearing off a measure of boiled peas inside his helmet.

Another thing is striking. The average poor Athenian
seems to have no purse. Or rather he uses the purse provided by nature. At every booth one can see unkempt
buyers solemnly taking their small change from their
mouths.[1] Happy the people that has not learned the
twentieth century wisdom concerning microbes ! For most
Athenians seem marvelously healthy.

Still one other fact is brought home constantly. "Fixed
prices" are absolutely unknown. The slightest transaction
involves a war of bargaining. Wits are matched against
wits, and only after a vast deal of wind do buyer and seller
reach a fair compromise. All this makes retail trade in
the Agora an excellent school for public affairs or litigation.

*   *   *   *   *   *   *

18. The Leisured Class in Athens. — Evidently Athens,
more than many later-day cities, draws clear lines between
the workers and the "gentlemen of leisure." There is no
distinction of dress between the numerous slaves and the
humbler free workers and traders; but there is obvious distinction between the artisan of bent shoulders who shambles out of yonder pungent tannery, with his scant garments
girded around him, and the graceful gentleman of easy gestures and flowing drapery who moves towards the Tholos.
There is great *political* democracy in Athens, but not so
much *social* democracy. "Leisure," *i.e.* exemption from

---

[1] A wealthier purchaser would, of course, have his own pouch, or more
probably one carried for him by a slave.

every kind of sordid, money-getting, hard work, is counted the true essential for a respectable existence, and to live on the efforts of others and to devote oneself to public service or to letters and philosophy is the open satisfaction or the private longing of every Athenian.

A great proportion of these, therefore, who frequent the Agora are not here on practical business, unless they have official duties at the government offices.[1] But in no city of any age has the gracious art of doing nothing been brought to such perfection. The Athenians are an intensely gregarious people. Everybody knows everybody else. Says an orator, "It is impossible for a man to be either a rascal or an honest man in this city without your all knowing it." Few men walk long alone; if they do keep their own company, they are frowned on as "misanthropes." The morning visit to the Agora "to tell or to hear some new thing"[2] will be followed by equally delightful idling and conversation later in the day at the Gymnasia, and later still, probably, at the dinner-party. Easy and unconventional are the personal greetings. A little shaking out of the mantle, an indescribable flourish with the hands. A free Greek will despise himself for "bowing," even to the Great King. To clasp hands implies exchanging a pledge, something far more than mere salutation.

"*Chaire*, Aristomenes!"

"*Chaire*, Cleandros!"

Such is the usual greeting, using an expressive word which can mean equally well "hail!" and "farewell!"

19. Familiar Types around the Agora. — These animated, eager-faced men whose mantles fall in statuesque folds prefer obviously to walk under the Painted Porch, or the blue

---

[1] To serve the state in any official capacity (usually without any salary attached to the office) would give the highest satisfaction to any Greek. The desire for participation in public affairs might be described as a mania.   [2] Acts of the Apostles, 17:21.

roof of heaven, while they evolve their philosophies, mature
their political schemes, or organize the material for their
orations and dramas, rather than to bend over desks within
close offices. Around the Athenian Agora, a true type of
this preference, and busy with this delightful idleness,
half a century earlier could have been seen a droll figure with
"indescribable nose, bald head, round body, eyes rolling and
twinkling with good humor," scantily clad, — an incorrigible
do-nothing, windbag, and hanger-on, a later century might assert, — yet history has given to him the name of Socrates.

Not all Athenians, of course, make such justifiable use of
their idleness. There are plenty of young men parading
about in long trailing robes, their hair oiled and curled most
effeminately, their fingers glittering with jewels, — "ring-
loaded, curly-locked coxcombs," Aristophanes, the comic poet,
has called them, — and they are here only for silly display.
Also there are many of their elders who have no philosophy
or wit to justify their continuous talking; nevertheless, all
considered, it must be admitted that the Athenians make a
use of their dearly loved "leisure," which men of a more
pragmatic race will do well to consider as the fair equivalent
of much frantic zeal for "business." Athenian "leisure"
has already given the world Pericles, Thucydides, Æschylus,
Sophocles, Euripides, Socrates, and Plato, not to name such
artists as Phidias, whose profession cannot exempt them
from a certain manual occupation.

20. The Barber Shops. — This habit of genteel idleness
naturally develops various peculiar institutions. For
example, the barber shops are almost club rooms. Few
Hellenes at this time shave their beards,[1] but to go with
unkempt whiskers and with too long hair is most disgrace-

[1] Alexander the Great (336–323 B.C.) required his soldiers to be shaved
(as giving less grasp for the enemy!), and the habit then spread generally
through the whole Hellenic world.

ful.   The barber shops, booths, or little rooms let into the
street walls of the houses, are therefore much frequented.
The good tonsors have all the usual arts.   They can dye
gray hair brown or black; they can wave or curl their patrons' locks (and an artificially curled head is no disgrace to
a man).   Especially, they keep a good supply of strong per-
fumes; for many people will want a little scent on their hair
each morning, even if they wish no other attention.   But it
is not an imposition to a barber to enter his shop, yet never
move towards his low stool before the shining steel mirror.
Anybody is welcome to hang around indefinitely, listening
to the proprietor's endless flow of talk.   He will pride himself on knowing every possible bit of news or rumor: Had
the Council resolved on a new fleet-building program?
Had the Tyrant of Syracuse's "four" the best chance in the
chariot race in the next Olympic games?   The garrulity of
barbers is already proverbial.

"How shall I cut your hair, sir?" once asked the court
tonsor of King Archelāus of Macedon.

"In silence," came the grim answer.

But the proprietor will not do all the talking.   Everybody
in the little room will join.   Wits will sharpen against wits;
and if the company is of a grave and respectable sort, the
conversation will grow brisk upon Plato's theory of the
"reality of ideas," upon Euripides's interpretation of the
relations of God to man, or upon the spiritual symbolism
of Scopas's bas-reliefs at Halicarnassus.

The barber shops by the Agora then are essential portions
of Athenian social life.   Later we shall see them supplemented by the Gymnasia; — but the Agora has detained us
long enough.   The din and crowds are lessening.   People
are beginning to stream homeward.   It lacks a little of noon
according to the "time-staff" (gnomon), a simple sun dial
which stands near one of the porticoes, and we will now
follow some Athenian gentleman towards his dwelling.

CHAPTER IV.

THE ATHENIAN HOUSE AND ITS FURNISHINGS.

21. Following an Athenian Gentleman Homeward. — Leaving the Agora and reëntering the streets the second impression of the residence districts becomes more favorable. There are a few bay trees planted from block to block; and ever and anon the monotonous house walls recede, giving space to display some temple, like the Fane of Hephæstos [1] near the Market Place, its columns and pediment flashing not merely with white marble, but with the green, scarlet, and gold wherewith the Greeks did not hesitate to decorate their statuary.

At street corners and opposite important mansions a Hermes-bust like those in the plaza rises, and a very few houses have a couple of pillars at their entrances and some outward suggestion of hidden elegance.

We observe that almost the entire crowd leaving the Agora goes on foot. To ride about in a chariot is a sign of undemocratic presumption; while only women or sick men will consent to be borne in a litter. We will select a sprucely dressed gentleman who has just been anointed in a barber's shop and accompany him to his home. He is neither one of the decidedly rich, otherwise his establishment would be exceptional, not typical, nor is he of course one of the hard-working poor. Followed by perhaps two clean and capable serving lads, he wends his way down several of the narrow lanes that lie under the northern brow

---

[1] Wrongly called the "Theseum" in modern Athens.

26

of the Acropolis.[1] Before a plain solid house door he halts
and cries *Pai! Pai!* ["Boy! Boy!"]. There is a rattle of
bolts and bars. A low-visaged foreign-born porter, whose
business it is to show a surly front to all unwelcome visitors,
opens and gives a kind of salaam to his master; while the
porter's huge dog jumps up barking and pawing joyously.

As we enter behind him (carefully advancing with right
foot foremost, for it is bad luck to tread a threshold with
the *left*) we notice above the lintel some such inscription as
"Let no evil enter here!" or "To the Good Genius," then a
few steps through a narrow passage bring us into the *Aula*,
the central court, the indispensable feature of every typical
Greek house.

22. The Type and Uses of a Greek House. — All domestic
architecture, later investigators will discover, falls into two
great categories — of the northern house and the southern
house. The northern house begins with a single large room,
"the great hall," then lesser rooms are added to it. It gets
its light from windows in the outer walls, and it is covered
by a single steep roof. The southern (Greek and Oriental)
house is a building inclosing a rectangular court. The
rooms, many or few, get their light from this court, while
they are quite shut off from the world outside. All in all,
for warm climates this style of house is far more airy, cool,
comfortable than the other. The wide open court becomes
the living room of the house save in very inclement weather.

Socrates is reported to have uttered what was probably
the average sensible view about a good house.[2] The good
house, he thought, should be cool in summer, and warm in
winter, convenient for the accommodation of the family and
its possessions. The central rooms should therefore be

---

[1] This would be a properly respectable quarter of the city, but we do not
know of any really "aristocratic residence district" in Athens.

[2] In Xenophon's *Memorabilia*, III. 8, §§ 9, 10.

lofty and should open upon the south, yet for protection in summer there should be good projecting eaves (over the court) and again the rooms on the northern exposure should be made lower. All this is mere sense, but really the average male Athenian does not care a great deal about his dwelling. He spends surprisingly little money beautifying it. Unless he is sick, he will probably be at home only for sleeping and eating. The Agora, the Public Assembly, the Jury Courts, the Gymnasium, the great religious festivals consume his entire day. " I never spend my time indoors," says Xenophon's model Athenian, " my wife is well able to run the household by herself."[1] Such being the case, even wealthy men have very simple establishments, although it is at length complained (*e.g.* by Demosthenes) that people are now building more luxurious houses, and are not content with the plain yet sufficient dwellings of the great age of Pericles.[2]

23. The Plan of a Greek House. — The plan of a Greek house naturally varies infinitely according to the size of its land plot, the size of the owner's family, his own taste, and wealth. It will usually be rectangular, with the narrower side toward the street; but this is not invariable. In the larger houses there will be two courts (*aulæ*), one behind the other, and each with its own circuit of dependent chambers. The court first entered will be the *Andronitis* (the Court of the Men), and may be even large enough to afford a considerable promenade for exercise. Around the whole of the open space run lines of simple columns, and above the opening swings an awning if the day is very hot. In the very center rises a small stone altar with a statue of Zeus the Protector (*Zeus Herkeïos*), where the father of the

---

[1] Xenophon, *Economics*, VII. 3.

[2] Very probably in such outlying Greek cities as Syracuse, Taras (Tarentum), etc., more elegant houses could be found than any at this time in Athens.

family will from time to time offer sacrifice, acting as the priest for the household. Probably already on the altar there has been laid a fresh garland; if not, the newcomers from the Agora have now fetched one.

The Andronitis is the true living room of the house: here the master will receive his visitors, here the male slaves will work, and the women also busy themselves (promptly retiring, however, on the appearance of masculine strangers). The decoration is very plain: the walls are neatly tinted with some kind of wash; the floor is of simple plaster, or, in a humbler house, common earth pounded hard.) Under the colonnade

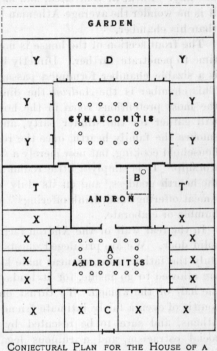

CONJECTURAL PLAN FOR THE HOUSE OF A
WEALTHY ATHENIAN.

A = Altar of Zeus Herkeios.
B = Altar of Hestia.
C = Entrance Hall.
D = Kitchen.
T = Thalamos.
T' = Anti-thalamos.
X = Rooms for the Men.
Y = Rooms for the Women.

at all four sides open the various chambers, possibly twelve in all. They really are cells or compartments rather than rooms, small and usually lighted only by their doors. Some are used for storerooms, some for sleeping closets for the male slaves and for the grown-up sons of the house, if there are any.   Dark, ill ventilated, and most scantily furnished, it is no wonder the average Athenian loves the Agora better than his chamber.

The front section of the house is now open to us, but it is time to penetrate farther.   Directly behind the open court is a sizable chamber forming a passage to the inner house.   This chamber is the *Andron*, the dining hall and probably the most pretentious room in the house.   Here the guests will gather for the dinner party, and here in one corner smokes the family hearth, once the real fire for the whole household cooking, but now merely a symbol of the domestic worship.   It is simply a little round altar sacred to Hestia, the hearth goddess,[1] and on its duly rekindled flame little "meat offerings and drink offerings" are cast at every meal, humble or elaborate.

In the rear wall of the Andron facing the Andronitis is a solid door.   We are privileged guests indeed if we pass it.   Only the father, sons, or near male kinsmen of the family are allowed to go inside, for it leads into the *Gynæconitis*, the hall of the women.   To thrust oneself into the Gynæconitis of even a fairly intimate friend is a studied insult at Athens, and sure to be resented by bodily chastisement, social ostracism, and a ruinous legal prosecution.   The Gynæconitis is in short the Athenian's holy of holies.   Their women are forbidden to participate in so much of public life that their own peculiar world is especially reserved to them.   To invade this world is not bad breeding; it is social sacrilege.

In the present house, the home of a well-to-do family, the Gynæconitis forms a second pillared court with adja-cent rooms of substantially the same size and shape as the Andronitis.   One of the rooms in the very rear is proclaimed by the clatter of pots and pans and the odor of a frying

---

[1] Who corresponds to the Roman goddess *Vesta*.

turbot to be the kitchen; others are obviously the sleeping closets of the slave women. On the side nearest to the front of the house, but opening itself upon this inner court, is at least one bed chamber of superior size. This is the *Thalamos*, the great bedroom of the master and mistress, and here are kept all the most costly furnishings and ornaments in the house. If there are grown-up unmarried daughters, they have another such bedroom (*anti-thalamos*) that is much larger than the cells of the slave girls. Another special room is set apart for the working of wool, although this chief occupation of the female part of the household is likely to be carried on in the open inner court itself, if the weather is fine. Here, around a little flower bed, slave girls are probably spinning and embroidering, young children playing or quarreling, and a tame quail is hopping about and watching for a crumb. There are in fact a great many people in a relatively small space; everything is busy, chattering, noisy, and confusing to an intruding stranger.

24. Modifications in the Typical Plan. — These are the essential features of an Athenian house. If the establishment is a very pretentious one, there may be a small garden in the rear carefully hedged against intruders by a lofty wall.[1] More probably the small size of the house lot would force simplifications in the scheme already stated. In a house one degree less costly, the Gynæconitis would be reduced to a mere series of rooms shut off in the rear. In more simple houses still there would be no interior section of the house at all. The women of the family would be provided for by a staircase rising from the main hall to a second story, and here a number of upper chambers would give the needful seclusion.[2] Of course as one goes down

[1] Such a luxury would not be common in city houses; land would be too valuable.

[2] Houses of more than two stories seem to have been unknown in Athens. The city lacked the towering rookeries of tenements (*insulæ*)

the social scale, the houses grow simpler and simpler. Small shops are set into the street wall at either side of the entrance door, and on entering one finds himself in a very limited and utterly dingy court with a few dirty compartments opening thence, which it would be absurd to dignify by the name of "rooms." Again one ceases to wonder that the male Athenians are not "home folk" and are glad to leave their houses to the less fortunate women!

25. Rents and House Values. — Most native Athenians own their houses. Houses indeed can be rented, usually by the foreign traders and visitors who swarm into the city; and at certain busy seasons one can hire "lodgings" for a brief sojourn. Rents are not unreasonable, 8 % or 8⅓ % of the value of the house being counted a fair annual return. But the average citizen is also a householder, because forsooth houses are very cheap. The main cost is probably for the land. The chief material used in building, sun-dried brick, is very unsubstantial,[1] and needs frequent repairs, but is not expensive. Demosthenes the Orator speaks of a "little house" (doubtless of the kind last described) worth only seven minæ [about $126.00], and this is not the absolute minimum. A very rich banker has had one worth 100 minæ [about $1800.00], and probably this is close to the maximum. The rent question is not therefore one of the pressing problems at Athens.

26. The Simple yet Elegant Furnishings of an Athenian Home. — These houses, even owned by the lordly rich, are surprisingly simple in their furnishings. The accumulation of heavy furniture, wall decorations, and bric-a-brac which will characterize the dwellings of a later age, would be

which were characteristic of Rome ; sometimes, however, a house seems to have been shared between several families.

[1] This material was so friable and poor that the Greek burglar was known as a " Wall-digger." It did not pay him to pick a lock ; it was simpler for him to quarry his way through the wall with a pickax.

utterly offensive to an Athenian — contradicting all his ideas of harmony and "moderation." The Athenian house lacks of course bookcases and framed pictures. It probably too lacks any genuine closets. Beds, couches, chairs (usually backless), stools, footstools, and small portable tables, — these alone seem in evidence. In place of bureaus, dressers, and cupboards, there are huge chests, heavy and carved, in which most of the household gear can be locked away. In truth, the whole style of Greek household life expresses that simplicity on which we have already commented. Oriental carpets are indeed met with, but they are often used as wall draperies or couch covers rather than upon the floors. Greek costume (see p. 43) is so simple that there is small need for elaborate chests of drawers, and a line of pegs upon the wall cares for most of the family wardrobe.

All this is true; yet what furniture one finds is fashioned with commendable grace. There is a marked absence of heavy and unhealthful upholstery; but the simple bed (four posts sustaining a springless cushion stuffed with feathers or wool) has its woodwork adorned with carving which is a true mean betwixt the too plain and the too ornate; and the whole bed is given an elegant effect by the magnificently embroidered scarlet tapestry which overspreads it. The lines of the legs of the low wooden tables which are used at the dinner parties will be a lesson (if we have time to study them) upon just proportion and the value of subtle curves. Moreover, the different household vessels, the stone and bronze lamps, the various table dishes, even the common pottery put to the humblest uses, all have a beauty, a chaste elegance, a saving touch of deft ornamentation, which transforms them out of "kitchen ware" into works of art. Those black water pots covered with red-clay figures which the serving maids are bearing so carelessly into the scullery at the screaming summons of the cook will be some day perchance the pride of a museum.

and teach a later age that costly material and aristocratic uses are not needful to make an article supremely beautiful.

Of course the well-to-do Athenian is proud to possess certain "valuables." He will have a few silver cups elegantly chased, and at least one diner's couch in the *andron* will be made of rare imported wood, and be inlaid with gilt or silver. On festival days the house will be hung with brilliant and elaborately wrought tapestries which will suddenly emerge from the great chests. Also, despite frowns and criticisms, the custom is growing of decorating one's walls with bright-lined frescoes after the manner of the Agora colonnades. In the course of a few generations the homes of the wealthier Greeks will come to resemble those of the Romans, such as a later age has resurrected at Pompeii.

CHAPTER V.

THE WOMEN OF ATHENS.

27. How Athenian Marriages are Arranged. — Over this typical Athenian home reigns the wife of the master. Public opinion frowns upon celibacy, and there are relatively few unmarried men in Athens. An Athenian girl is brought up with the distinct expectation of matrimony.[1] Opportunities for a romance almost never will come her way; but it is the business of her parents to find her a suitable husband. If they are kindly people of good breeding, their choice is not likely to be a very bad one. If they have difficulties, they can engage a professional "matchmaker," a shrewd old woman who, for a fee, will hunt out an eligible young man. Marriage is contracted primarily that there may be legitimate children to keep up the state and to perpetuate the family. That the girl should have any will of her own in the matter is almost never thought of. Very probably she has never seen "Him," save when they both were marching in a public religious procession, or at some rare family gathering (a marriage or a funeral) when there were outside guests. Besides she will be "given away" when only about fifteen, and probably has formed no intelligent opinion or even prejudices on the subject.

If the young man (who will marry at about thirty) is independent in life, the negotiations will be with him directly. If he is still dependent on the paternal allowance, the two

[1] The vile custom of exposing unwelcome female babies probably created a certain preponderance of males in Attica, and made it relatively easy to marry off a desirable young girl.

sets of parents will usually arrange matters themselves, and demand only the formal consent of the prospective bridegroom. He will probably accept promptly this bride whom his father has selected; if not, he risks a stormy encounter with his parents, and will finally capitulate. He has perhaps never seen "Her," and can only hope things are for the best; and after all she is so young that his friends tell him that he can train her to be very useful and obedient if he will only take pains. The parents, or, failing them, the guardians, adjust the dowry — the lump sum which the bride will bring with her towards the new establishment.[1] Many maxims enjoin "marry only your equal in fortune." The poor man who weds an heiress will not be really his own master; the dread of losing the big dowry will keep him in perpetual bondage to her whims.

28. Lack of Sentiment in Marriages. — Sometimes marriages are arranged in which any sentiment is obviously prohibited. A father can betroth his daughter by will to some kinsman, who is to take her over as his bride when he takes over the property. A husband can bequeath his wife to some friend who is likely to treat her and the orphan children with kindness. Such affairs occur every day. Do the Athenian women revolt at these seemingly degrading conditions, wherein they are handed around like slaves, or even cattle? — According to the tragic poets they do. Sophocles (in the *Tereus*) makes them lament,

"We women are nothing; — happy indeed is our childhood, for *then* we are thoughtless; but when we attain maidenhood, lo! we are driven away from our homes, sold as merchandise, and compelled to marry and say 'All's well.'"

Euripides is even more bitter in his *Medea:* —

---

[1] The dowry was a great protection to the bride. If her husband divorced her (as by law he might), the dowry must be repaid to her guardians with 18 per cent. interest.

> Surely of creatures that have life and wit,
> We women are of all things wretchedest,
> Who first must needs, as buys the highest bidder,
> Thus buy a husband, and our body's master.[1]

29. Athenian Marriage Rites. — However, thus runs public custom. At about fifteen the girl must leave her mother's fostering care and enter the house of the stranger. The wedding is, of course, a great ceremony; and here, if nowhere else, Athenian women can surely prepare, flutter, and ordain to their heart's content. After the somewhat stiff and formal betrothal before witnesses (necessary to give legal effect to the marriage), the actual wedding will probably take place, — perhaps in a few days, perhaps with a longer wait till the favorite marriage month Gamelion [January].[2] Then on a lucky night of the full moon the bride, having, no doubt tearfully, dedicated to Artemis her childish toys, will be decked in her finest and will come down, all veiled, into her father's torchlit aula, swarming now with guests. Here will be at last that strange master of her fate, the bridegroom and his best man (*paranymphos*). Her father will offer sacrifice (probably a lamb), and after the sacrifice everybody will feast on the flesh of the victim; and also share a large flat cake of pounded sesame seeds roasted and mixed with honey. As the evening advances the wedding car will be outside the door. The mother hands the bride over to the groom, who leads her to the chariot, and he and the groomsman sit down, one on either side, while with torches and song the friends go with the car in jovial procession to the house of the young husband.

"Ho, Hymen! Ho, Hymen! Hymenæos! Io!"

So rings the refrain of the marriage song; and all the

---

[1] Way's translation.
[2] This winter month was sacred to Hera, the marriage guardian.

doorways and street corners are crowded with onlookers
to shout fair wishes and good-natured raillery.

At the groom's house there is a volley of confetti to
greet the happy pair. The bride stops before the threshold
to eat a quince.[1] There is another feast, — possibly riotous
fun and hard drinking. At last the bride is led, still
veiled, to the perfumed and flower-hung marriage chamber.
The doors close behind the married pair. Their friends
sing a merry rollicking catch outside, the *Epithalamium*.
The great day has ended. The Athenian girl has experienced the chief transition of her life.

30. The Mental Horizon of Athenian Women. — Despite
the suggestions in the poets, probably the normal Athenian
woman is neither degraded nor miserable. If she is a girl
of good ancestry and the usual bringing up, she has never
expected any other conditions than these. She knows that
her parents care for her and have tried to secure for her a
husband who will be her guardian and solace when they are
gone. Xenophon's ideal young husband, Ischomachus, says
he married his wife at the age of fifteen.[2] She had been
"trained to see and to hear as little as possible"; but her
mother had taught her to have a sound control of her
appetite and of all kinds of self-indulgence, to take wool
and to make a dress of it, and to manage the slave maids in
their spinning tasks. She was at first desperately afraid of
her husband, and it was some time before he had "tamed"
her sufficiently to discuss their household problems freely.
Then Ischomachus made her join with him in a prayer to
the gods that "he might teach and she might learn all that
could conduce to their joint happiness"; after which they
took admirable counsel together, and her tactful and ex-

[1] The symbol of fertility.
[2] See Xenophon's "The Economist," VII ff. The more pertinent passages are quoted in W. S. Davis's *Readings in Ancient History*, vol. I, pp
265–271.

perienced husband (probably more than twice her age)
trained her into a model housewife.

31. The Honor paid Womanhood in Athens. — Obviously
from a young woman with a limited intellectual horizon
the Athenian gentleman can expect no mental companion-
ship; but it is impossible that he can live in the world as
a keenly intelligent being, and not come to realize the
enormous value of the "woman spirit" as it affects all
things good.   Hera, Artemis, Aphrodite, above all Pallas-
Athena, — city-warder of Athens, — who are they all but
idealizations of that peculiar genius which wife, mother,
and daughter show forth every day in their homes?   An
Athenian never allows his wife to visit the Agora.   She
cannot indeed go outside the house without his express permission, and only then attended by one or two serving
maids; public opinion will likewise frown upon the man
who allowed his wife to appear in public too freely[1];
nevertheless there are compensations.   Within her home
the Athenian woman is within her kingdom.   Her husband
will respect her, because he will respect himself.   Brutal
and harsh he may possibly be, but that is because he is
also brutal and harsh in his outside dealings.   In extreme
cases an outraged wife can sue for divorce before the
archon.   And very probably in ninety-nine cases out of a
hundred the Athenian woman is contented with her lot:
partly because she knows of nothing better; partly because
she has nothing concrete whereof to complain.

Doubtless it is because an Athenian house is a "little
oasis of domesticity," tenderly guarded from all insult, — a
miniature world whose joys and sorrows are not to be

[1] Hypereides, the orator, says, "The woman who goes out of her own
home ought to be of such an age that when men meet her, the question
is not 'Who is her husband?' but 'Whose mother is she?'"   Pericles, in
the great funeral oration put in his mouth by Thucydides, says that the
best women are those who are talked of for good or ill the very least.

shared by the outer universe, — that the Athenian treats the
private affairs of his family as something seldom to be
shared, even with an intimate friend. Of individual women
we hear and see little in Athens, but of *noble womanhood*
a great deal. By a hundred tokens, delightful vase paintings, noble monuments, poetic myths, tribute is paid to the
self-mastery, the self-forgetfulness, the courage, the gentle-
ness "of the wives and mothers who have made Athens
the beacon of Hellas"; and there is one witness better
than all the rest. Along the "Street of the Tombs," by
the gate of the city, runs the long row of stelæ (funeral
monuments), inimitable and chaste memorials to the beloved dead; and here we meet, many times over, the por-
trayal of a sorrow too deep for common lament, the sorrow
for the lovely and gracious figures who have passed into
the great Mystery. Along the Street of the Tombs the
wives and mothers of Athens are honored not less than the
wealthy, the warriors, or the statesmen.

   32. The Sphere of Action of Athenian Women. — Assuredly
the Athenian house mother cannot match her husband in
discussing philosophy or foreign politics, but she has her
own home problems and confronts them well. A dozen or
twenty servants must be kept busy. From her, all the
young children must get their first education, and the girls
probably everything they are taught until they are married.
Even if she does not meet many men, she will strive val-
iantly to keep the good opinion of her husband. If she has
shapely feet and hands (whereon great stress is laid in
Hellas), she will do her uttermost to display them to the
greatest advantage [1]; and she has, naturally, plenty of other
vanities (see p. 49). Her husband has turned over to her
the entire management of the household. This means

   [1] The custom of wearing sandals instead of shoes of course aided the
developing of beautiful feet.

that if he is an easy-going man, she soon understands his home business far better than he does himself, and really has him quite at her mercy. Between caring for her husband's wants, nursing the sick slaves, acting as arbitress in their inevitable disputes, keeping a constant watch upon the storeroom, and finally in attending to the manufacture of nearly all the family clothing, she is not likely to rust in busy idleness, or sit complaining of her lot. At the many great public festivals she is always at least an onlooker and often she marches proudly in the magnificent processions. She is allowed to attend the tragedies in the theater.[1] Probably, too, the family will own a country farm, and spend a part

SPINNING.

of the year thereon. Here she will be allowed a delightful freedom of movement, impossible in the closely built city. All in all, then, she will complain of too much enforced activity rather than of too much idleness.

Nevertheless our judgment upon the Athenian women is mainly one of regret. Even if not discontented with their

[1] Not the comedies — they were too broad for refined women. But the mere fact that Athenian ladies seem to have been allowed to attend the tragedies is a tribute to their intellectual capacities. Only an acute and intelligent mind can follow Æschylus, Sophocles, and Euripides.

lot, they are not realizing the full possibilities which Providence has placed within the reach of womanhood, much less the womanhood of the mothers of the warriors, poets, orators, and other immortals of Athens. One great side of civilization which the city of Athens might develop and realize is left unrealized. *This civilization of Athens is too masculine;* it is therefore one sided, and in so far it does not realize that ideal "Harmony" which is the average Athenian's boast.

CHAPTER VI.

ATHENIAN COSTUME.

33. The General Nature of Greek Dress. — In every age the important kingdom of dress has been reserved for the peculiar sovereignty of woman. This is true in Athens, though not perhaps to the extent of later ages. Still an Athenian lady will take an interest in "purple and fine linen" far exceeding that of her husband, and where is there a more fitting place than this in which to answer for an Athenian, the ever important question "wherewithal shall I be clothed"?

Once again the Athenian climate comes in as a factor, this time in the problem of wardrobe. Two general styles of garment have divided the allegiance of the world, — the clothes that are *put on* and the clothes that are *wrapped around*. The former style, with its jackets, trousers, and leggins, is not absolutely unknown to the Athenians, — their old enemies, the Persians, wear these[1]; but such clumsy, inelegant garments are despised and ridiculed as fit only for the "Barbarians" who use them. They are not merely absurdly homely; they cannot even be thrown off promptly in an emergency, leaving the glorious human form free to put forth any noble effort. The Athenians wear the wrapped style of garments, which are, in final analysis, one or two large square pieces of cloth flung skilfully around the body and secured by a few well-placed

[1] The Persians no doubt learned to use this style of garment during their life on the cold, windy steppes of Upper Asia, before they won their empire in the more genial south.

43

pins. This costume is infinitely adjustable; it can be expanded into flowing draperies or contracted into an easy working dress by a few artful twitches. It can be nicely adjusted to meet the inevitable sense of "beauty" bred in the bone of every Athenian. True, on the cold days of midwinter the wearers will go about shivering; but cold days are the exception, warm days the rule, in genial Attica.[1]

This simplicity of costume has produced certain important results. There are practically no tailors in Athens, only cloth merchants, bleachers, and dyers. Again fashions (at least in the actual cut of the garments) seldom change. A cloak that was made in the days of Alcibiades (say 420 B.C.) can be worn with perfect propriety to-day (360 B.C.) if merely it has escaped without severe use or moth holes. It may be more usual this year to wear one's garments a little higher or a little more trailing than formerly; but *that* is simply a matter for a shifting of the pins or of the girdle.

As a result, the Athenian seldom troubles about his "spring" or "winter" suit. His simple woolen garments wear a very long time; and they have often been slowly and laboriously spun and woven by his wife and her slave girls. Of course even a poor man will try to have a few changes of raiment, — something solid and coarse for every day, something of finer wool and gayer color for public and private festivals. The rich man will have a far larger wardrobe, and will pride himself on not being frequently seen in the same dress; yet even his outfit will seem very meager to the dandies of a later age.

34. The Masculine Chiton, Himation, and Chlamys. — The

---

[1] The whole civilization of Athens was, of course, based on a climate in which artificial heat would be very little needed. A pot of glowing charcoal might be used to remove the chill of a room in the very coldest weather. Probably an Athenian would have regarded a climate in which furnace heat was demanded nearly eight months in the year as wholly unfit for civilized man.

essential garments of an Athenian man are only two — the *chiton* and the *himation*. The chiton may be briefly described as an oblong of woolen cloth large enough to wrap around the body somewhat closely, from the neck down to just above the knees. The side left open is fastened by fibulæ — elegantly wrought pins perhaps of silver or gold; in the closed side there is a slit for the arm. There is a girdle, and, if one wishes, the skirt of the chiton may be pulled up through it, and allowed to hang down in front, giving the effect of a blouse. The man of prompt action, the soldier, traveler, worker, is "well girded," — his chiton is drawn high, but the deliberate old gentleman who parades the Agora, discussing poetry or statecraft, has his chiton falling almost to a trailing length. Only occasionally short sleeves are added to this very simple garment; they are considered effeminate, and are not esteemed. If one's arms get cold, one can protect them by pulling up the skirt, and wrapping the arms in the blouse thus created.

An Athenian gentleman when he is in the house wears nothing but his chiton; it is even proper for him to be seen wearing nothing else upon the streets, but then more usually he will add an outer cloak, — his *himation*.

The himation is even simpler than the chiton. It is merely a generous oblong woolen shawl. There are innumerable ways of arranging it according to the impulse of the moment; but usually it has to be worn without pins, and that involves wrapping it rather tightly around the body, and keeping one of the hands confined to hold the cloak in place. That is no drawback, however, to a genteel wearer. It proclaims to the world that *he* does not have to work, wearing his hands for a living; therefore he can keep them politely idle.[1] The adjustment of the himation is a work

---

[1] Workingmen often wore no himation, and had a kind of chiton (an exōmis) which was especially arranged to leave them with free use of their arms.

of great art.   A rich man will often have a special slave
whose business it is to arrange the hang and the folds before his master moves forth in public; and woe to the care-
less fellow if the effect fails to display due elegance and
dignity !

There is a third garment sometimes worn by Athenians.
Young men who wish to appear very active, and genuine
travelers, also wear a *chlamys*, a kind of circular mantle or
cape which swings jauntily over their shoulders, and will
give good protection in foul weather.

There are almost no other masculine garments.   No
shirts (unless the chiton be one), no underwear.   In their
costume, as in so many things else, the Athenians exemplify
their oft-praised virtue of simplicity.

35. The Dress of the Women. — The dress of the women
is like that of the men, but differs, of course, in complexity.
They also have a chiton,[1] which is more elaborately made,
especially in the arrangement of the blouse; and probably
there is involved a certain amount of real *sewing*[2]; not
merely of *pinning*.

Greater care is needed in the adjustment of the " zone "
(girdle), and half sleeves are the rule with women, while
full sleeves are not unknown.   A Greek lady again cannot
imitate her husband, and appear in public in her chiton
only.   A himation, deftly adjusted, is absolutely indispensable whenever she shows herself outside the house.

These feminine garments are all, as a rule, more elaborately embroidered, more adorned with fringes and tassels,
than those of the men.   In arranging her dress the Athenian lady is not bound by the rigid precepts of fashion.

---

[1] This robe was sometimes known by the Homeric name of *peplos.*
[2] Probably with almost all Greek garments the main use of the needle
was in the embroidery merely, or in the darning of holes and rents.   It
was by no means an essential in the real manufacture.

Every separate toilette is an opportunity for a thousand
little niceties and coquetries which she understands exceedingly well. If there is the least excuse for an expedition
outside the house, her ladyship's bevy of serving maids will
have a serious time of it. While their mistress cools herself with a huge peacock-feather fan, one maid is busy over
her hair; a second holds the round metallic mirror before
her; a third stands ready to extend the jewel box whence
she can select finger rings, earrings, gold armlets, chains
for her neck and hair, as well as the indispensable brooches
whereon the stability of the whole costume depends.
When she rises to have her himation draped around her,
the directions she gives reveal her whole bent and character. A dignified and modest matron will have it folded
loosely around her entire person, covering both arms and
hands, and even drawing it over her head, leaving eyes and
nose barely visible. Younger ladies will draw it close
around the body so as to show the fine lines of their waists
and shoulders. And in the summer heat the himation (for
the less prudish) will become a light shawl floating loose
and free over the shoulders, or only a kind of veil drawn
so as to now conceal, now reveal, the face.

Children wear miniature imitations of the dress of their
elders. Boys are taught to toughen their bodies by refrain-
ing from thick garments in cold weather. In hot weather
they can frequently be seen playing about with very little
clothing at all!

36. Footwear and Head Coverings. — Upon his feet the
Athenian frequently wears nothing. He goes about his
home barefoot; and not seldom he enjoys the delight of
running across the open greensward with his unsandaled
feet pressing the springing ground; but normally when he
walks abroad, he will wear *sandals*, a simple solid pair of
open soles tied to his feet by leather thongs passing between

the toes. For hard country walking and for hunting there is something like a high leather boot,[1] though doubtless these are counted uncomfortable for ordinary wear. As for the sandals, simple as they are, the Attic touch of elegance is often upon them. Upon the thongs of the sandals there is usually worked a choice pattern, in some brilliant color or even gilt.

The Athenians need head coverings even less than foot-gear. Most of them have thick hair; baldness is an uncommon affliction; everybody is trained to walk under the full glare of Helios with little discomfort. Of course certain trades require hats, *e.g.* sailors who can be almost identified by their rimless felt caps. Genteel travelers will wear wide-brimmed hats; but the ladies, as a rule, have no head-gear besides their tastefully arranged hair, although they will partly atone for the lack, by having a maid walk just behind them with a gorgeously variegated parasol.

37. The Beauty of the Greek Dress. — Greek costume, then, is something fully sharing in the national character-istics of harmony, simplicity, individuality. It is easy to see how admirably this style of dress is adapted to furnish ever ready models and inspiration for the sculptor.[2] Un-conventional in its arrangement, it is also unconventional in its color. A masculine crowd is not one unmitigated swarm of black and dark grays or browns, as with the multitudes of a later age. On the contrary, white is counted theoreti-cally the most becoming color on any common occasion for either sex;[3] and on festival days even grave and elderly men will appear with chitons worked with brilliant em-

---

[1] Actors, too, wore a leather boot with high soles to give them extra height — the *cothurnus.*

[2] "The chiton became the mirror of the body," said the late writer, Achilles Tatius.

[3] No doubt farmers and artisans either wore garments of a non-com-mittal brown, or, more probably, let their originally white costume get utterly dirty.

broidery along the borders, and with splendid himatia of some single clear hue—violet, red, purple, blue, or yellow. As for the costume of the groom at a wedding, it is far indeed from the "conventional black" of more degenerate days. He may well wear a purple-edged white chiton of fine Milesian wool, a brilliant scarlet himation, sandals with blue thongs and clasps of gold, and a chaplet of myrtle and violets. His intended bride is led out to him in even more dazzling array. Her white sandal-thongs are embroidered with emeralds, rubies, and pearls. Around her neck is a necklace of gold richly set,—and she has magnificent golden armlets and pearl eardrops. Her hair is fragrant with Oriental nard, and is bound by a purple fillet and a chaplet of roses. Her ungloved fingers shine with jewels and rings. Her main costume is of a delicate saffron, and over it all, like a cloud, floats the silvery tissue of the nuptial veil.

38. Greek Toilet Frivolities. — From the standpoint of inherent fitness and beauty, this Athenian costume is the noblest ever seen by the world. Naturally there are ill-advised creatures who do not share the good taste of their fellows, or who try to deceive the world and themselves as to the ravages of that arch-enemy of the Hellene, — Old Age. Athenian women especially (though the men are not without their follies) are sometimes fond of rouge, false hair, and the like. Auburn hair is especially admired, and many fine dames bleach their tresses in a caustic wash to obtain it. The styles of feminine hair dressing seem to change from decade to decade much more than the arrangements of the garments. Now it is plaited and crimped hair that is in vogue, now the more beautiful "Psyche-knots"; yet even in their worst moods the Athenian women exhibit a sweet reasonableness. They have not yet fallen into the clutches of the Parisian hairdresser.

WINGATE JUNIOR COLLEGE

The poets, of course, ridicule the foibles of the fair sex.[1]
Says one : —

> The golden hair Nikylla wears
> Is hers, who would have thought it ?
> She swears 'tis hers, and true she swears
> For I know where she bought it !

And again : —

> You give your cheeks a rosy stain,
> With washes dye your hair ;
> But paint and washes both are vain
> To give a youthful air.
> An art so fruitless then forsake,
> Which, though you much excel in,
> You never can contrive to make
> Old Hecuba young Helen.

But enough of such scandals ! All the best opinion —
masculine and feminine — frowns on these follies. Let us
think of the simple, dignified, and æsthetically noble costume of the Athenians as not the least of their examples to
another age.

[1] Translated in Falke's *Greece and Rome* (English translation, p. 69).
These quotations probably date from a time considerably later than the
hypothetical period of this sketch ; but they are perfectly proper to apply
to conditions in 360 B.C.

CHAPTER VII.

THE SLAVES.

39. Slavery an Integral Part of Greek Life. — An Athenian lady cares for everything in her house, — for the food supplies, for the clothing, yet probably her greatest task is to manage the heterogeneous multitude of slaves which swarm in every wealthy or even well-to-do mansion.[1]

Slaves are everywhere: not merely are they the domestic servants, but they are the hands in the factories, they run innumerable little shops, they unload the ships, they work the mines, they cultivate the farms. Possibly there are more able-bodied male slaves in Attica than male free men, although this point is very uncertain. Their number is the harder to reckon because they are not required to wear any distinctive dress, and you cannot tell at a glance whether a man is a mere piece of property, or a poor but very proud and important member of the "Sovereign Demos [People] of Athens."

No prominent Greek thinker seems to contest the right-eousness and desirability of slavery. It is one of the usual, nay, inevitable, things pertaining to a civilized state. Aristotle the philosopher puts the current view of the case very clearly. "The lower sort of mankind are *by nature* slaves, and it is better for all inferiors that they should be under the rule of a master. The use made of slaves and of tame animals is not very different; for both by their bodies

---

[1] The Athenians never had the absurd armies of house slaves which characterized Imperial Rome; still the numbers of their domestic servants were, from a modern standpoint, extremely large.

51

minister to the needs of life." The intelligent, enlightened, progressive Athenians are naturally the "masters"; the stupid, ignorant, sluggish minded Barbarians are the "inferiors." Is it not a plain decree of Heaven that the Athenians are made to rule, the Barbarians to serve?—No one thinks the subject worth serious argument.

Of course the slave cannot be treated quite as one would treat an ox. Aristotle takes pains to point out the desirability of holding out to your "chattel" the hope of freedom, if only to make him work better; and the great philosopher in his last testament gives freedom to five of his thirteen slaves. Then again it is recognized as clearly against public sentiment to hold fellow Greeks in bondage. It is indeed done. Whole towns get taken in war, and those of the inhabitants who are not slaughtered are sold into slavery.[1] Again, exposed children, whose parents have repudiated them, get into the hands of speculators, who raise them "for market." There is also a good deal of kidnapping in the less civilized parts of Greece like Ætolia. Still the proportion of genuinely *Greek* slaves is small. The great majority of them are "Barbarians," men born beyond the pale of Hellenic civilization.

40. The Slave Trade in Greece. — There are two great sources of slave supply: the Asia Minor region (Lydia and Phrygia, with Syria in the background), and the Black Sea region, especially the northern shores, known as Scythia. It is known to innumerable heartless "traders" that human flesh commands a very high price in Athens or other Greek cities. Every little war or raid that vexes those barbarous countries so incessantly is followed by the sale of the unhappy captives to speculators who ship them on, stage by stage, to Athens. Perhaps there is no war; the

[1] For example, the survivors, after the capture of Melos, in the Peloponnesian War.

supply is kept up then by deliberate kidnapping on a large scale, or by piracy.[1] In any case the arrival of a chain gang of fettered wretches at the Peiræus is an everyday sight. Some of these creatures are submissive and tame (perhaps they understand some craft or trade); these can be sold at once for a high price. Others are still doltish and stubborn. They are good for only the rudest kind of labor, unless they are kept and trained at heavy expense. These brutish creatures are frequently sold off to the mines, to be worked to death by the contractors as promptly and brutally as one wears out a machine ; or else they become public galley slaves, when their fate is practically the same. But we need not follow such horrors.

The remainder are likely to be purchased either for use upon the farm, the factory, or in the home. There is a regular "circle" at or near the Agora for traffic in them. They are often sold at auction. The price of course varies with the good looks, age,[2] or dexterity of the article, or the abundance of supply. "Slaves will be high" in a year when there has been little warfare and raiding in Asia Minor. "Some slaves," says Xenophon, "are well worth two minæ [$36.00] and others barely half a mina [$9.00]; some sell up to five minæ [$90.00] and even for ten [$180.00]. Nicias, the son of Nicaretus, is said to have given a talent [over $1000.00] for an overseer in the mines."[3] The father of Demosthenes owned a considerable factory. He had thirty-two sword cutters worth about five minæ each, and twenty couch-makers (evidently less skilled) worth together 40 minæ [about $720.00]. A girl who is

[1] A small but fairly constant supply of slaves would come from the seizure of the persons and families of bankrupt debtors, whose creditors, especially in the Orient, might sell them into bondage.

[2] There was probably next to no market for old women ; old men in broken health would also be worthless. Boys and maids that were the right age for teaching a profitable trade would fetch the most.

[3] Xenophon, *Memorabilia*, ii. 5, § 2.

handsome and a clever flute player, who will be readily hired for supper parties, may well command a very high price indeed, say even 30 minæ [about $540.00].

41. The Treatment of Slaves in Athens. — Once purchased, what is the condition of the average slave? If he is put in a factory, he probably has to work long hours on meager rations. He is lodged in a kind of kennel; his only respite is on the great religious holidays. He cannot contract valid marriage or enjoy any of the normal conditions of family life. Still his evil state is partially tempered by the fact that he has to work in constant association with free workmen, and he seems to be treated with a moderate amount of consideration and good camaraderie. On the whole he will have much less to complain of (if he is honest and industrious) than his successors in Imperial Rome.

In the household, conditions are on the whole better. Every Athenian citizen tries to have at least *one* slave, who, we must grant, may be a starving drudge of all work. The average gentleman perhaps counts ten to twenty as sufficient for his needs. We know of households of fifty. There must usually be a steward, a butler in charge of the storeroom and cellar, a marketing slave, a porter, a baker, a cook,[1] a nurse, perhaps several lady's maids, the indispensable attendant for the master's walks (a graceful, well-favored boy, if possible), the pedagogue for the children, and in really rich families, a groom, and a mule boy. It is the business of the mistress to see that all these creatures are kept busy and reasonably contented. If a slave is reconciled to his lot, honest, cheerful, industrious, his condition is not miserable. Athenian slaves are allowed a surprising amount of liberty, so most visitors to the city complain. A slave may be flogged most cruelly, but he cannot be put to

---

[1] Who, however, could not be trusted to cook a formal dinner. For such purpose an expert must be hired.

death at the mere whim of his master. He cannot enter
the gymnasium, or the public assembly; but he can visit the
temples. As a humble member of the family he has a
small part usually in the family sacrifices. But in any case
he is subject to one grievous hardship: when his testimony
is required in court he must be "put to the question" by
torture. On the other hand, if his master has wronged him
intolerably, he can take sanctuary at the Temple of Theseus,
and claim the privilege of being sold to some new owner.
A slave, too, has still another grievance which may be no
less galling because it is sentimental. His name (given him
arbitrarily perhaps by his master) is of a peculiar category,
which at once brands him as a bondman: Geta, Manes, Dro-
mon, Sosias, Xanthias, Pyrrhias, — such names would be
repudiated as an insult by a citizen.

42. Cruel and Kind Masters. — Slavery in Athens, as everywhere else, is largely dependent upon the character of the
master; and most Athenian masters would not regard crude
brutality as consistent with that love of elegance, harmony,
and genteel deliberation which characterizes a well-born
citizen. There do not lack masters who have the whip
continually in their hands, who add to the raw stripes
fetters and branding, and who make their slaves unceasingly miserable; but such masters are the exception, and
public opinion does not praise them. Between the best
Athenians and their slaves there is a genial, friendly relation, and the master will put up with a good deal of real
impertinence, knowing that behind this forwardness there
is an honest zeal for his interests.

Nevertheless the slave system of Athens is not commendable. It puts a stigma upon the glory of honest manual
labor. It instills domineering, despotic habits into the owners, cringing subservience into the owned. Even if a slave
becomes freed, he does not become an Athenian citizen; he

is only a "metic," a resident foreigner, and his old master, or some other Athenian, must be his patron and representative in every kind of legal business. It is a notorious fact that the *mere state* of slavery robs the victim of his self-respect and manhood. Nevertheless nobody dreams of abolishing slavery as an institution, and the Athenians, comparing themselves with other communities, pride themselves on the extreme humanity of their slave system.

43. The "City Slaves" of Athens. — A large number of nominal "slaves" in Athens differ from any of the creatures we have described. The community, no less than an individual, can own slaves just as it can own warships and temples. Athens owns "city slaves" (*Demosioi*) of several varieties. The clerks in the treasury office, and the checking officers at the public assemblies are slaves; so too are the less reputable public executioners and torturers; in the city mint there is another corps of slave workmen, busy coining "Athena's owls" — the silver drachmas and four-drachma pieces. But chiefest of all, *the city owns its public police force.* The "Scythians" they are called from their usual land of origin, or the "bowmen," from their special weapon, which incidentally makes a convenient cudgel in a street brawl. There are 1200 of them, always at the disposal of the city magistrates. They patrol the town at night, arrest evil-doers, sustain law and order in the Agora, and especially enforce decorum, if the public assemblies or the jury courts become tumultuous. They have a special cantonment on the hill of Areopagus near the Acropolis. "Slaves" they are of course in name, and under a kind of military discipline; but they are highly privileged slaves. The security of the city may depend upon their loyal zeal. In times of war they are auxiliaries. Life in this police force cannot therefore be burdensome, and their position is envied by all the factory workers and the house servants.

CHAPTER VIII.

THE CHILDREN.

44. The Desirability of Children in Athens. — Besides the oversight of the slaves the Athenian matron has naturally the care of the children. A childless home is one of the greatest of calamities. It means a solitary old age, and still worse, the dying out of the family and the worship of the family gods. There is just enough of the old superstitious "ancestor worship" left in Athens to make one shudder at the idea of leaving the "deified ancestors" without any descendants to keep up the simple sacrifices to their memory. Besides, public opinion condemns the childless home as not contributing to the perpetuation of the city. How Corinth, Thebes, or Sparta will rejoice, if it is plain that Athens is destroying herself by race suicide! So at least *one* son will be very welcome. His advent is a day of happiness for the father, of still greater satisfaction for the young mother.

45. The Exposure of Infants. — How many more children are welcome depends on circumstances. Children are expensive luxuries. They must be properly educated and even the boys must be left a fair fortune.[1] The girls must always have good dowries, or they cannot "marry according to their station." Public opinion, as well as the law, allows a father (at least if he has one or two children already) to exercise a privilege, which later ages will pronounce one of the foulest blots on Greek civilization. After the birth of a child there is an anxious day or two for the poor young

---

[1] The idea of giving a lad a "schooling" and then turning him loose to earn his own living in the world was contrary to all Athenian theory and practice.

mother and the faithful nurses. — Will he 'nourish' it ? Are there boys enough already ? Is the disappointment over the birth of a daughter too keen ? Does he dread the curtailment in family luxuries necessary to save up for an allowance or dowry for the little stranger ? Or does the child promise to be puny, sickly, or even deformed ? If any of these arguments carry adverse weight, there is no appeal against the father's decision. He has until the fifth day after the birth to decide. In the interval he can utter the fatal words " Expose it ! " The helpless creature is then put in a rude cradle, or more often merely in a shallow pot and placed near some public place ; *e.g.* the corner of the Agora, or near a gymnasium, or the entrance to a temple. Here it will soon die of mere hunger and neglect, unless rescued. If the reasons for exposure are evident physical defects, no one will touch it. Death is certain. If, however, it seems healthy and well formed, it is likely to be taken up and cared for. Not out of pure compassion, however. The harpies who raise slaves and especially slave girls, for no honest purposes, are prompt to pounce upon any promising looking infant. They will rear it as a speculation ; if it is a girl, they will teach it to sing, dance, play. The race of light women in Athens is thus really recruited from among the very best families. The fact is well known, but it is constantly winked at. Aristophanes, the comic poet, speaks of this exposure of children as a common feature of Athenian life. Socrates declares his hearers are vexed when he robs them of pet ideas, "like women who have had their children taken from them." There is little or nothing for men of a later day to say of this custom save condemnation.[1]

---

[1] About the only boon gained by this foul usage was the fact that, thanks to it, the number of physically unfit persons in Athens was probably pretty small, for no one would think of bringing up a child which, in its first babyhood, promised to be a cripple.

46. The Celebration of a Birth. — But assuredly in a majority of cases, the coming of a child is more than welcome. If a girl, tufts of wool are hung before the door of the happy home; if a boy, there is set out an olive branch. Five days after the birth, the nurse takes the baby, wrapped almost to suffocation in swaddling bands, to the family hearth in the *andron*, around which she runs several times, followed doubtless, in merry, frolicking procession, by most of the rest of the family. The child is now under the care of the family gods. There is considerable eating and drinking. Exposure now is no longer possible. A great load is off the mind of the mother. But on the "tenth day" comes the real celebration and the feast. This is the "name day." All the kinsmen are present. The house is full of incense and garlands. The cook is in action in the kitchen. Everybody brings simple gifts, along with abundant wishes of good luck. There is a sacrifice, and during the ensuing feast comes the naming of the child. Athenian names are very short and simple.[1] A boy has often his father's name, but more usually his grandfather's, as, *e.g.*, Themistocles, the son of Neocles, the son of Themistocles: the father's name being usually added in place of a surname. In this way certain names will become a kind of family property, and sorrowful is the day when there is no eligible son to bear them!

The child is now a recognized member of the community. His father has accepted him as a legitimate son, one of his prospective heirs, entitled in due time to all the rights of an Athenian citizen.

47. Life and Games of Young Children. — The first seven years of a Greek boy's life are spent with his nurses and his mother. Up to that time his father takes only un-

---

[1] Owing to this simplicity and the relatively small number of Athenian names, a directory of the city would have been a perplexing affair.

official interest in his welfare. Once past the first perilous "five days," an Athenian baby has no grounds to complain of his treatment. Great pains are taken to keep him warm and well nourished. A wealthy family will go to some trouble to get him a skilful nurse, those from Sparta being in special demand, as knowing the best how to rear healthy infants. He has all manner of toys, and Aristotle the philosopher commends their frequent donation; otherwise, he says, children will be always "breaking things in the house." Babies have rattles. As they grow older they have dolls of painted clay or wax, sometimes with movable hands and feet, and also toy dishes, tables, wagons, and animals. Lively boys have whipping toys, balls, hoops, and swings. There is no lack of pet dogs, nor of all sorts of games on the blind man's buff and "tag" order.[1] Athenian

THE MATERNAL SLIPPER.

children are, as a class, very active and noisy. Plato speaks feelingly of their perpetual "roaring." As they grow larger, they begin to escape more and more from the narrow quarters of the courts of the house, and play in the streets.

48. Playing in the Streets. — Narrow, dirty, and dusty as the streets seem, children, even of good families, are allowed to play in them. After a rain one can see boys floating

---

[1] It is not always easy to get the exact details of such ancient games, for the "rules" have seldom come down to us; but generally speaking, the games of Greek children seem extremely like those of the twentieth century.

toy boats of leather in every mud puddle, or industriously
making mud pies. In warm weather the favorite if cruel
sport is to catch a beetle, tie a string to its legs, let it fly
off, then twitch it back again. Leapfrog, hide-and-seek,
etc., are in violent progress down every alley. The streets
are not at all ideal playgrounds. Despite genteel ideas of
dignity and moderation, there is a great deal of foul talk
and brawling among the passers, and Athenian children
have receptive eyes and ears. Yet on the other hand, there
is a notable regard and reverence for childhood. With all
its frequent callousness and inhumanity, Greek sentiment
abhors any brutality to young children. Herodotus the
historian tells of the falling of a roof, whereby one hundred
and twenty school children perished, as being a frightful
calamity,[1] although recounting cold-blooded massacres of
thousands of adults with never a qualm; and Herodotus is
a very good spokesman for average Greek opinion.

49. The First Stories and Lessons. — Athens has no kin-
dergartens. The first teaching which children will receive
is in the form of fables and goblin tales from their mothers
and nurses, — usually with the object of frightening them
into " being good," — tales of the spectral Lamiæ, or of the
horrid witch Mormo who will catch naughty children; or
of Empusa, a similar creature, who lurks in shadows and
dark rooms; or of the Kobaloi, wild spirits in the woods.
Then come the immortal fables of Æsop with their obvious
application towards right conduct. Athenian mothers and
teachers have no two theories as to the wisdom of corporal
punishment. The rod is never spared to the spoiling of the
child, although during the first years the slipper is sufficient. Greek children soon have a healthy fear of their
nurses; but they often learn to love them, and funeral monuments will survive to perpetuate their grateful memory.

[1] Herodotus, VI. 27.

50. The Training of Athenian Girls. — Until about seven years old brothers and sisters grow up in the *Gynæconitis* together. Then the boys experience a complete change in their lives, when they are sent to school. The girls will continue about the house until the time of their marriage. It is only in the rarest of cases that the parents feel it needful to hire any kind of tutor for *them*. What the average girl knows is simply what her mother can teach her. Perhaps a certain number of Athenian women (of good family, too) are downright illiterate; but this is not very often the case. A normal girl will learn to read and write, with her mother for school mistress.[1] Very probably she will be taught to dance, and sometimes to play on some instrument, although this last is not quite a proper accomplishment for young women of good family. Hardly any one dreams of giving a woman any systematic intellectual training.[2] Much more important it is that she should know how to weave, spin, embroider, dominate the cook, and superintend the details of a dinner party. She will have hardly time to learn these matters thoroughly before she is "given a husband," and her childhood days are forever over (see p. 35).

Meantime her brother has been started upon a course of education which, both in what it contains and in what it omits, is one of the most interesting and significant features of Athenian life.

[1] There has come down to us a charming Greek terra-cotta (it is true, not from Athens) showing a girl seated on her mother's knee, and learning from a roll which she holds.

[2] Plato suggested in his *Republic* (V. 451 f.) that women should receive the same educational opportunities as the men. This was a proposition for Utopia and never struck any answering chord.

CHAPTER IX.

THE SCHOOLBOYS OF ATHENS.

51. Athenians Generally Literate. — Education is not compulsory by law in Athens, but the father who fails to give his son at least a modicum of education falls under a public contempt, which involves no slight penalty. Practically all Athenians are at least literate. In Aristophanes's famous comedy, *The Knights,* a boorish " sausage-seller " is introduced, who, for the purposes of the play, must be one of the very scum of society, and he is made to cry, " Only consider now my education! I can but barely read, just in a kind of way." [1] Evidently if illiterates are not very rare in Athens, the fellow should have been made out utterly ignorant. " He can neither swim [2] nor say his letters," is a common phrase for describing an absolute idiot. When a boy has reached the age of seven, the time for feminine rule is over ; henceforth his floggings, and they will be many, are to come from firm male hands. .

52. Character Building the Aim of Athenian Education. — The true education is of course begun long before the age of seven. *Character not book-learning, is the main object of Athenian education, i.e.* to make the boy self-contained, modest, alert, patriotic, a true friend, a dignified gentleman, able to appreciate and participate in all that is true, harmo-

[1] Aristophanes, *Knights*, ll. 188–189.
[2] Swimming was an exceedingly common accomplishment among the Greeks, naturally enough, so much of their life being spent upon or near the sea.

nious, and beautiful in life. To that end his body must be
trained, not apart from, but along with his mind. Plato
makes his character Protagoras remark, " As soon as a child
understands what is said to him, the nurse, the mother,
the pedagogue, and the father vie in their efforts to make
him good, by showing him in all that he does that '*this* is
right,' and '*that* is wrong'; 'this is pretty,' and 'that is
ugly'; so that he may learn what to follow and what to
shun. If he obeys willingly — why, excellent. If not, then
try by threats and blows to correct him, as men straighten a
warped and crooked sapling." Also after he is fairly in
school " the teacher is enjoined to pay more attention to his
morals and conduct than to his progress in reading and
music."

53. The Schoolboy's Pedagogue. — It is a great day for an
Athenian boy when he is given a pedagogue. This slave
(perhaps purchased especially for the purpose) is not his
teacher, but he ought to be more than ordinarily honest,
kindly, and well informed. His prime business is to accompany the young master everywhere out-of-doors, especially
to the school and to the gymnasium ; to carry his books and
writing tablets; to give informal help upon his lessons; to
keep him out of every kind of mischief; to teach him social
good manners; to answer the thousand questions a healthy
boy is sure to ask ; and finally, in emergencies, if the schoolmaster or father is not at hand, to administer a needful
whipping. A really capable pedagogue can mean everything to a boy; but it is asking too much that a purchased
slave should be an ideal companion.[1] Probably many pedagogues are responsible for their charges' idleness or downright depravity. It is a dubious system at the best.

---

[1] No doubt frequently the pedagogue would be an old family servant
of good morals, loyalty, and zeal. In that case the relation might be
delightful.

The assigning of the pedagogue is simultaneous with the beginning of school days; and the Athenians are not open to the charge of letting their children waste their time during possible study hours. As early as Solon's day (about 590 B.C.) a law had to be passed forbidding schools to open *before* daybreak, or to be kept open after dusk. This was in the interest not of good eyesight, but of good morals. Evidently schools had been keeping even longer than through the daylight. In any case, at gray dawn every yawning schoolboy is off, urged on by his pedagogue, and his tasks will continue with very little interruption through the entire day. It is therefore with reason that the Athenian lads rejoice in the very numerous religious holidays.

54. An Athenian School. — Leaving the worthy citizen's home, where we have lingered long chatting on many of the topics the house and its denizens suggest, we will turn again to the streets to seek the school where one of the young sons of the family has been duly conducted (possibly, one may say, driven) by his pedagogue. We have not far to go. Athenian schools have to be numerous, because they are small. To teach children of the poorer classes it is enough to have a modest room and a few stools; an unrented shop will answer. But we will go to a more pretentious establishment. There is an anteroom by the entrance way where the pedagogues can sit and doze or exchange gossip while their respective charges are kept busy in the larger room within. The latter place, however, is not particularly commodious. On the bare wall hang book-rolls, lyres, drinking vessels, baskets for books, and perhaps some simple geometrical instruments. The pupils sit on rude, low benches, each lad with his boxwood tablet covered with wax [1] upon his lap,

[1] This wax tablet was practically a slate. The letters written could be erased with the blunt upper end of the metallic stylus, and the whole surface of the tablet could be made smooth again by a judicious heating.

and presumably busy, scratching letters with his stylus. The master sits on a high chair, surveying the scene. He cultivates a grim and awful aspect, for he is under no delusion that "his pupils love him." "He sits aloft," we are told, "like a juryman, with an expression of implacable wrath, before which the pupil must tremble and cringe."[1]

Athenian schoolboys have at least their full share of idleness, as well as of animal spirits. There is soon a loud whisper from one corner. Instantly the ruling tyrant rises. "Antiphon! I have heard you. Come forward!" If Antiphon is wise, he will advance promptly and submit as cheerfully as possible to a sound caning; if folly possesses him, he will hesitate. At a nod from the master two older boys, who serve as monitors, will seize him with grim chuckles. He will then be fortunate if he escapes being tied to a post and flogged until his back is one mass of welts, and his very life seems in danger. It will be useless for him to complain to his parents. A good schoolmaster is supposed to flog frequently to earn his pay; if he is sparing with the rod or lash, he is probably lacking in energy. Boys will be boys, and there is only one remedy for juvenile shortcomings.

This diversion, of course, with its attendant howling, interrupts the course of the school, but presently matters again become normal. The scholars are so few that probably there is only one teacher, and instruction is decidedly "individual," although poetry and singing are very likely taught "in concert."

55. The School Curriculum. — As to the subjects studied, the Athenian curriculum is well fixed and limited: letters, music, and gymnastics. Every lad must have a certain amount of all of these. The gymnastics will be taught later

---

[1] The quotation is from the late writer Libanius, but it is perfectly true for classic Athens.

.n the day by a special teacher at a "wrestling school."
The "music" may also be taught separately. The main
effort with a young boy is surely to teach him to read and
write. And here must be recalled the relative infrequency
of complete books in classic Athens.[1] To read public placards, inscriptions of laws, occasional epistles, commercial
documents, etc., is probably, for many Athenians, reading
enough. The great poets he will learn by ear rather than
by eye; and he may go through a long and respected life
and never be compelled to read a really sizable volume from
end to end. So the teaching of reading is along very simple
lines. It is perhaps simultaneous with the learning of
writing. The twenty-four letters are learned by sheer
power of memory; then the master sets lines upon the
tablets to be copied. As soon as possible the boy is put
to learning and writing down passages from the great poets.
Progress in mere literacy is very rapid. There is no waste
of time on history, geography, or physical science; and between the concentration on a single main subject and the
impetus given by the master's rod the Athenian schoolboy
soon becomes adept with his letters. Possibly a little
arithmetic is taught him, but only a little. In later life, if he
does not become a trader or banker, he will not be ashamed
to reckon simple sums upon his fingers or by means of
pebbles; although if his father is ambitious to have him
become a philosopher, he may have him taught something of
geometry.

Once more we see the total absence of "vocational studies"
in this Athenian education. The whole effort is to develop
a fair, noble, free, and lofty character, not to earn a living.
To set a boy to study with an eye to learning some profitable trade is counted illiberal to the last degree. It is for

[1] One gets the impression that books — in the sense of complete volumes
— were much rarer in Athens than in Imperial Rome, or in the later Middle Ages up to the actual period of the invention of printing.

this reason that practical arithmetic is discouraged, yet a
little knowledge of the art of outline drawing is allowed;
for though no gentleman intends to train his son to be a
great artist, the study will enable him to appreciate good
sculpture and painting. Above all the schoolmaster, who,
despite his brutal austerity, ought to be a clear-sighted and
inspiring teacher, must lose no opportunity to instil moral
lessons, and develop the best powers of his charges. Theognis, the old poet of Megara, states the case well: —

> To rear a child is easy ; but to teach
> Morals and manners is beyond our reach.
> To make the foolish wise, the wicked good,
> That science never yet was understood.

56. The Study of the Poets. — It is for the developing of
the best moral and mental qualities in the lads that they
are compelled to memorize long passages of the great poets
of Hellas. Theognis, with his pithy admonitions cast in
semi-proverb form, the worldly wisdom of Hesiod, and of
Phocylides are therefore duly flogged into every Attic schoolboy.[1] But the great text-book, dwarfing all others, is
Homer, — "the Bible of the Greeks," as later ages will call
it. Even in the small school we visit, several of the pupils
can repeat five or six long episodes from both the *Iliad* and
the *Odyssey*, and there is one older boy present (an extraordinary, but by no means an unprecedented case) who
can repeat *both* of the long epics word for word.[2] Clearly
the absence of many books has then its compensations.
The average Athenian lad has what seems to be a simply
marvelous memory.

And what an admirable text-book and "second reader"

---

[1] Phocylides, whose gnomic poetry is now preserved to us only in scant
fragments, was an Ionian, born about 560 B.C. His verses were in great
acceptance in the schools.

[2] For such an attainment see Xenophon's *Symposium*, 3 : 5.

the Homeric poems are! What characters to imitate: the high-minded, passionate, yet withal loyal and lovable Achilles who would rather fight gloriously before Troy (though death in the campaign is certain) than live a long life in ignoble ease at home at Phthia; or Odysseus, the "hero of many devices," who endures a thousand ills and surmounts them all; who lets not even the goddess Calypso seduce him from his love to his "sage Penelope"; who is ever ready with a clever tale, a plausible lie, and, when the need comes, a mighty deed of manly valor. The boys will all go home to-night with firm resolves to suffer all things rather than leave a comrade unavenged, as Achilles was tempted to do and nobly refused, and to fight bravely, four against forty, as Odysseus and his comrades did, when at the call of duty and honor they cleared the house of the dastard suitors. True, philosophers like Plato complain: "Homer gives to lads very undignified and unworthy ideas of the gods"; and men of a later age will assert: "Homer has altogether too little to say about the cardinal virtues of truthfulness and honesty."[1] But making all allowances the *Iliad* and the *Odyssey* are still the two grandest secular text-books the world will ever know. The lads are infinitely the better for them.

Three years, according to Plato, are needed to learn the rudiments of reading and writing before the boys are fairly launched upon this study of the poets. For several years more they will spend most of their mornings standing respectfully before their master, while he from his chair reads to them from the roll of one author or another, — the

[1] The virtue of unflinching *honesty* was undoubtedly the thing least cultivated by the Greek education. Successful prevarication, *e.g.* in the case of Odysseus, was put at altogether too high a premium. It is to be feared that the average Athenian schoolboy was only partially truthful. The tale of "George Washington and the cherry tree" would never have found favor in Athens. The great Virginian would have been blamed for failing to concoct a clever lie.

pupils repeating the lines, time and again, until they have learned them, while the master interrupts to explain every nice point in mythology, in real or alleged history, or a moot question in ethics.

57. The Greeks do not study Foreign Languages. — As the boys grow older the scope of their study naturally increases; but in one particular their curriculum will seem strangely limited. *The study of foreign languages has no place in a Greek course of study.* That any gentleman should learn say Persian, or Egyptian (unless he intended to devote himself to distant travel), seems far more unprofitable than, in a later age, the study of say Patagonian or Papuan will appear.[1] Down at the Peiræus there are a few shipmasters, perhaps, who can talk Egyptian, Phœnician, or Babylonish. They need the knowledge for their trade, but even they will disclaim any cultural value for their accomplishment. The euphonious, expressive, marvelously delicate tongue of Hellas sums up for the Athenian almost all that is valuable in the world's intellectual and literary life. What has the outer, the "Barbarian," world to give him? — Nothing, many will say, but some gold darics which will corrupt his statesmen, and some spices, carpets, and similar luxuries which good Hellenes can well do without. The Athenian lad will never need to crucify the flesh upon Latin, French, and German, or an equivalent for his own Greek. Therein perhaps he may be heavily the loser, save that his own mother tongue is so intricate and full of subtle possibilities that to learn to make the full use thereof is truly a matter for lifelong education.

58. The Study of " Music." — But the Athenian has a substitute for this omission of foreign language study: *Music.*

---

[1] This fact did not prevent the Greeks from having a considerable respect for the traditions and lore of, *e.g.*, the Egyptians, and from borrowing a good many non-Greek usages and inventions; but all this could take place without feeling the least necessity for studying foreign languages.

This is something more comprehensive than "the art of combining tones in a manner to please the ear" [Webster]. It is practically the study of whatever will develop the noble powers of the emotions, as contrasted to the mere intellect.[1] Indeed everything which comes within the ample provinces of the nine Muses, even sober history, might be included in the term. However, for special purposes, the study of "Music" may be considered as centering around playing instruments and singing. The teacher very likely resides in a house apart from the master of the school of letters. Aristophanes gives this picture of the good old customs for the teaching of music. "The boys from the same section of the town have to march thinly clad and draw up in good order — though the snow be thick as meal — to the house of the harp master. There he will teach them [some famous tune] raising a mighty melody. If any one acts silly or turns any quavers, he gets a good hard thrashing for 'banishing the Muses!'"[2]

Learning to sing is probably the most important item, for every boy and man ought to be able to bear his part in the great chorals which are a notable element in most religious festivals; besides, a knowledge of singing is a great aid to appreciating lyric poetry, or the choruses in tragedy, and in learning to declaim. To learn to sing elaborate solo pieces is seldom necessary, — it is not quite genteel in grown-up persons, for it savors a little too much of the professional. So it is also with instrumental music. The Greeks lack the piano, the organ, the elaborate bass instruments of a later day. Their flutes and harps, although very sweet, might seem thin to a twentieth-century critic.

[1] Aristotle [*Politics*, V. (or VIII.) 1] says that the literary education is to train the mind; while music, though of no practical use, "provides a noble and liberal employment of leisure."

[2] Aristophanes's *The Clouds*. The whole passage is cited in Davis's *Readings in Ancient History*, vol. I, pp. 252–255.

But one can gain considerable volume by the great *number* of instruments, and nearly everybody in Athens can pick at the lyre after a fashion. The common type of harp is the lyre, and it has enough possibilities for the average boy. The more elaborate *cithera* is usually reserved for professionals.[1] An Athenian lad is expected to be able to accompany his song upon his own lyre and to play in concert with his fellows.

The other instrument in common use is the *flute*. At its simplest, this is a mere shepherd's pipe. Anybody can make one with a knife and some rushes. Then come elaborations; two pipes are fitted together into one wooden mouthpiece. Now, we really have an instrument with possibilities. But it is not in such favor in the schools as the lyre. You cannot blow day after day upon the flute and not distort your cheeks permanently. Again the gentleman's son will avoid "professionalism." There are amateur flute players moving in the best society, but the more fastidious frown upon the instrument, save for hired performers.

59. The Moral Character of Greek Music. — Whether it is singing, harp playing, or flute playing, a most careful watch is kept upon the *character* of the music taught the lads. The master who lets his pupils learn many soft, dulcet, languishing airs will find his charges' parents extremely angry, even to depriving him of their patronage. Very soft music, in "Lydian modes," is counted effeminate, fit only for the women's quarters and likely to do boys no good. The riotous type also, of the "Ionic mode," is fit only for drinking songs and is even more under the ban.[2] What is especially in favor

---

[1] For the details of these harp types of instruments see Dictionary of Antiquities.

[2] The "Phrygian mode" from which the "Ionic" was derived was still more demoralizing; it was counted "orgiastic," and proper only in certain excited religious rhapsodies.

is the stern, strenuous Dorian mode. This will make boys hardy, manly, and brave. Very elaborate music with trills and quavers is in any case frowned upon. It simply delights the trained ear, and has no reaction upon the character; and of what value is a musical presentation unless it leaves the hearers and performer better, worthier men? Let the average Athenian possess the opportunity, and he will infallibly stamp with disapproval a great part of both the popular and the classical music of the later ages.[1]

60. The Teaching of Gymnastics. — The visits to the reading school and to the harp master have consumed a large part of the day; but towards afternoon the pedagogues will conduct their charges to the third of the schoolboys' tyrants: the gymnastic teacher. Nor do his parents count this the least important of the three. Must not their sons be as physically "beautiful" (to use the common phrase in Athens) as possible, and must they not some day, as good citizens, play their brave part in war? The *palæstras* (literally "wrestling grounds") are near the outskirts of the city, where land is cheap and a good-sized open space can be secured. Here the lads are given careful instruction under the constant eye of an expert in running, wrestling, boxing, jumping, discus hurling, and javelin casting. They are not expected to become professional athletes, but their parents will be vexed if they do not develop a healthy tan all over their naked bodies,[2] and if they do not learn at least moderate proficiency in the sports and a certain amount of familiarity with elementary military maneuvers. Of course

[1] We have extremely few Greek melodies preserved to us, and these few are not attractive to the modern ear. All that can fairly be said is that the Hellenes were obviously such æsthetic, harmoniously minded people that it is impossible their music should have failed in nobility, beauty, and true melody.

[2] To have a pale, untanned skin was "womanish" and unworthy of a free Athenian citizen.

boys of marked physical ability will be encouraged to think
of training for the various great " games " which culminate
at Olympia, although enlightened opinion is against the pro-
moting of professional athletics; and certain extreme philosophers question the wisdom of any extensive physical culture
at all, " for (say they) is not the human mind the real thing
worth developing?"[1]

Weary at length and ready for a hearty meal and sleep,
the boys are conducted homeward by their pedagogues.

As they grow older the lads with ambitious parents
will be given a more varied education. Some will be put
under such teachers of the new rhetoric and oratory, now in
vogue, as the famous Isocrates, and be taught to play the
orator as an aid to inducing their fellow citizens to bestow
political advancement. Certain will be allowed to become
pupils of Plato, who has been teaching his philosophy out at
the groves of the Academy, or to join some of his rivals in
theoretical wisdom. Into these fields, however, we cannot
follow them.

61. The Habits and Ambitions of Schoolboys. — It is a
clear fact, that by the age say of thirteen, the Athenian
education has had a marked effect upon the average schoolboy. Instead of being " the most ferocious of animals," as
Plato, speaking of his untutored state describes him, he is
now " the most amiable and divine of living beings." The
well-trained lad goes now to school with his eyes cast upon
the ground, his hands and arms wrapped in his chiton,
making way dutifully for all his elders. If he is addressed
by an older man, he stands modestly, looking downward
and blushing in a manner worthy of a girl. He has been
taught to avoid the Agora, and if he must pass it, never to

[1] The details of the boys' athletic games, being much of a kind with those
followed by adults at the regular public gymnasia, are here omitted
See Chap. XVII.

linger. The world is full of evil and ugly things, but he is taught to hear and see as little of them as possible. When men talk of his healthy color, increasing beauty, and admire the graceful curves of his form at the wrestling school, he must not grow proud. He is being taught to learn relatively little from books, but a great deal from hearing the conversation of grave and well-informed men. As he grows older his father will take him to all kinds of public gatherings and teach him the working details of the "Democratic Government" of Athens. He becomes intensely proud of his city. It is at length his chief thought, almost his entire life. A very large part of the loyalty which an educated man of a later age will divide between his home, his church, his college, his town, and his nation, the Athenian lad will sum up in two words, — "my *polis*"; *i.e.* the city of Athens. His home is largely a place for eating and sleeping; his school is not a great institution, it is simply a kind of disagreeable though necessary learning shop; his church is the religion of his ancestors, and this religion is warp and woof of the government, as much a part thereof as the law courts or the fighting fleet; his town and his nation are alike the sovran city-state of Athens. Whether he feels keenly a wider loyalty to Hellas at large, as against the Great King of Persia, for instance, will depend upon circumstances. In a real crisis, as at Salamis, — yes. In ordinary circumstances when there is hot feud with Sparta, — no.

62. The "Ephebi." — The Athenian education then is admirably adapted to make the average lad a useful and worthy citizen, and to make him modest, alert, robust, manly, and a just lover of the beautiful, both in conduct and in art. It does not, however, develop his individual bent very strongly; and it certainly gives him a mean view of the dignity of labor. He will either become a leisurely gentleman, whose only proper self-expression will come in warfare,

politics, or philosophy; or — if he be poor — he will at least
envy and try to imitate the leisure class.

By eighteen the young Athenian's days of study will
usually come to a close. At that age he will be given a
simple festival by his father and be formally enrolled in his
paternal *deme*.[1] His hair, which has hitherto grown down
toward his shoulders, will be clipped short. He will allow
his beard to grow. At the temple of Aglaurus he will (with
the other youths of his age) take solemn oath of loyalty to
Athens and her laws. For the next year he will serve as a
military guard at the Peiræus, and receive a certain training in soldiering. The next year the state will present him
with a new shield and spear, and he will have a taste of
rougher garrison duty at one of the frontier forts towards
Bœotia or Megara.[2] Then he is mustered out. He is an
ephebus no longer, but a full-fledged citizen, and all the
vicissitudes of Athenian life are before him.

[1] One of the hundred or more petty townships or precincts into which
Attica was divided.

[2] These two years which the *ephebi* of Athens had to serve under arms
have been aptly likened to the military service now required of young
men in European countries.

CHAPTER X.

THE PHYSICIANS OF ATHENS.

63. The Beginnings of Greek Medical Science. — As we move about the city we cannot but be impressed by the high average of fine physiques and handsome faces. Your typical Greek is fair in color and has very regular features. The youths do not mature rapidly, but thanks to the gymnasia and the regular lives, they develop not merely admirable, but healthy, bodies. The proportion of hale and hearty *old* men is great; and probably the number of invalids is considerably smaller than in later times and in more artificially reared communities.[1] Nevertheless, the Athenians are certainly mortal, and subject to bodily ills, and the physician is no unimportant member of society, although his exact status is much less clearly determined than it will be in subsequent ages.

Greek medicine and surgery, as it appears in Homer, is simply a certain amount of practical knowledge gained by rough experience, largely supplemented by primitive superstition. It was quite as important to know the proper prayers and charms wherewith to approach "Apollo the Healer," as to understand the kind of herb poultice which would keep wounds from festering. Homer speaks of Asclepius; however, in early days he was not a god, but simply a skilful leach. Then as we approach historic times the physician's art becomes more regular. Asclepius is elevated

---

[1] A slight but significant witness to the general healthiness of the Greeks is found in the very rare mention in their literature of such a common ill as *toothache*.

into a separate and important deity, although it is not till
420 B.C. that his worship is formally introduced into Athens.
Long ere that time, however, medicine and surgery had won
a real place among the practical sciences. The sick man
stands at least a tolerable chance of rational treatment,
and of not being murdered by wizards and fanatical ex-
orcists.

64. Healing Shrines and their Methods. — There exist in
Athens and in other Greek cities real sanataria[1]; these are
temples devoted to the healing gods (usually Asclepius, but
sometimes Apollo, Aphrodite, and Hera). Here the patient
is expected to sleep over night in the temple, and the god
visits him in a dream, and reveals a course of treatment
which will lead to recovery. Probably there is a good
deal of sham and imposture about the process. The canny
priests know more than they care to tell about how the
patient is worked into an excitable, imaginative state; and
of the very human means employed to produce a satisfactory
and informing dream.[2] Nevertheless it is a great deal to
convince the patient that he is sure of recovery, and that
nobody less than a god has dictated the remedies. The
value of mental therapeutics is keenly appreciated. Attached to the temple are skilled physicians to "interpret"
the dream, and opportunities for prolonged residence with
treatment by baths, purgation, dieting, mineral waters, sea
baths, all kinds of mild gymnastics, etc. Entering upon
one of these temple treatments is, in short, anything but sur-
rendering oneself to unmitigated quackery. Probably a
large proportion of the former patients have recovered;
and they have testified their gratitude by hanging around

[1] The most famous was at Epidaurus, where the Asclepius cult seems to
have been especially localized.
[2] The "healing sleep" employed at these temples is described, in a
kind of blasphemous parody, in Aristophanes's *Plutus*. (Significant passages are quoted in Davis's *Readings in Ancient History*, vol. I, pp. 258–261.)

the shrine little votive tablets,[1] usually pictures of the
diseased parts now happily healed, or, for internal maladies,
a written statement of the nature of the disease. This is
naturally very encouraging to later patients : they gain confidence by knowing that many cases similar to their own
have been thus cured.

These visits to the healing temples are, however, expensive : not everybody has entire faith in them; for many
lesser ills also they are wholly unnecessary. Let us look,
then, at the regular physicians.

65. An Athenian Physician's Office. — There are salaried
public medical officers in Athens, and something like a public
dispensary where free treatment is given citizens in simple
cases; but the average man seems to prefer his own doctor.[2]
We may enter the office of Menon, a "regular private prac-
titioner," and look about us. The office itself is a mere
open shop in the front of a house near the Agora; and, like
a barber's shop, is something of a general lounging place.
In the rear one or two young disciples (doctors in embryo)
and a couple of slaves are pounding up drugs in mortars.
There are numbers of bags of dried herbs and little glass
flasks hanging on the walls. Near the entrance is a statue
of Asclepius the Healer, and also of the great human founder
of the real medical science among the Greeks — Hippocrates.

Menon himself is just preparing to go out on his professional calls. He is a handsome man in the prime of life,
and takes great pains with his personal appearance. His
himation is carefully draped. His finger rings have excellent cameos. His beard has been neatly trimmed, and he
has just bathed and scented himself with delicate Assyrian

---

[1] Somewhat as in the various Catholic pilgrimage shrines (*e.g.* Lourdes)
to-day.

[2] We know comparatively little of these public physicians; probably
they were mainly concerned with the health of the army and naval force,
the prevention of epidemics, etc.

nard. He will gladly tell you that he is in no wise a fop, but that it is absolutely necessary to produce a pleasant personal impression upon his fastidious, irritable patients. Menon himself claims to have been a personal pupil of the great Hippocrates,[1] and about every other reputable Greek physician will make the same claim. He has studied more or less in a temple of Asclepius, and perhaps has been a member of the medical staff thereto attached. He has also become a member of the Hippocratic brotherhood, a semi-secret organization, associated with the Asclepius cult, and carefully cherishing the dignity of the profession and the secret arts of the guild.

66. The Physician's Oath. — The oath which all this brotherhood has sworn is noble and notable. Here are some of the main provisions : —

" I swear by Apollo the Physician, and Asclepius and Hygeia; a [Lady Health] and Panaceia [Lady All-Cure] to honor as my parents the master who taught me this art, and to admit to my own instruction only his sons, my own sons, and those who have been duly inscribed as pupils, and who have taken the medical oath, and no others. I will prescribe such treatment as may be for the benefit of my patients, according to my best power and judgment, and preserve them from anything hurtful or mischievous. I will never, even if asked, administer poison, nor advise its use. I will never give a criminal draught to a woman. I will maintain the purity and integrity of my art. Wherever I go, I will abstain from all mischief or corruption, or any immodest action. If ever I hear any secret I will not divulge it. If I keep this oath, may the gods give me success in life and in my art. If I break this oath, may all the reverse fall upon me." [2]

---

[1] Who was still alive, an extremely old man. He died in Thessaly in 357 B.C., at an alleged age of 104 years.

[2] For the unabridged translation of this oath, see Smith's *Dictionary of Antiquities* (revised edition), vol. II, p. 154.

67. The Skill of Greek Physicians. — Menon's skill as a physician and surgeon is considerable. True, he has only a very insufficient conception of anatomy. His *theoretical* knowledge is warped, but he is a shrewd judge of human nature and his *practical* knowledge is not contemptible. In his private pharmacy his assistants have compounded a great quantity of drugs which he knows how to administer with much discernment. He has had considerable experience in dealing with wounds and sprains, such as are common in the wars or in the athletic games. He understands that Dame Nature is a great healer, who is to be assisted rather than coerced; and he dislikes resorting to violent remedies, such as bleedings and strong emetics. Ordinary fevers and the like he can attack with success. He has no modern anæsthetics or opium, but has a very insufficient substitute in mandragora. He can treat simple diseases of the eye; and he knows how to put gold filling into teeth. His surgical instruments, however, are altogether too primitive. He is personally cleanly; but he has not the least idea of antiseptics; the result is that obscure internal diseases, calling for grave operations, are likely to baffle him. He will refuse to operate, or if he does operate the chances are against the patient.[1] In other words, his medical skill is far in advance of his surgery.

Menon naturally busies himself among the best families of Athens, and commands a very good income. He counts it part of his equipment to be able to persuade his patients, by all the rules of logic and rhetoric, to submit to disagreeable treatment; and for that end has taken lessons in informal oratory from Isocrates or one of his associates. Some of Menon's competitors (feeling themselves less eloquent) have actually a paid rhetorician whom they can take

---

[1] Seemingly a really serious operation was usually turned over by the local physician to a traveling surgeon, who could promptly disappear from the neighborhood if things went badly.

to the bedside of a stubborn invalid, to induce him by
irrefutable arguments to endure an amputation.[1]

No such honor of course is paid to the intellects of the
poorer fry, who swarm in at Menon's surgery. Those who
cannot pay to have him bandage them himself, perforce put
up with the secondary skill and wisdom of the "disciples."
The drug-mixing slaves are expected to salve and physic
the patients of their own class; but there seems to be a law
against allowing them to attempt the treatment of free-born
men.

68. Quacks and Charlatans. — Unluckily not everybody is
wise enough to put up with the presumably honest efforts
of Menon's underlings. There appears to be no law against
allowing anybody who wishes to pose as a physician, and
to sell his inexperience and his quack nostrums. Vendors
of every sort of cure-all abound, as well as creatures who
work on the superstitious and pretend to cure by charms and
hocus-pocus. In the market there is such a swarm of these
charlatans of healing that they bring the whole medical
profession into contempt. Certain people go so far as to
distrust the efficacy of any part of the lore of Asclepius. Says
one poet tartly: —

> The surgeon Menedemos, as men say,
> Touched as he passed a Zeus of marble white;
> Neither the marble nor his Zeus-ship might
> Avail the god — they buried him to-day.

And again even to dream of the quacks is dangerous: —

> Diophantes, sleeping, saw
> Hermas the physician:
> Diophantes never woke
> From that fatal vision.[2]

[1] Plato tells how Gorgias, the famous rhetorician, was sometimes thus
hired. A truly Greek artifice — this substitution of oratory for chloroform!

[2] Both of these quotations probably date from later than 360 B.C., but
they are perfectly in keeping with the general opinion of Greek quackery.

All in all, despite Menon's good intentions and not despicable skill, it is fortunate the gods have made "Good Health" one of their commonest gifts to the Athenians. Constant exercise in the gymnasia, occasional service in the army, the absence of cramping and unhealthful office work, and a climate which puts out-of-door existence at a premium, secure for them a general good health that compensates for most of the lack of a scientific medicine.

CHAPTER XI.

THE FUNERALS.

69. An Athenian's Will. — All Menon's patients are to-day set out upon the road to recovery. Hipponax, his rival, has been less fortunate. A wealthy and elderly patient, Lycophron, died the day before yesterday. As the latter felt his end approaching, he did what most Athenians may put off until close to the inevitable hour — he made his will, and called in his friends to witness it; and one must hope there can be no doubt about the validity, the signets attached, etc., for otherwise the heirs may find themselves in a pretty lawsuit.

The will begins in this fashion : "The Testament of Lycophron the Marathonian.[1]   May all be well : — but if I do not recover from this sickness, thus do I bestow my estate." Then in perfectly cold-blooded fashion he proceeds to give his young wife and the guardianship of his infant daughter to Stobiades, a bachelor friend who will probably marry the widow within two months or less of the funeral. Lycophron gives also specific directions about his tomb; he gives legacies of money or jewelry to various old associates; he mentions certain favorite slaves to receive freedom, and as specifically orders certain others (victims of his displeasure) to be kept in bondage. Lastly three reliable friends are named as executors.

70. The Preliminaries of a Funeral. — An elaborate funeral is the last perquisite of every Athenian. Even if Lycophron

---

[1] In all Athenian legal documents, it was necessary to give the deme of the interested party or parties.

had been a poor man he would now receive obsequies seemingly far out of proportion to his estate and income. It is even usual in Greek states to have laws restraining the amount which may be spent upon funerals, — otherwise great sums may be literally "burned up" upon the funeral pyres. When now the tidings go out that Lycophron's nearest relative has "closed his mouth," after he has breathed his last, all his male kinsfolk and all other persons who *hope* to be remembered in the will promptly appear in the Agora in black himatia[1] and hasten to the barber shops to have their heads shaved. The widow might shave her hair likewise, with all her slave maids, did not her husband, just ere his death, positively forbid such disfigurements. The women of the family take the body in charge the minute the physician has declared that all is over. The customary obol is put in the mouth of the corpse,[2] and the body is carefully washed in perfumed water, clothed in festal white; then woolen fillets are wound around the head, and over these a crown of vine leaves. So arrayed, the body is ready to be laid out on a couch in the front courtyard of the house, with the face turned toward the door so as to seem to greet everybody who enters. In front of the house there stands a tall earthen vase of water, wherewith the visitors may give themselves a purifying sprinkling, after quitting the polluting presence of a dead body.

71. Lamenting the Dead. — Around this funeral bed the relatives and friends keep a gloomy vigil. The Athenians after all are southern born, and when excited seem highly emotional people. There are stern laws dating from Solon's

[1] In the important city of Argos, however, *white* was the proper funeral color.

[2] This was not originally (as later asserted) a fee to Charon the ferryman to Hades, but simply a "minimum precautionary sum, for the dead man's use" (Dr. Jane Harrison), placed in the mouth, where a Greek usually kept his small change.

day against the worst excesses, but what now occurs seems violent enough. The widow is beating her breast, tearing her hair, gashing her cheeks with her finger nails. Lycophron's elderly sister has ashes sprinkled upon her gray head and ever and anon utters piteous wails. The slave women in the background keep up a hideous moaning. The men present do not think it undignified to utter loud lamentation and to shed frequent tears. Least commendable of all (from a modern standpoint) are the hired dirge singers, who maintain a most melancholy chant, all the time beating their breasts, and giving a perfect imitation of frantic grief. This has probably continued day and night, the mourners perhaps taking turns by relays.

All in all it is well that Greek custom enjoins the actual funeral, at least, on the second day following the death.[1] The "shade" of the deceased is not supposed to find rest in the nether world until after the proper obsequies.[2] To let a corpse lie several days without final disposition will bring down on any family severe reproach. In fact, on few points are the Greeks more sensitive than on this subject of prompt burial or cremation. After a land battle the victors are bound never to push their vengeance so far as to refuse a " burial truce " to the vanquished ; and it is a doubly unlucky admiral who lets his crews get drowned in a sea fight, without due effort to recover the corpses afterward and to give them proper disposition on land.

72. The Funeral Procession. — The day after the " layingout" comes the actual funeral. Normally it is held as early as possible in the morning, before the rising of the sun. Perhaps while on the way to the Agora we have passed,

---

[1] It must be remembered that the Greeks had no skilled embalmers at their service, and that they lived in a decidedly warm climate.

[2] See the well-known case of the wandering shade of Patroclus demanding the proper obsequies from Achilles (*Iliad*, XXIII. 71).

well outside the city, such a mournful procession. The
youngest and stoutest of the male relatives carry the litter :
although if Lycophron's relatives had desired a really extrav-
agant display they might have employed a mule car. Ahead
of the bier march the screaming flute players, earning their
fees by no melodious din. Then comes the litter itself with
the corpse arrayed magnificently for the finalities, a honey
cake set in the hands,[1] a flask of oil placed under the head.
After this come streaming the relatives in irregular procession : the widow and the chief heir (her prospective second
husband !) walking closest, and trying to appear as demon-
strative as possible : nor (merely because the company is
noisy and not stoical in its manner) need we deny that there
is abundant genuine grief. All sorts of male acquaintances
of the deceased bring up the rear, since it is good form to proclaim to wide Athens that Lycophron had hosts of friends.[2]

73. The Funeral Pyre. — So the procession moves through
the still gloomy streets of the city, — doubtless needing
torch bearers as well as flute players, — and out through some
gate, until the line halts in an open field, or better, in a quiet
and convenient garden. Here the great funeral pyre of
choice dry fagots, intermixed with aromatic cedar, has been
heaped. The bier is laid thereon. There are no strictly religious ceremonies. The company stands in a respectful
circle, while the nearest male kinsman tosses a pine link
upon the oil-soaked wood. A mighty blaze leaps up to
heaven, sending its ruddy brightness against the sky now
palely flushed with the bursting dawn. The flutists play in
softer measures. As the fire rages a few of the relatives toss

[1] The original idea of the honey cake was simply that it was a friendly
present to the infernal gods ; later came the conceit that it was a sop to
fling to the dog Cerberus, who guarded the entrance to Hades.

[2] Women, unless they were over sixty years of age, were not allowed to
join in funeral processions unless they were first cousins, or closer kin,
of the deceased.

upon it pots of rare unguents; and while the flames die
down, thrice the company shout their farewells, calling their
departed friend by name — "Lycophron! Lycophron! Lycophron!"

So fierce is the flame it soon sinks into ashes. As soon as
these are cool enough for safety (a process hastened by
pouring on water or wine) the charred bones of the deceased
are tenderly gathered up to be placed in a stately urn. The
company, less formally now, returns to Athens, and that night
there will probably be a great funeral feast at the house of
the nearest relative, everybody eating and drinking to
capacity "to do Lycophron full honor"; for it is he who is
imagined as being now for the last time the host.

74. Honors to the Memory of the Dead. — Religion seems
to have very little place in the Athenian funeral : there are
no priests present, no prayers, no religious hymns. But the
dead man is now conceived as being, in a very humble and
intangible way, a deity himself : his good will is worth propitiating; his memory is not to be forgotten. On the third,
ninth, and thirtieth days after the funeral there are simple
religious ceremonies with offerings of garlands, fruits, liba-
tions and the like, at the new tomb; and later at certain
times in the year these will be repeated. The more enlightened will of course consider these merely graceful re-
membrances of a former friend ; but there is a good deal of
primitive ancestor worship even in civilized Athens.

Burning is the usual method for the Greeks to dispose of
their dead, but the burial of unburned bodies is not unknown to them. Probably, however, the rocky soil and the
limited land space around Athens make regular cemeteries
less convenient than elsewhere : still it would have been
nothing exceptional if Lycophron had ordered in his will
that he be put in a handsome pottery coffin to be placed in
a burial ground pertaining to his family.

ATHENIAN FUNERAL MONUMENT.

A lady is gazing upon her casket of jewels before bidding them eternal farewell. Note the admirable restraint yet pathos of the scene.

75. The Beautiful Funeral Monuments. — If the noisy funeral customs permitted to the Athenians may repel a later day observer, there can be only praise for the Athenian tombs, or rather the funeral monuments (*stēlæ*) which might be set over the urns of ashes or the actual coffins. Nearly every Athenian family has a private field which it uses for sepulchral purposes: but running outside of the city, near the Itonian Gate along the road to the Peiræus, the space to either side of the highway has been especially appropriated for this purpose. Walking higher along this " Street of the Tombs " we can make a careful survey of some of the most touching memorials of Athenian life.

The period of hot, violent grief seems now over; the mourners have settled down in their dumb sense of loss. This spirit of calm, noble resignation is what is expressed upon these monuments. All is chaste, dignified, simple. There are no labored eulogies of the deceased; no frantic expressions of sorrow; no hint (let it be also said) of any hope of reunions in the Hereafter. Sometimes there is simply a plain marble slab or pillar marked with the name of the deceased; and with even the more elaborate monuments the effort often is to concentrate, into one simple scene, the best and worthiest that was connected with the dear departed. Here is the noble mother seated in quiet dignity extending her hand in farewell to her sad but steadfast husband, while her children linger wonderingly by; here is the athlete, the young man in his pride, depicted not in the moment of weakness and death, but scraping his glorious form with his strigil, after some victorious contest in the games; here is the mounted warrior, slain before Corinth whilst battling for his country, represented in the moment of overthrowing beneath his flying charger some despairing foe. We are made to feel that these Athenians were fair and beautiful in their lives, and that in their deaths they were not unworthy. And we

marvel, and admire these monuments the more when we
realize that they are not the work of master sculptors but
of ordinary paid craftsmen. We turn away praising the
city that could produce such noble sculpture and call it
mere handicraft, and praising also the calm poise of soul,
uncomforted by revealed religion, which could make these
monuments common expressions of the bitterest, deepest,
most vital emotions which can ever come to men.[1]

[1] As Von Falke (*Greece and Rome*, p. 141) well says of these monuments,
" No skeleton, no scythe, no hour-glass is in them to bring a shudder to
the beholder. As they [the departed] were in life, mother and daughter,
husband and wife, parents and children, here they are represented together, sitting or standing, clasping each other's hands and looking at one
another with love and sympathy as if it were their customary affectionate
intercourse. What the stone perpetuates is the love and happiness they
enjoyed together, while yet they rejoiced in life and the light of day.''

CHAPTER XII.

TRADE, MANUFACTURES, AND BANKING.

76. The Commercial Importance of Athens. — While the funeral mourners are wending their slow way homeward we have time to examine certain phases of Athenian life at which we have previously glanced, then ignored. Certain it is, most " noble and good " gentlemen delight to be considered persons of polite uncommercial leisure; equally certain it is that a good income is about as desirable in Athens as anywhere else, and many a stately "Eupatrid," who seems to spend his whole time in dignified walks, discoursing on politics or philosophy, is really keenly interested in trades, factories, or farms, of which his less nobly born stewards have the active management. Indeed one of the prime reasons for Athenian greatness is the fact that Athens is the richest and greatest commercial city of Continental Hellas, with only Corinth as a not formidable rival.[1]

To understand the full extent of Athenian commercial prosperity we must visit the Peiræus, yet in the main city itself will be found almost enough examples of the chief kinds of economic activity.

77. The Manufacturing Activities of Athens. — Attica is the seat of much manufacturing. Go to the suburbs: everywhere is the rank odor of the tanneries; down at the

---

[1] Syracuse in distant Sicily was possibly superior to Athens in commerce and economic prosperity, although incomparably behind her in the empire of the arts and literature.

harbors are innumerable ship carpenters and sail and
tackle makers, busy in the shipyards; from almost every
part of the city comes the clang of hammer and anvil where
hardware of all kinds is being wrought in the smithies; and
finally the pottery makers are so numerous as to require
special mention hereafter. But no list of all the manufacturing activities is here possible; enough that practically
every known industry is represented in Athens, and the

AT THE SMITHY.

"industrial" class is large.[1] A very large proportion of the
industrial laborers are slaves, but by no means all. A good
many are real Athenian citizens; a still larger proportion
are "metics" (resident foreigners without political
rights). The competition of slave labor, however, tends
to keep wages very low. An unskilled laborer will have to
be content with his 3 obols (9 cents) per day; but a trained
workman will demand a drachma (18 cents) or even more.
There are no labor unions or trade guilds. A son usually,

[1] For a very suggestive list of the numerous kinds of Greek industries
(practically all of which would be represented in Athens) see H. J.
Edwards, in Whibley's *Companion to Greek Studies*, p. 431.

though not invariably, follows his father's profession.
Each industry and line of work tends to have its own little
street or alley, preferably leading off the Agora. "The
Street of the Marble Workers," the "Street of the Box
Makers," and notably the "Street of the Potters" contain
nearly all the workshops of a given kind. Probably you
can find no others in the city. Prices are regulated by custom and competition; in case any master artisan is suspected of "enhancing" the price of a needful commodity,
or his shady business methods seem dangerous to the public,
there is no hesitation in invoking an old law or passing a
new one in the Assembly to bring him to account.

Manufacturers are theoretically under a social ban, and
indeed yonder petty shoemaker, who, with his two apprentices, first makes up his cheap sandals, then sells them over
the low counter before his own shop, is very far from being
a "leisurely" member of the "noble and the good." But
he who, like the late Lycophron, owns a furniture factory
employing nigh threescore slaves, can be sure of lying
down on his couch at a dinner party among the very best;
for, as in twentieth century England, even manufacture and
"trade," if on a sufficiently large scale, cover a multitude of
social sins.[1]

78. The Commerce of Athens. — Part of Athenian wealth
comes from the busy factories, great and small, which seem
everywhere; still more riches come in by the great commerce which will be found centered at the Peiræus. Here
is the spacious *Deigma*, a kind of exchange-house where
ship masters can lay out samples of their wares on display,

[1] Plato, probably echoing thoughtful Greek opinion, considered it bad
for manufacturers to be either too wealthy or too poor; thus a potter getting too rich will neglect his art, and grow idle; if, however, he cannot
afford proper tools, he will manufacture inferior wares, and his sons will
be even worse workmen than he. Such comment obviously comes from
a society where most industrial life is on a small scale.

and sell to the important wholesalers, who will transmit to the petty shopkeepers and the "ultimate consumer."[1]

There are certain articles of which various districts make a specialty, and which Athens is constantly importing: Bœotia sends chariots; Thessaly, easy chairs; Chios and Miletos, bedding; and Miletos, especially, very fine woolens. Greece in general looks to Syria and Arabia for the much-esteemed spices and perfumes; to Egypt for papyri for the book rolls; to Babylonia for carpets. To discuss the whole problem of Athenian commerce would require a book in itself; but certain main facts stand out clearly. One is that Attica herself has extremely few natural products to export — only her olive oil, her Hymettus honey, and her magnificent marbles — dazzling white from Pentelicos, gray from Hymettus, blue or black from Eleusis. Again we soon notice the great part which *grain* plays in Athenian commerce. Attica raises such a small proportion of the necessary breadstuffs, and so serious is the crisis created by any shortage, that all kinds of measures are employed to compel a steady flow of grain from the Black Sea ports into the Peiræus. Here is a law which Demosthenes quotes to us : —

"It shall not be lawful for any Athenian or any metic in Attica, or any person under their control [*i.e.* slave or freedman] to lend out money on a ship which is not commissioned to bring grain to Athens."

A second law, even more drastic, forbids any such person to transport grain to any harbor but the Peiræus. The penalties for evading these laws are terrific. At set intervals also the Public Assembly (Ecclesia) is in duty bound

[1] Of course a very large proportion of Greek manufactured wares were never exported, but were sold direct by the manufacturer to the consumer himself. This had various disadvantages; but there was this large gain: *only one profit* was necessary to be added to the mere cost of production. This aided to make Greece (from a modern standpoint) a paradise of low prices.

to consider the whole state of the grain trade : while the dealers in grain who seem to be cornering the market, and forcing up the price of bread, are liable to prompt and disastrous prosecution.

79. The Adventurous Merchant Skippers. — Foreign trade at Athens is fairly well systematized, but it still partakes of the nature of an adventure. The name for "skipper" (naukleros) is often used interchangeably for "merchant." Nearly all commerce is by sea, for land routes are usually slow, unsafe, and inconvenient[1]; the average foreign trader is also a shipowner, probably too the actual working captain. He has no special commodity, but will handle everything which promises a profit. A war is breaking out in Paphlagonia. Away he sails thither with a cargo of good Athenian shields, swords, and lances. He loads up in that barbarous but fertile country with grain; but leaves enough room in his hold for some hundred skins of choice wine which he takes aboard at Chios. The grain and wine are disembarked at the Peiræus. Hardly are they ashore ere rumor tells him that salt herring[2] are abundant and especially cheap at Corcyra; and off he goes for a return cargo thereof, just lingering long enough to get on a lading of Athenian olive oil.

80. Athenian Money-changers and Bankers. — An important factor in the commerce of Athens is the " Money-changer." There is no one fixed standard of coinage for Greece, let alone the Barbarian world. Athens strikes its money on a standard which has very wide acceptance, but Corinth has another standard, and a great deal of business is also transacted in Persian gold darics. The result is that at the Peiræus

[1] Naturally there was a safe land route from Athens across the Isthmus to Corinth and thence to Sparta or towards Elis; again, there would be fair roads into Bœotia.

[2] Salt fish were a very usual and important article of Greek commerce

and near the Agora are a number of little "tables" where
alert individuals, with strong boxes beside them, are ready
to sell foreign coins to would-be travelers, or exchange
darics for Attic drachmæ, against a pretty favorable
commission.

This was the beginning of the Athenian banker; but from
being a mere exchanger he has often passed far beyond, to
become a real master of credit and capital.   There are several of these highly important gentlemen who now have a
business and fortune equal to that of the famous Pasion,
who died in 370 B.C.   While the firm of Pasion and Company
was at its height, the proprietor derived a net income of at
least 100 minæ (over $1800) per year from his banking;
and more than half as much extra from a shield factory.[1]

81. A Large Banking Establishment. — Enter now the
"tables" of Nicanor.   The owner is a metic; perhaps he
claims to come from Rhodes, but the shrewd cast of his eye
and the dark hue of his skin gives a suggestion of the Syrian
about him.   In his open office a dozen young half-naked
clerks are seated on low chairs — each with his tablets
spread out upon his knees laboriously computing long
sums.[2]   The proprietor himself acts as the cashier.   He has
not neglected the exchange of foreign moneys; but that is a
mere incidental.   His first visitor this morning presents a
kind of letter of credit from a correspondent in Syracuse
calling for one hundred drachmæ.   " Your voucher? " asks
Nicanor.   The stranger produces the half of a coin broken in
two across the middle.   The proprietor draws a similar half

---

[1] These sums seem absurdly small for a great money magnate, but the
very high purchasing power of money in Athens must be borne in mind.
We know a good deal about Pasion and his business from the speeches
which Demosthenes composed in the litigation which arose over his estate.

[2] Without the Arabic system of numerals, elaborate bookkeeping surely
presented a sober face to the Greeks.   Their method of numeration was
very much like that with the so-called Roman numerals.

coin from a chest. The parts match exactly, and the money
is paid on the spot. The next comer is an old acquaintance,
a man of wealth and reputation; he is followed by two
slaves bearing a heavy talent of coined silver which he
wishes the banker to place for him on an advantageous loan,
against a due commission. The third visitor is a well-born
but fast and idle young man who is squandering his patri-
mony on flute girls and chariot horses. He wishes an
advance of ten minæ, and it is given him—against the mort-
gage of a house, at the ruinous interest of 36 per cent, for
such prodigals are perfectly fair prey. Another visitor is
a careful and competent ship merchant who is fitting for a
voyage to Crete, and who requires a loan to buy his return
cargo. Ordinary interest, well secured, is 18 per cent, but
a sea voyage, even at the calmest season, is counted extra
hazardous. The skipper must pay 24 per cent at least.
A poor tradesman also appears to raise a trifle by pawning
two silver cups; and an unlucky farmer, who cannot meet
his loan, persuades the banker to extend the time "just
until the next moon"[1]—of course at an unmerciful com-
pounding of interest.

82. Drawbacks to the Banking Business. — Nicanor has no
paper money to handle, no stocks, no bonds, — and the line
between legitimate interest and scandalous usury is by no
means clearly drawn. There is at least one good excuse for
demanding high interest. It is notoriously hard to collect
bad debts. Many and many a clever debtor has persuaded
an Athenian jury that *all* taking of interest is somewhat
immoral, and the banker has lost at least his interest, sometimes too his principal. So long as this is the case, a
banker's career has its drawbacks; and Demosthenes in a

---

[1] "Watching the moon," *i.e.* the end of the month when the debts become due, appears to have been the melancholy recreation of many Athenian debtors. See Aristophanes's *Clouds*, l. 18.

recent speech has commended the choice by Pasion's son of
a factory worth 60 minæ per year, instead of his father's
banking business worth nominally 100.   The former was so
much more secure than an income depending on "other
people's money!"

Finally it must be said that while Nicanor and Pasion
have been honorable and justly esteemed men, many of
their colleagues have been rogues.   Many a "table" has been
closed very suddenly, when its owner absconded, or col-
lapsed in bankruptcy, and the unlucky depositors and
creditors have been left penniless, during the "rearrange-
ment of the tables," as the euphemism goes.

83. The Pottery of Athens. — There is one other form of
economic activity in Athens which deserves our especial
notice, different as it is from the bankers' tables, — the
manufacture of earthen vases.   A long time might be spent
investigating the subject; here there is room only for a
hasty glance.   For more than two hundred years Attica
has been supplying the world with a pottery which is in
some respects superior to any that has gone before, and
also (all things considered) to any that will follow, through
nigh two and a half millenniums.   The articles are primarily tall vases and urns, some for mere ornament or for
religious purposes, — some for very humble household utility;
however, besides the regular vases there is a great variety
of dishes, plates, pitchers, bowls, and cups all of the same
general pattern, — a smooth, black glaze [1] covered with figures in the delicate red of the unglazed clay.   At first the
figures had been in black and the background in red, but by
about 500 B.C. the superiority of the black backgrounds had
been fully realized and the process perfected.   For a long
time Athens had a monopoly of this beautiful earthenware,
but now in 360 B.C. there are creditable manufactories in

---

[1] Sometimes this glaze tended to a rich olive green or deep brown.

other cities, and especially in the Greek towns of Southern
Italy. The Athenian industry is, however, still considerable; in fifty places up and down the city, but particularly
in the busy quarter of the Ceramicus, the potters' wheels are
whirling, and the glazers are adding the elegant patterns.

**84. Athenian Pottery an Expression of the Greek Sense of
Beauty.** — Athens is proud of her traditions of naval and
military glory; of the commerce of the Peiræus; of her
free laws and constitution; of her sculptured temples, her
poets, her rhetoricians and philosophers. Almost equally
well might she be proud of her vases. They are not made
— let us bear clearly in mind — by avowed artists, servants
of the Muses and of the Beautiful; they are the regular
commercial products of work-a-day craftsmen. But what
craftsmen! In the first place, they have given to every
vase and dish a marvelous individuality. There seems to
be absolutely no duplication of patterns.[1] Again, since
these vases are made for Greeks, they must — no matter
how humble and commonplace their use — be made beautiful — elegantly shaped, well glazed, and well painted:
otherwise, no matter how cheap, they will never find a
market.

The process of manufacture is simple, yet it needs a
masterly touch. After the potter has finished his work at
the wheel and while the clay is still soft, the decorator
makes his rough design with a blunt-pointed stylus. A line
of black glaze is painted around each figure. Then the black
background is freely filled in, and the details within the
figures are added. A surprisingly small number of deft lines
are needed to bring out the whole picture.[2] Sometimes the

[1] It is asserted that of the many thousands of extant Greek vases
that crowd the shelves of modern museums, there are nowhere two
patterns exactly alike.

[2] In this respect the Greek vase paintings can compete with the best
work in the Japanese prints.

glaze is thinned out to a pale brown, to help in the drawing of the interior contours. When the design is completed,
we have an amount of life and expression which with the
best potters is little short of startling. The subjects treated
are infinite, as many as are the possible phases of Greek
life. Scenes in the home and on the farm; the boys and
their masters at school; the warriors, the merchants, the
priests sacrificing, the young gallants serenading a sweetheart; all the tales, in short, of poet-lore and mythology, —
time would fail to list one tenth of them. Fairly we can
assert that were all the books and formal inscriptions about
the Athenians to be blotted out, these vase paintings,
almost photographs one might say, of Athenian daily life,
would give us back a very wide knowledge of the habits of
the men in the city of Athena.

The potters are justly proud of their work; often they do
not hesitate to add their signatures, and in this way later
ages can name the "craftsmen" who have transmitted to
them these objects of abiding beauty. The designers also
are accommodating enough to add descriptive legends of the
scenes which they depict, — Achilles, Hercules, Theseus,
and all the other heroes are carefully named, usually with
the words written above or beside them.

The pottery of Athens, then, is truly Athenian; that is to
say, it is genuinely elegant, ornamental, simple, and distinctive. The best of these great vases and mixing bowls are
works of art no less than the sculptures of Phidias upon
the Parthenon.

CHAPTER XIII.

THE ARMED FORCES OF ATHENS.

85. Military Life at Athens. — Hitherto we have seen almost nothing save the peaceful civic side of Athenian life, but it is a cardinal error to suppose that art, philosophy, farming, manufacturing, commerce, and bloodless home politics sum up the whole of the activities of Attica. Athens is no longer the great imperial state she was in the days of Pericles, but she is still one of the greatest military powers in Greece,[1] and on her present armed strength rests a large share of her prestige and prosperity. Her fleet, which is still her particular boast, must of course be seen at the Peiræus; but as we go about the streets of the main city we notice many men, who apparently had recently entered their house doors as plain, harmless citizens, now emerging, clad in all the warrior's bravery, and hastening towards one of the gates. Evidently a review is to be held of part of the citizen army of Athens. If we wish, we can follow and learn much of the Greek system of warfare in general and of the Athenian army in particular.

Even at the present day, when there is plenty of complaint that Athenians are not willing to imitate the sturdy campaigning of their fathers, the citizens seem always at war, or getting ready for it. Every citizen, physically fit, is liable to military service from his eighteenth to his sixtieth year. To make efficient soldiers is really the main

---

[1] Of course the greatest military power of Greece had been Sparta until 371 B.C., when the battle of Leuctra made Thebes temporarily "the first land power."

end of the constant physical exercise. If a young man
takes pride in his hard and fit body, if he flings spears in
the stadium, and learns to race in full armor, if he goes on
long marches in the hot sun, if he sleeps on the open hill-
side, or lies on a bed of rushes watching the moon rise over
the sea, — it is all to prepare himself for a worthy part in
the " big day " when Athens will confront some old or new
enemy on the battlefield. A great deal of the conversation
among the younger men is surely not about Platonic ideals,
Demosthenes's last political speech, nor the best fighting
cocks; it is about spears, shield-straps, camping ground,
rations, ambuscades, or the problems of naval warfare.

It is alleged with some show of justice that by this time
Athenians are so enamored with the pleasures of peaceful
life that they prefer to pay money for mercenary troops
rather than serve themselves on distant expeditions; and
certain it is that there are plenty of Arcadians, Thracians,
and others, from the nations which supply the bulk of the
mercenaries, always in Athenian pay in the outlying garrisons. Still the old military tradition and organization for
the citizens is kept up, and half a generation later, when
the freedom of Athens is blasted before Philip the Macedonian at Chæroneia, it will be shown that if the Athenian
militia does not know how to conquer, it at least knows
how to die. So we gladly follow to the review, and gather
our information.

86. The Organization of the Athenian Army. — After a
young ephebus has finished his two years of service in the
garrisons he returns home subject to call at the hour of
need. When there is necessity to make up an army, enough
men are summoned to meet the required number and no
more. Thus for a small force only the eligibles between
say twenty and twenty-four years of age would be summoned; but in a crisis all the citizens are levied up to

the very graybeards. The levy is conducted by the ten
Strategi (at once 'generals,' 'admirals,' and 'war ministers'),
who control the whole armed power of Athens. The
recruits summoned have to come with three days' rations
to the rendezvous, usually to the Lyceum wrestling ground
just outside the city. In case of a general levy the old
men are expected to form merely a home guard for the walls;
the young men must be ready for hard service over seas.

The organization of the Athenian army is very simple;
each of the ten Attic tribes sends its own special battalion
or *taxis*, which is large or small according to the total size
of the levy.[1] These *taxeis* are subdivided into companies or
lochoi, of about an average of 100 men each. The *taxeis* are
each under a tribe-colonel (*taxiarch*), and each company
under its captain (*locharch*). The ten strategi theoretically
command the whole army together, but since bitter experience teaches that ten generals are usually nine too many,
a special decree of the people often entrusts the supreme
command of a force to one commander, or at most to not
over three. The other strategi must conduct other expeditions, or busy themselves with their multifarious home
duties.

87. The Hoplites and the Light Troops. — The unit of the
Athenian citizen army, like practically all Greek armies, is
the heavy armed infantry soldier, the *hoplite*. An army
of " three thousand men " is often an army of so many hoplites, unless there is specific statement to the contrary.
But really it is of six thousand men, to be entirely accurate:
for along with every hoplite goes an attendant, a "light-
armed man," either a poor citizen who cannot afford a regular suit of armor,[2] or possibly a trusted slave. These

---

[1] Thus if 3000 men were called out, the average *taxis* would be 300
strong; but if 6000, then 600.

[2] The hoplite's panoply (see description later) was sufficiently expensive to imply that its owner was at least a man in tolerable circumstances.

"light-armed men" carry the hoplites' shields until the battle, and most of the baggage. They have javelins, and sometimes slings and bows. They act as skirmishers before the actual battle: and while the hoplites are in the real death-grip they harass the foe as they can, and guard the camp. When the fight is done they do their best to cover the retreat, or slaughter the flying foe if their own hoplites are victorious.

88. The Cavalry and the Peltasts. — There are certain divisions of the army besides the hoplites and this somewhat ineffective light infantry. There is a cavalry corps of 1000. Wealthy young Athenians are proud to volunteer therein; it is a sign of wealth to be able to provide your war horse. The cavalry too is given the place of honor in the great religious processions; and there is plenty of chance for exciting scouting service on the campaign. Again, the cavalry service has something to commend it in that it is accounted *much safer* than the infantry![1] The cavalry is, however, a rather feeble fighting instrument. Greek riders have no saddles and no stirrups. They are merely mounted on thin horse pads, and it is very hard to grip the horse with the knees tightly enough to keep from being upset ignominiously while wielding the spear. The best use for the cavalry perhaps is for the riders to take a sheaf of javelins, ride up and discharge them at the foe as skirmishers, then fall back behind the hoplites; though after the battle the horsemen will have plenty to do in the retreat or the pursuit.

The Athenians have of course the Scythian police archers to send into any battle near Athens; they can also hire

[1] Greeks could seldom have been brought to imitate the reckless medieval cavaliers. The example of Leonidas at Thermopylæ was more commended than imitated. Outside of Sparta at least, few Greeks would have hesitated to flee from a battlefield, when the day (despite their proper exertions) had been wholly lost.

mercenary archers from Crete, but the Greek bows are relatively feeble, only three or four feet long — by no means equal to the terrible yew bows which will win glory for England in the Middle Ages. There has also come into vogue, especially since the Peloponnesian war, an improved kind of light-javelin-men, — the "Peltasts," — with small shields, and light armor, but with extra long lances. In recent warfare this type of soldier, carefully trained and agile, has been known to defeat bodies of the old-style over-encumbered hoplites.[1] Nevertheless, most veteran soldiers still believe that the heavy infantryman is everything, and the backbone of nearly every Greek army is still surely the hoplite. He will continue to be the regular fighting unit until the improved "phalanx," and the "Companion Cavalry" of Philip and Alexander of Macedon teach the captains of the world new lessons.

89. The Panoply of the Hoplite. — We have passed out one of the gates and are very likely in a convenient open space south and east of the city stretching away toward the ever visible slopes of gray Hymettus. Here is a suitable parade ground. The citizen soldiers are slipping on their helmets and tightening up their cuirasses. Trumpets blow from time to time to give orders to "fall in" among the respective *lochoi* and *taxeis*. There is plenty of time to study the arms and armor of the hoplites during these preliminaries.

A very brief glance at the average infantryman's defensive weapons tells us that to be able to march, maneuver, and fight efficiently in this armor implies that the Athenian soldier is a well-trained athlete. The whole panoply weighs many pounds.[2] The prime parts in the armor are the

[1] Especially the Athenian general Iphicrates was able to cut to pieces a *mora* (brigade) of Spartan hoplites, in 392 B.C., by skilful use of a force of peltasts.

[2] Possibly fifty or more — we have no correct means for an exact estimate.

helmet, the cuirass, the greaves, and the shield. Every able-bodied citizen of moderate means has this outfit hanging in his andronitis, and can don it at brief notice. The *helmet* is normally of bronze; it is cut away enough in front to leave the face visible, but sometimes a cautious individual will insist on having movable plates (which can be turned up and down) to protect the cheeks.[1] Across the top there

runs a firm metal ridge to catch any hard down-right blow, and set into the ridge is a tall nodding crest either of horsehair or of bright feathers — in either case the joy and glory of the wearer.

Buckled around the soldier's body is the *cuirass*. It comprises a breastplate and a back piece of bronze, joined by thongs, or by straps with a buckle. The metal comes down to the hips.

HOPLITE IN ARMOR.

Below it hangs a thick fringe of stout strips of leather strengthened with bright metallic studs, and reaching halfway to the knees. From this point to the knees the legs are bare, but next come the *greaves*, thin pliable plates of bronze fitted to the shape of the leg, and opening at the back. They have to be slipped on, and then are fastened at knees and ankle with leathern straps.

---

[1] The "Corinthian" type of helmets came more closely over the face, and the cheek protectors were not movable; these helmets were much like the closed helms of the medieval knights. The Spartans, in their contempt for danger, wore plain pointed steel caps which gave relatively little protection

But the warrior's main protection is his *shield*. With a strong, large shield you can fight passing well without any regular body armor; while with the best outfit of the latter you are highly vulnerable without your shield. To know how to swing your shield so as to catch every possible blow, to know how to push and lunge with it against an enemy, to know how to knock a man down with it, if needs be, *that* is a good part of the soldier's education. The shield is sometimes round, but more often oval. It is about four feet by the longest diameter. It is made of several layers of heavy bull's hide, firmly corded and riveted together, and has a good metal rim and metal boss in the center. On the inside are two handles so that it can be conveniently wielded on the left arm.[1] These shields are brilliantly painted, and although the Greeks have no heraldic devices, there are all manner of badges and distinguishing marks in vogue. Thus all Theban shields are blazoned with a club; Sicyonian shields are marked with the initial " Sigma " (Σ), and we note that the Athenian shields are all marked Alpha (A).[2]

90. The Weapons of a Hoplite. — The hoplites have donned their armor. Now they assume their offensive weapons. Every man has a lance and a sword. The *lance* is a stout weapon with a solid wooden butt, about six feet long in all. It is really too heavy to use as a javelin. It is most effective as a pike thrust fairly into a foeman's face, or past his shield into a weak spot in his cuirass. The sword is usually kept as a reserve weapon in case the lance gets broken. It is not over 25 inches in length, making rather a huge double-edged vicious knife than a saber; but it is terrible for cut

[1] Earlier Greek shields seem to have been very large and correspondingly heavy. These had only a single handle; and to aid in shifting them they were swung on straps passed over the left shoulder.

[2] This last is a matter of safe inference rather than of positive information.

and thrust work at very close quarters. Simple as these
weapons are, they are fearful instruments of slaughter in
well-trained hands, and the average Greek has spent a considerable part of his life in being taught how to use them.

91. Infantry Maneuvers. — The final trumpets have blown,
and the troops fall into their places. Each tribal *taxis* lines
up its *lochoi*. The Greeks have no flags nor standards.
There is a great deal of shouting by the subaltern officers,
and running up and down the ranks. Presently everything
is in formal array. The hoplites stand in close order, each
man about two feet from the next,[1] leaving no gaps between
each division from end to end of the lines. The men are set in
eight long ranks. This is the normal *phalanx*[2] order. Only
those in front can actually lunge and strike at the enemy.
The men in the rear will add to the battering force of the
charge, and, crowding in closely, wedge themselves promptly
to the front, when any of the first rank goes down.

It is an imposing sight when the strategos in charge of
the maneuvers, a stately man in a red chlamys, gives the
final word " March ! "

Loud pipes begin screaming. The long lines of red, blue,
and orange plumes nod fiercely together. The sun strikes
fire out of thousands of brandished lance tips. The phalanx
goes swinging away over the dusty parade ground, the sub-
alterns up and down the files muttering angrily to each
inapt recruit to " Keep your distance : " or " Don't advance
your shield." The commandant duly orders the " Half
turn : " " Left " or " Right turn : " " Formation by squares,"
and finally the critical " Change front to rear." If this last

---

[1] The object would be to give each man just enough distance to let him
make fair use of his lance, and yet have his shield overlap that of his
neighbor.

[2] The " phalanx " is sometimes spoken of as a Macedonian innovation,
but Philip and Alexander simply improved upon an old Greek military
formation.

maneuver is successfully accomplished, the strategos will compliment the drill sergeants; for it is notoriously difficult to turn a ponderous phalanx around and yet make it keep good order. The drilling goes on until the welcome order comes, "Ground arms!" and every perspiring soldier lets his heavy shield slip from his arm upon the ground.

92. The Preliminaries of a Greek Battle. — Later in the day, if these are happy times of peace, the whole phalanx, so bristling and formidable, will have resolved itself into its harmless units of honest citizens all streaming home for dinner.

Our curiosity of course asks how does this army act upon the campaign; what, in other words, is a typical Greek battle? This is not hard to describe. Greek battles, until lately, have been fought according to set formulæ in which there is little room for original generalship, though much for ordinary circumspection and personal valor. A battle consists in the charging together of two phalanxes of hoplites of about equal numbers. If one army greatly over-matches the other, the weaker side will probably retire without risking a contest. With a common purpose, there-fore, the respective generals will select a broad stretch of level ground for the struggle, since stony, hilly, or uneven ground will never do for the maneuvering of hoplites. The two armies, after having duly come in sight of one another, and exchanged defiances by derisive shouts, catcalls, and trumpetings, will probably each pitch its camp (protected by simple fortifications) and perhaps wait over night, that the men may be well rested and have a good dinner and breakfast. The soldiers will be duly heartened up by being told of any lucky omens of late, — how three black crows were seen on the right, and a flash of lightning on the left; and the seers and diviners with the army will, at the general's orders, repeat any hopeful oracles they can remember or fabricate, *e.g.* predicting ruin for Thebes, or victory for Athens. In the morning the soldiers have breakfast, then the lines are carefully arrayed a little beyond bowshot from the enemy, who are preparing themselves in similar fashion. Every man has his arms in order, his spear point and sword just from the whetstone, and every buckle made fast. The general (probably in sight of all the men) will cause the seers to kill a chicken, and examine its entrails. "The omens are good; the color is favorable; the gods are with us!"[1] he announces: and then, since he is a Greek among Greeks, he delivers in loud voice an harangue to as many as can hear him, setting forth the patriotic issues at stake in the battle, the call of the fatherland to its sons, the glory of brave valor, the shame of cowardice, probably ending with some practical directions about "Never edging to the right!" and exhorting his men to raise as loud a war-cry as possible, both to encourage themselves and to demoralize the enemy.

93. Joining the Battle. — The troops answer with a cheer, then join in full chorus in the "*Pœan* —" a fierce rousing charging-song that makes every faint-heart's blood leap faster. Another pæan bellowed from the hostile ranks indicates that similar preliminaries have been disposed of there. The moment the fierce chorus ends, the general (who probably is at the post of danger and honor — the right wing) nods to his corps of pipers. The shrill flutes cut the air. The whole phalanx starts forward like one man, and the enemy seem springing to meet it. The tossing color, the flashing arms and armor, make it a sight for men and gods. If the enemy has a powerful archery force, as had the Persians at Marathon, then the phalanx is allowed to advance on the run, — for at all costs one must get

---

[1] It may be suspected that it was very seldom the omens were *allowed* to be unfavorable when the general was really resolved on battle.

through the terrible zone of the arrow fire and come to grips; but if their bowmen are weak, the hoplites will be restrained,—it is better not to risk getting the phalanx disorganized. Running or marching the troops will emit a terrible roaring: either the slow deep "*A! la! la! la!*" or something quicker, "*Eleleū!*" "*Eleleū!*" and the flutes will blow all the while to give the time for the marching.

Closer at hand the two armies will fairly spring into unfriendly embrace. The generals have each measured his enemy's line and extended his own to match it.[1] With files of about equal depth, and well-trained men on both sides, the first stage of this death grapple is likely to be a most fearful yet indecisive pushing: the men of the front ranks pressing against each other, shield to shield, glaring out of their helmets like wild beasts against the foemen three feet away, and lunging with their lances at any opening between the hostile shields or above them. The comrades behind wedge in the front ranks closer and closer. Men are crushed to death, probably without a wound, just by this hellish impact. The shouts and yells emitted are deafening. There is an unearthly clashing of steel weapons on bronze armor. Every now and then a shrill, sharp cry tells where a soldier has been stabbed, and has gone down in the press, probably to be trampled to death instantly. In this way the two writhing, thrusting phalanxes continue to push on one another at sheer deadlock, until a cool observer might well wonder whether the battle would not end simply with mutual extermination.

---

[1] Any sudden attempt to extend your line *beyond* the foe's, so as to outflank him, would probably have produced so much confusion in your own phalanx as to promise certain disaster. Of course for an inferior force to accept battle by thinning its line, to be able by extending to meet the long lines of the enemy, would involve the greatest risk of being broken through at the center. The best remedy for inferior numbers was manifestly to decline a decisive battle.

94. The Climax and End of the Battle. — But look away now from the center, towards the two wings. What the generals of *both* contending armies have feared and warned against has come to pass. Every hoplite is admirably covered by his great shield on his left side; but his right is unprotected. It is almost impossible to resist the impulse to take a step toward the right to get under the cover of a comrade's shield. And he in turn has been edging to the right likewise. The whole army has in fact done so, and likewise the whole phalanx of the enemy. So after a quarter of an hour of brisk fighting, the two hosts, which began by joining with lines exactly facing each other, have each edged along so much that each overlaps the other on the right wing, thus:

What will happen now is easy to predict with assurance up to a certain point. The overlapping right wings will *each* promptly turn the left flank of their enemies, and falling upon the foe front and rear catch them almost helpless. The hoplite is an admirable soldier when standing shoulder to shoulder with his comrades facing his foe; but once beset in the rear he is so wedged in by the press that it is next to impossible for him to turn and fight effectively. Either he will be massacred as he stands or the panic will spread betimes, and simultaneously both left wings will break formation and hurry off the field in little better than flight.

Now will come the real test of discipline and deliberate valor. Both centers are holding stoutly. Everything rests on the respective victorious right wings. Either they will foolishly forget that there is still fighting elsewhere on the field, and with ill-timed huzzaing pursue the men they have just routed, make for their camp to plunder it, or worse

still, disperse to spoil the slain; or, if they can heed their
general's entreaties, keep their ranks, and wheeling around
come charging down on the rear of the enemy's center. If
one right wing does this, while the hostile right wing has
rushed off in heedless pursuit, the battle is infallibly won
by the men who have kept their heads; but if both right
wings turn back, then the real death grapple comes when
these two sets of victors in the first phase of the contest
clash together in a decisive grapple.

By this time the original phalanx formations, so orderly,
and beautiful, have become utterly shattered. The field is
covered by little squares or knots of striking, cursing, raging men — clashing furiously together. If there are any
effective reserves, now is the time to fling them into the
scale. The hitherto timorous light troops and armor bearers
rush up to do what they can. Individual bravery and valor
count now to the uttermost. Little by little the contest
turns against one side or the other. The crucial moment
comes. The losing party begins to fear itself about to be
surrounded. Vain are the last exhortations of the officers
to rally them. "Every man for himself!" rings the cry;
and with one mad impulse the defeated hoplites rush
off the field in rout. Since they have been at close grip
with their enemies, and now must turn their ill-protected
backs to the pursuing spears, the massacre of the defeated
side is sometimes great. Yet not so great as might be
imagined. Once fairly beaten, you must strip off helmet
and cuirass, cast away shield and spear, and run like a hare.
You have lightened yourself now decidedly. But your foe
must keep *his* ponderous arms, otherwise he cannot master
you, if he overtakes you. Therefore the vanquished can
soon distance the victors unless the latter have an unusually
efficient cavalry and javelin force. However, the victors are
likely to enter the camp of the vanquished, and to celebrate duly that night dividing the plunder.

95. The Burial Truce and the Trophy after the Battle. — A few hours after the battle, while the victors are getting breath and refreshing themselves, a shamefaced herald, bearing his sacred wand of office, presents himself. He is from the defeated army, and comes to ask a burial truce. This is the formal confession of defeat for which the victors have been waiting. It would be gross impiety to refuse the request; and perhaps the first watch of the night is spent by detachments of both sides in burying or burning the dead.

The fates of prisoners may be various. They may be sold as slaves. If the captors are pitiless and vindictive, it is not contrary to the laws of war to put the prisoners to death in cold blood; but by the fourth century B.C. Greeks are becoming relatively humane. Most prisoners will presently be released against a reasonable ransom paid by their relatives.

The final stage of the battle is the trophy: the visible sign on the battlefield that here such-and-such a side was victorious. The limbs are lopped off a tree, and some armor captured from the foe is hung upon it. After indecisive battles sometimes both sides set up trophies; in that case a second battle is likely to settle the question. Then when the victors have recovered from their own happy demoralization, they march into the enemy's country; by burning all the farmsteads, driving off the cattle, filling up the wells, girdling the olive and fruit trees, they reduce the defeated side (that has fled to its fortified town) to desperation. If they have any prisoners, they threaten to put them to death. The result, of course, is frequently a treaty of peace in favor of the victors.

96. The Siege of Fortified Towns. — If, however, one party cannot be induced to risk an open battle; or if, despite a defeat, it allows the enemy to ravage the fields, and yet persists in defending the walls of its town,—the war is likely to be tedious and indecisive. It is notorious that Greeks dislike hard sieges. The soldiers are the fellow townsmen of the generals. If the latter order an assault with scaling ladders and it is repulsed with bloody loss, the generals risk a prosecution when they get home for "casting away the lives of their fellow citizens."[1] In short, fifty men behind a stout wall and "able to throw anything" are in a position to defy an army.

The one really sure means of taking a town is to build a counter wall around it and starve it out,—a slow and very expensive, though not bloody process. Only when something very great is at stake will a Greek city-state attempt this.[2] There is always another chance, however. Almost every Greek town has a discontented faction within its walls, and many a time there will be a traitor who will betray a gate to the enemy; and then the siege will be suddenly ended in one murderous night.

97. The Introduction of New Tactics. — Greek battles are thus very simple things as a rule. It is the general who, accepting the typical conditions as he finds them, and avoiding any gross and obvious blunders, can put his men in a state of perfect fitness, physical and moral, that is likely to win the day. Of late there has come indeed a spirit of innovation. At Leuctra (371 B.C.) Epaminondas the Theban defeated the Spartans by the unheard-of device of massing a part of his hoplites fifty deep (instead of the orthodox eight or twelve) and crushing the Spartan right wing by

[1] In siege warfare Oriental kings had a great advantage over Greek commanders. The former could sacrifice as many of their "slaves" as they pleased, in desperate assaults. The latter had always to bear in mind their accountability at home for any desperate and costly attack.

[2] As in the siege of Potidæa (432–429 B.C.), when if Athens had failed to take the place, her hold upon her whole empire would have been jeopardized.

the sheer weight of his charge, before the rest of the line
came into action at all. If the experiment had not suc-
ceeded, Epaminondas would probably have been denounced
by his own countrymen as a traitor, and by the enemy
as a fool, for varying from the time-honored long, "even
line" phalanx; and the average general will still prefer to
keep to the old methods ; then if anything happens, *he* at
least will not be blamed for any undue rashness. Only in
Macedon, King Philip II (who is just about to come to the
throne) will not hesitate to study the new battle tactics of
Epaminondas, and to improve upon them.

The Athenians will tell us that their citizen hoplites are
a match for any soldiers in Greece, except until lately the
Spartans, and now (since Leuctra) possibly the Thebans.
But Corinthians, Argives, Sicyonians, they can confront
most readily. They will also add, quite properly, that the
army of Athens is in the main for home defense. She
does not claim to be a preëminently military state. The
glory of Athens has been the mastery of the sea. Our next
excursion must surely be to the Peiræus.

CHAPTER XIV.

THE PEIRÆUS AND THE SHIPPING.

98. The " Long Walls " down to the Harbor Town. — It is some five miles from the city to the Peiræus, and the most direct route this time lies down the long avenue laid between the Long Walls, and running almost directly southwest.[1] The ground is quite level. If we could catch glimpses beyond the walls, we would see fields, seared brown perhaps by the summer sun, and here and there a bright-kerchiefed woman gleaning among the wheat stubble. The two walls start from Athens close together and run parallel for some distance, then they gradually diverge so as to embrace within their open angle a large part of the circumference of the Peiræus. This open space is built up with all kinds of shops, factories, and houses, usually of the less aristocratic kind. In fact, all the noxious sights and odors to be found in Athens seem tenfold multiplied as we approach the Peiræus.

The straight highroad is swarming with traffic: clumsy wagons are bringing down marble from the mountains; other wains are headed toward Athens with lumber and bales of foreign wares. Countless donkeys laden with panniers are

---

[1] These were the walls whereof a considerable section was thrown down by Lysander after the surrender of Athens [404 B.C.]. The demolition was done to the " music of flute girls," and was fondly thought by the victors to mean the permanent crippling of Athens, and therefore " the first day of the liberty of Greece." In 393 B.C., by one of the ironies of history, Conon, an Athenian admiral, but in the service of the king of Persia, who was then at war with Sparta, appeared in the Peiræus, and *with Persian men and money* rebuilt the walls amid the rejoicings of the Athenians.

117

being flogged along. A great deal of the carrying is done
by half-naked sweating porters; for, after all, slave-flesh is
almost as cheap as beast-flesh. So by degrees the two walls
open away from us: before us now expands the humming
port town; we catch the sniff of the salt brine, and see the
tangle of spars of the multifarious shipping. Right ahead,
however, dominating the whole scene, is a craggy height,—

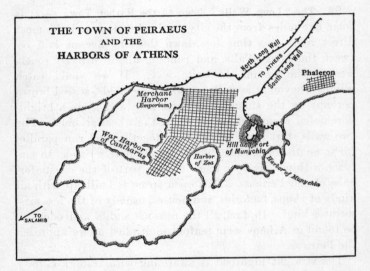

THE TOWN OF PEIRAEUS
AND THE
HARBORS OF ATHENS

the hill of Munychia, crowned with strong fortifications, and
with houses rising terrace above terrace upon its slopes. At
the very summit glitters in its white marble and color work
the temple of Artemis Munychia, the guardian goddess of
the port town and its citadel.[1]

99. Munychia and the Havens of Athens. — Making our
way up a steep lane upon the northwestern slope, we pass

[1] This fortress of Munychia, rather than the Acropolis in Athens, was
the real citadel of Attica. It dominated the all-important harbors on
which the very life of the state depended.

within the fortifications, the most formidable near Athens.
A band of young ephebi of the garrison eye us as we enter;
but we seem neither Spartans nor Thebans and are not
molested. From a convenient crag near the temple, the
whole scheme of the harbors of Athens is spread out before
us, two hundred and eighty odd feet below. Behind us is
the familiar plain of Athens with the city, the Acropolis,
and the guardian mountains. Directly west lies the expanse of roof of the main harbor town, and then beyond is
the smooth blue expanse of the " Port of the Peiræus," the
main mercantile harbor of Athens. Running straight down
from Munychia, southwest, the land tapers off into a rocky
promontory, entirely girt with strong fortifications. In this
stretch of land are two deep round indentations. Cups of
bright water they seem, communicating with the outer sea only
by narrow entrances which are dominated by stout castles.
Zea is the name of the more remote; the " haven " of
Munychia is that which seems opening almost at our feet.
These both are full of the naval shipping, whereof more
hereafter. To the eastward, and stretching down the coast,
is a long sandy beach whereon the blue ripples are crumbling
between the black fishing boats drawn up upon the strand.
This is Phaleron, the old harbor of Athens before Themistocles fortified the *Peiræus* — merely an open roadstead in
fact, but still very handy for small craft, which can be
hauled up promptly to escape the tempest.

100. The Glorious View from the Hill of Munychia. — These
are the chief points in the harbors; but the view from Munychia is most extensive. Almost everything in sight has
its legend or its story in sober history. Ten miles away to
the southward rise the red rocky hills of Ægina, Athens'
old island enemy; and the tawny headlands of the Argolic
coast are visible yet farther across the horizon. Again, as
we follow the purplish ridge of Mount Ægaleos as it runs

down the Attic coast to westward, we come to a headland, then to a belt of azure water, about a mile wide, then the reddish hills of an irregular island. Every idler on the citadel can tell us all the story. On that headland on a certain fateful morning sat Xerxes, lord of the Persians, with his sword-hands and mighty men about him and his ships before him, to look down on the naval spectacle and see how his slaves would fight. The island beyond is "holy Salamis," and in this narrow strip of water has been the battle which saved the life of Hellas. Every position in the contest seems clearly in sight, even the insignificant islet of Psyttaleia, where Aristeides had landed his men after the battle, and massacred the Persians stationed there "to cut off the Greeks who tried to escape."

The water is indescribably blue, matching the azure of the sky. Ships of all kinds under sails or oars are moving lightly over the havens and the open Saronic bay. It is a matchless spectacle — albeit very peaceful. We now descend to the Peiræus proper and examine the merchant shipping and wharves, leaving the navy yards and the fighting triremes till later.

101. The Town of Peiræus. — The Peiræus has all the life of the Athenian Agora many times multiplied. Everywhere there is work and bustle. Aristophanes has long since described the impression it makes on strangers,[1] — sailors clamoring for pay, rations being served out, figureheads being burnished, men trafficking for corn, for onions, for leeks, for figs, — "wreaths, anchovies, flute girls, blackened eyes, the hammering of oars from the dock yards, the fitting of rowlocks, boatswains' pipes, fifes, and whistling." There is such confusion one can hardly analyze one's surroundings. However, we soon discover the Peiræus has certain advantages over Athens itself. The streets are

---

[1] *Acharn.* 54 ff.

much wider and are quite straight,[1] crossing at right angles,
unlike the crooked alleys of old Athens which seem nothing
but built-up cow trails.   Down at the water front of the main
harbor (the "Peiræus" harbor to distinguish it from Zea
and Munychia) we find about one third, nearest the entrance
passage and called the Cantharus, reserved for the use of
the war navy.   The remainder is turned over to the mer-
chantmen.   This section is the famous *Emporium*, which is
such a repository of foreign wares that Isocrates boasts that

FISHERMEN.

here one can easily buy all those things which it is extremely
hard to purchase anywhere else in Hellas.   Along the shore
run five great stoas or colonnades, all used by the traders
for different purposes ; — among them are the Long Stoa
(*Makra' Stoa'*), the *Deigma* (see p. 93) used as a sample
house by the wholesalers, and the great Corn Exchange
built by Pericles.   Close down near the wharves stands also
a handsome and frequented temple, that of Athena Euploia
(Athena, Giver of good Voyages), to whom many a shipman

---

[1] Pericles employed the famous architect Hippodamus to lay out the
Peiræus.   It seems to have been arranged much like many of the newer
American cities.

offers prayer ere hoisting sail, and many another comes to
pay grateful vows after surviving a storm.[1] Time fails us
for mentioning all the considerable temples farther back
in the town.   The Peiræus in short is a semi-independent
community; with its shrines, its agoras, its theaters, its court
rooms, and other public buildings.   The population contains
a very high percentage of metics, and downright Barbarians, — indeed, long-bearded Babylonians, clean bronze
Egyptians, grinning Ethiopians, never awaken the least comment, they are so familiar.

102. The Merchant Shipping. — We can now cast more
particular eyes upon the shipping.   Every possible type is
represented.   The fishing craft just now pulling in with loads
of shining tunnies caught near Ægina are of course merely
broad open boats, with only a single dirty orange sail swinging in the lagging breeze.   Such vessels indeed depend
most of the time upon their long oars.   Also just now there
goes across the glassy surface of the harbor a slim graceful
rowing craft, pulling eight swiftly plying oars to a side.   She
is a *Lembus :* probably the private cutter of the commandant of
the port.   Generally speaking, however, we soon find that all
the larger Greek ships are divided into two categories, the
" long ships " and the " round ships. "   The former depend
mainly on oars and are for war; the latter trust chiefly to
sail power and are for cargo.   The craft in the merchant
haven are of course nearly all of this last description.

Greeks are clever sailors.   They never feel really happy
at a great distance from the sea which so penetrates their
little country; nevertheless, they have not made all the
progress in navigation which, considering the natural ingenuity of the race, might well be expected.   The prime difficulty is that Greek ships very seldom have comfortable cabins.

[1] There seems to have been still another precinct, sacred to "Zeus and
Athena the Preservers," where it was very proper to offer thanksgivings
after a safe voyage.

The men expect to sleep on shore every night possible. Only in a great emergency, or when crossing an exceptionally wide gulf or channel,[1] can a captain expect the average crew to forego the privilege of a warm supper and bivouac upon the strand. This means (since safe anchorages are by no means everywhere) the ships must be so shallow and light they can often be hauled up upon the beach. Even with a pretty large crew, therefore, the limit to a manageable ship is soon reached ; and during the whole of the winter season all long-distance voyaging has to be suspended ; while, even in summer, nine sailors out of ten hug close to the land, despite the fact that often the distance of a voyage is thereby doubled.

However, the ships at Peiræus, if not large in size, are numerous enough. Some are simply big open boats with details elaborated. They have a small forecastle and poop built over, but the cargo in the hold is exposed to all wind and weather. The propulsion comes from a single unwieldy square sail swinging on a long yard the whole length of the vessel. Other ships are more completely decked, and depend on two square sails in the place of one. A few, however, are real "deep sea" vessels — completely decked, with two or even three masts ; with cabins of tolerable size, and forward and aft curious projections, like turrets, — the use whereof is by no means obvious, but we soon gather that pirates still abound on the distant seas, and that these turrets are useful when it comes to repelling boarders. The very biggest of these craft run up to 250 gross tons (later day register),[2] although with these ponderous defense-works they seem considerably larger. The average of the ships, however, will reckon only 30 to 40 tons or even smaller. It is really a mistake, any garrulous sailor will tell us, to build merchant ships much

---

[1] For example, the trip from Crete to Cyrene — which would be demanded first, before coasting along to Egypt.

[2] The Greeks reckoned their ships by their capacity in talents (= about 60 lbs.), e.g. a ship of 500 talents, of 2000, or (among the largest) 10,000.

bigger. It is impossible to make sailing vessels of the Greek model and rig sail very close to the wind; and in every contrary breeze or calm, recourse must be had to the huge oars piled up along the gunwales. Obviously it is weary work propelling a large ship with oars unless you have a huge and expensive crew, — far better then to keep to the smaller vessels.

103. The Three War Harbors and the Ship Houses. — Many other points about these "round ships" interest us; but such matters they share with the men-of-war, and our inspection has now brought us to the navy yard. There are strictly three separate navy yards, one at each of the harbors of Munychia, Zea, and Cantharus, for the naval strength of Athens is so great that it is impossible to concentrate the entire fleet at one harbor. Each of these establishments is protected by having two strong battlements or breakwaters built out, nearly closing the respective harbor entrances. At the end of each breakwater is a tower with parapets for archers, and capstans for dragging a huge chain across the harbor mouth, thus effectively sealing the entrance to any foe.[1] The Zea haven has really the greatest warship capacity, but the Cantharus is a good type for the three.[2] As we approach it from the merchant haven, we see the shelving shore closely lined with curious structures which do not easily explain themselves. There are a vast number of dirty, shelving roofs, slightly tilted upward towards the land side, and set at right angles to the water's edge. They are each about 150 feet long, some 25 feet wide, about 20 feet high, and are set up side by side with no passage between.

[1] Ancient harbors were much harder to defend than modern ones, because there was no long-range artillery to prevent an enemy from thrusting into an open haven among defenseless shipping.

[2] Zea had accommodation for 196 triremes, Munychia, 82, and the Cantharus, 94.

On close inspection we discover these are ship houses. Under each of the roofs is accommodated the long slim hull of a trireme, kept safe from sea and weather until the time of need, when a few minutes' work at a tackle and capstan will send it down into harbor, ready to tow beside a wharf for outfitting.

104. The Great Naval Arsenal. — The ship houses are not the only large structures at the navy yard. Here is also the great naval arsenal, a huge roofed structure open at the sides and entirely exposed to public inspection. Here between the lines of supporting columns can be seen stacked up the staple requisites for the ships, — great ropes, sail boxes, anchors, oars, etc. Everybody in Athens is welcome to enter and assure himself that the fleet can be outfitted at a minute's notice[1]; and at all times crews of half-naked, weather-beaten sailors are rushing hither and yon, carrying or removing supplies to and from the wharves where their ships are lying.

105. An Athenian Trierarch. — Among this unaristocratic crowd we observe a dignified old gentleman with an immaculate himation and a long polished cane. Obsequious clerks and sailing masters are hanging about him for his orders; it is easy to see that he is a *trierarch*—one of the wealthiest citizens on whom it fell, in turn, at set intervals, to provide the less essential parts of a trireme's outfit, and at least part of the pay for the crew for one year, and to be generally responsible for the efficiency and upkeep of the vessel.[2] This is a year of peace, and the patriotic pressure

[1] This arsenal was replaced a little later than the hypothetical time of this narrative by one designed by the famous architect, Philo. It was extremely elegant as well as commodious, with handsome columns, tiled roofs, etc. In 360 B.C., however, the arsenal seems to have been a strictly utilitarian structure.

[2] Just how much of the rigging and what fraction of the pay of the crew the government provided is by no means clear from our evidence.

to spend as much on your warship as possible is not so great
as sometimes; still Eustathius, the magnate in question,
knows that he will be bitterly criticised (nay, perhaps prosecuted in the courts) if he does not do "the generous thing."
He is therefore ordering an extra handsome figurehead;
promising a bonus to the rowing master if he can get his
hands to row in better rhythm than the ordinary crew; and
directing that wine of superior quality be sent aboard for
the men.[1] It will be an anxious year in any case for Eustathius.   He has ill wishers who will watch carefully to see if
the vessel fails to make a creditable record for herself during
the year, and whether she is returned to the ship house or
to the next trierarch in a state of good repair.   If the craft
does not then appear seaworthy, her last outfitter may be
called upon to rebuild her completely, a matter which will
eat up something like a talent.   Public service therefore does
not provide beds of roses for the rich men of Athens.

Eustathius goes away towards one of the wharves, where
his trireme, the *Invincible*, is moored with her crew aboard
her.   Let us examine a typical Athenian warship.

106. The Evolution of the Trireme. — The genesis of the
trireme was the old *penteconter* ("fifty-oar ship") which, in
its prime features, was simply a long, narrow, open hull,
with slightly raised prow and stern cabins, pulling twenty-
five oars to a side.   There are a few penteconters still in
existence, though the great naval powers have long since
scorned them.   It was a good while before the battle of
Salamis that the Greek sea warriors began to feel the need

It is certain that a public-spirited and lavish trierarch could almost ruin
himself (unless very wealthy) during the year he was responsible for the
vessel.

[1] According to various passages in Demosthenes, the cost of a trierarchy
for a year varied between 40 minæ (say $540) and a talent (about
$1000), very large sums for Athenians. The question of the amount
of time spent in active service in foreign waters would of course do much
to determine the outlay.

of larger warships.   It was impossible to continue the simple scheme of the penteconter.   To get more oars all on one tier you must make a longer boat, but you could not increase the beam, for, if you did, the whole craft would get so heavy that it would not row rapidly; and the penteconter was already so long in relation to its beam as to be somewhat unsafe.   A device was needed to get more oars into the water without increasing the length over much.   The

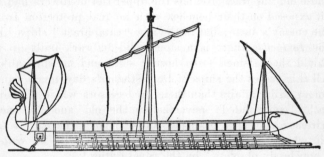

AN ATHENIAN TRIREME.

The scheme for the sails is conjectural, and no attempt is made to show the exact number of oars.

result was the *bireme* (two-banker) which was speedily replaced by the still more efficient *trireme* (three-banker), the standard battleship of all the Greek navies.[1]

107. The Hull of a Trireme. — The *Invincible* has a hull of fir strengthened by a solid oak keel, very essential if she is to be hauled up frequently.   Her hull is painted black, but there is abundance of scarlet, bright blue, and gilding upon her prow, stern, and upper works.   The slim hull itself is about 140 feet long, 14 feet wide, and rides the harbor so

[1] By the end of the fourth century B.C. vessels with four and five banks of oars (quadriremes and quinqueremes) had become the regular fighting ships, but they differed probably only in size, not in principle, from the trireme.

lightly as to show that it draws very little water; for the
warship, even more perhaps than the merchantman, is built
on the theory that her crew must drag her up upon the
beach almost every night.

While we study the vessel we are soon told that, although
triremes have been in general use since, say, 500 B.C., nevertheless the ships that fought at Salamis were decidedly
simpler affairs than those of three generations later. In
those old "aphract" vessels the upper tier of rowers had to
sit exposed on their benches with no real protection from
the enemy's darts; but in the new "cataphract" ships like
the *Invincible* there is a stout solid bulwark built up to
shield the oarsmen from hostile sight and missiles alike.
All this makes the ships of Demosthenes's day much hand-
somer, taller affairs than their predecessors which Themistocles commanded; nevertheless the old and the new
triremes have most essentials in common. The day is far
off when a battleship twenty years old will be called
" hopelessly obsolete " by the naval critics.[1]

The upper deck of the trireme is about eleven feet above
the harbor waves, but the lowest oar holes are raised barely
three feet. Into the intervening space the whole complicated
rowing apparatus has to be crammed with a good deal of
ingenuity. Running along two thirds of the length of the
hull nearly the whole interior of the vessel is filled with a
series of seats and foot rests rising in sets of three. Each
man has a bench and a kind of stool beneath him, and sits
close to a porthole. The feet of the lowest rower are near
the level of the water line; swinging two feet above him
and only a little behind him is his comrade of the second
tier; higher and behind in turn is he of the third.[2] Run-

[1] There is some reason for believing that an Athenian trireme was kept
in service for many years, with only incidental repairs, and then could
still be counted as fit to take her place in the line of battle.

[2] The exact system by which these oar benches were arranged, the crew
taught to swing together (despite the inequalities in the length of their

ning down the center of the ship on either side of these complicated benches is a broad, central gangway, just under the upper deck.   Here the supernumeraries will take refuge from the darts in battle, and here the regular rowers will have to do most of their eating, resting, and sleeping when they are not actually on the benches or on shore.

108. The Rowers' Benches of a Trireme. — With her full complement of rowers the benches of the *Invincible* fairly swarm with life.   There are 62 rowers to the upper tier (*thranites*), 58 for the middle tier (*zygites*), and 54 for the lower (*thalamites*), each man with his own individual oar. The *thranites* with the longest oars (full 13 feet 6 inches) have the hardest pull and the largest pay, but not one of the 174 oarsmen holds a sinecure.   In ordinary cruising, to be sure, the trireme will make use of her sails, to help out a single bank of oars which must be kept going almost all the time.   Even then it is weary work to break your back for a couple of hours taking your turn on the benches.   But in battle the trireme almost never uses sails.   She becomes a vast, many-footed monster, flying over the foam; and the pace of the three oar banks, swinging together, becomes maddening.   Behind their bulwarks the rowers can see little of what is passing.   Everything is dependent upon their rowing together in absolute rhythm come what may, and giving instant obedience to orders.   The trireme is in one sense like a latter-day steamer in her methods of propulsion; but the driving force is 174 straining, panting humans, not insensate water vapor and steel.

109. The Cabins, Rigging, and Ram of a Trireme. — Forward and aft of the rowers' benches and the great central gangway are the fore and stern cabins.   They furnish something akin to tolerable accommodations for the officers and a favored

oars), and several other like problems connected with the trireme, have received no satisfactory solution by modern investigators.

fraction of the crew. Above the forecastle rises a carved proudly curving prow, and just abaft it are high bulwarks to guard the javelin men when at close quarters with the foe. There is also on either side of the prow a huge red or orange " eye " painted around the hawse holes for the anchors. Above the stern cabin is the narrow deck reserved for the pilot, the " governor " of the ship, who will control the whole trireme with a touch now on one, now on the other, of the huge steering paddles which swing at the sides near the stern. Within the stern cabin itself is the little altar, sacred to the god or goddess to whom the vessel is dedicated, and on which incense will be burned before starting on a long cruise and before going into battle. Two masts rise above the deck, a tall mainmast nearly amidships, and a much smaller mast well forward. On each of these a square sail (red, orange, blue, or even, with gala ships, purple) will be swung from a long yard, while the vessel is cruising; but it is useless to set sails in battle. One could never turn the ship quickly enough to complete the maneuvers. The sails and yards will ordinarily be sent ashore as the first measure when the admiral signals " clear ship for action."

We have now examined all of the *Invincible* except her main weapon, — her beak; for the trireme is really herself one tremendous missile to be flung by the well-trained rowers at the ill-starred foe. Projecting well in front of the prow and close to the water line are three heavy metal spurs serrated one above the other, somewhat thus[1]:

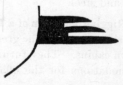

[1] Probably at Salamis and in the earlier Athenian navy the ram had been composed of a single long, tapering beak.

Let this fang once crash against a foeman's broadside, and
his timbers are crushed in like eggshells.

110. The Officers and Crew of a Trireme. — So much for
the *Invincible* herself, but obviously she is a helpless thing
without an efficient crew. The life of an oarsman is far
from luxurious, but the pay seems to be enough to induce a
goodly number of *thetes* (the poorest class of the Athenian
citizens) to accept service, and the rest can be supplied by
hired metics or any kind of foreign nondescript who can be
brought into discipline. The rowers are of course the real
heart and soul of the trireme; but they are useless without
proper training. Indeed it was the superior discipline of
the Athenian crews which in the days of Themistocles and
Pericles gave Athens the supremacy of the seas. The nominal, and sometimes actual, commander of the trireme is her
trierarch; but obviously a cultivated old gentleman like
Eustathius is no man to manage the ship in a sea fight. He
will name some deputy, perhaps a stout young friend or a
son, for the real naval work. Even he may not possess great
experience. The real commander of the *Invincible* is the
"governor" (*kybernates*), a gnarled old seaman, who has
spent all his life upon the water. Nominally his main duty
is to act as pilot, but actually he is in charge of the whole
ship; and in battle the trierarch (if aboard) will be very
glad to obey all his "suggestions." Next to the "governor"
there is the *proireus*, another experienced sailor who will
have especial charge of the forecastle in battle. Next in
turn are two "oar-masters" (*toixarchoi*), who are each responsible for the discipline and working of one of the long rowers'
benches; and following in grade, though highly important,
are the *keleustēs*, and the *triēraulēs*, who, by voice and by
flute respectively, will give the time and if needs be encouragement to the rowers. These are all the regular officers, but
naturally for handling the sails and anchors some common

sailors are desirable. The *Invincible* carries 17 of these. She also has 10 marines (*epibatœ*), men trained to fight in hoplites' armor and to repel boarders. The Persian ships at Salamis carried 30 such warriors, and often various Greek admirals have crowded their decks with these heavy marines; but the true Athenian sea warrior disdains them. Given a good helmsman and well-trained rowers, and you can sink your opponent with your ram, while he is clumsily trying to board you. Expert opinion considers the *epibatœ* somewhat superfluous, and their use in most naval battles as disgracefully unscientific.

111. A Trireme at Sea. — A trireme, then, is an heroic fighting instrument. She goes into battle prepared literally to do or die. If her side is once crushed, she fills with water instantly, and the enemy will be too busy and too inhumane to do anything but cheer lustily when they see the water covered with struggling wretches. But the trireme is also a most disagreeable craft before and after the battle. Her light draft sets her tossing on a very mild sea. In the hot southern climate, with very little ventilation beneath the upper deck, with nigh two hundred panting, naked human beings wedged in together below so closely that there is scarce room for one more, the heat, the smells, the drudgery, are dreadful. No wonder the crew demand that the trierarch and governor "make shore for the night," or that they weary of the incessant grating of the heavy oars upon the thole-pins.

Thus the *Invincible* will seem to any squeamish voyager, but not so to a distant spectator. For him a trireme is a most marvelous and magnificent sight. A sister ship, the *Danaë*,[1] is just entering the Peiræus from Lemnos (an isle still under the Athenian sovranty). Her upper works have

[1] The Greek ships seem to have been named either for mythological characters, or for desirable qualities and virtues.

been all brightened for the home-coming. Long, brilliant streamers trail from her sail yards and poop. The flute player is blowing his loudest. The marines stand on the forecastle in glittering armor. A great column of foam is spouting from her bow.[1] Her oars, eighty-seven to the side, pumiced white and hurling out the spray, are leaping back and forth in perfect unison. The whole vessel seems a thing of springing, ardent life. It is, indeed, a sight to stir the blood. No later sailing ship in her panoply of canvas, no steam battleship with her grim turrets and smoking funnels can ever match the spectacle of a trireme moving in her rhythm and glory.

112. The Tactics of a Naval Battle. — Imagination can now picture a Greek naval battle, fifty, a hundred, two hundred, or more of these splendid battleships flying in two hostile lines to the charge.[2] Round and round they will sail, each pilot watching the moment when an unlucky maneuver by the foe will leave a chance for an attack; and then will come the sudden swinging of the helm, the frantic "Pull hard!" to the oarsmen, the rending crash and shock as the ram tears open the opponent's side, to be followed by almost instant tragedy. If the direct attack on the foe's broadside fails, there is another maneuver. Run down upon your enemy as if striking bow to bow; the instant before contact let your aim swerve — a little. Then call to your men to draw in their oars like lightning while the enemy are still working theirs. If your oarsmen can do the trick in time, you can now ride down the whole of the foemen's exposed oar bank, while saving your own. He is left crippled and helpless, like a huge centipede with all the legs on one side

[1] At her best a trireme seems to have been capable of making 8 to 9 knots per hour.

[2] A more detailed picture of an ancient naval battle and its tactics can be found in the author's historical novel, *A Victor of Salamis* (Chap. XXIX).

stripped away. You can now back off deliberately, run out your oars, and in cold blood charge his exposed flank. If he does not now surrender, his people are dead men. Excellent to describe! Not always so excellent in performance. Everything depends on the perfect discipline and handiness of your crew.

113. The Naval Strength of Athens. — The strength of Athens is still upon the sea. Despite her defeats in the Peloponnesian War she has again the first navy in Hellas. All in all she can send out 400 triremes and since each trireme represents a crew of over 200 men, this means that Athens can dispose of over 80,000 souls in her navy, whereof, however, only a minor fraction are Athenian citizens. Athens is quite right in thus laying stress upon her sea power. Her long walls and the Peiræus make her practically an island. Even after Chæroneia, Philip of Macedon will be obliged to give her honorable terms, — she has still her great navy. Only after the defeat of her fleet at Amorgos in 322 B.C. will she have to know all the pangs of vassalage to Macedon.

CHAPTER XV.

AN ATHENIAN COURT TRIAL.

114. The Frequency of Litigation in Athens. — The visit to the Peiræus and the study of the shipping have not been too long to prevent a brief visit to one of the most characteristic scenes of Athenian life — a law court. Athens is notorious for the fondness which her citizens display for litigation. In fact it is a somewhat rare and exceptionally peaceable, harmless, and insignificant citizen who is not plaintiff or defendant in some kind of action every few years or so. Says Aristophanes, "The cicada [grasshopper] sings for only a month, but the people of Athens are buzzing with lawsuits and trials their whole life long." In the jury courts the contentious, tonguey man can spread himself and defame his enemies to his heart's content; and it must be admitted that in a city like Athens, where everybody seems to know everybody else's business almost every citizen is likely to have a number both of warm friends and of bitter enemies. Athenians do not have merely "cold acquaintances," or "business rivals," as will men of the twentieth century. They make no pretenses to "Christian charity." They freely call an obnoxious individual their "personal foe" (*echthros*), and if they can defeat, humiliate, and ruin him, they bless the gods. The usual outlet for such ill-feeling is a fierce and perhaps mutually destructive lawsuit.

Then too, despite Athenian notions of what constitutes a gentleman, many citizens are people of utterly penurious, niggardly habits. Frequently enough the fellow who can
135

discuss all Socrates's theories with you is quarreling with his neighbor over the loan of salt or a lamp wick or some meal for sacrifice.[1] If one of the customary "club-dinners"[2] is held at his house, he will be caught secreting some of the vinegar, lamp oil, or lentils. If he has borrowed something, say some barley, take care; when he returns it, he will measure it out in a vessel with the bottom dented inward. A little ill feeling, a petty grievance carefully cultivated,— the end in due time will be a lawsuit, costly far out of proportion to the originating cause.

115. Prosecutions in Athens.— Athens does not draw a sharp line between public and private litigation. There is no "state" or "district attorney" to prosecute for offenses against public order. Any full citizen can prosecute anybody else upon such a criminal charge as murder, no less than for a civil matter like breach of contract. All this leads to the growth of a mischievous clan — the *sycophants*. These harpies are professional accusers who will prosecute almost any rich individual upon whom they think they can fasten some technical offense. Their gains are from two quarters. If they convict the defendant, about half of the fine or property taken will go to the informer. But very likely there will be no trial. The victim (either consciously guilty, or innocent but anxious to avoid the risk) will pay a huge blackmail at the first threat of prosecution, and the case is hushed up.

It is true there are very heavy penalties for trumped-up cases, for unwarranted threat of legal proceedings, for perjured evidence ; still the abuse of the sycophants exists, and a great many of the lawsuits originate with this uncanny tribe.

---

[1] Persons of this kidney are delineated to us as typical characters by Theophrastus.

[2] The nearest modern equivalent is a " basket lunch."

116. The Preliminaries to a Trial. — There are official arbitrators to settle petty cases, but it is too often that one or both parties declare "the dicasts must settle it," and the lawsuit has to take its way. Athenian legal methods are simple. Theoretically there are no professional lawyers, and every man must look out for himself. The first business is to file your complaint with one of the magistrates (usually one of nine *archons*), and then with two witnesses give formal summons to your opponent, the defendant, to appear on a set day in court If he has defaulted, the case is usually ended then in your favor. This hearing before the magistrate is in any event an important part of the trial. Here each side proffers the laws it cites to sustain its claims, and brings its witnesses, who can be more or less cross-examined. All the pertinent testimony is now written down, and the tablets sealed up by the magistrate. At the final trial this evidence will be merely *read* to the jury, the witness in each instance standing up before the court and admitting, when duly asked, "This is my testimony on the case."

Free men testify under oath, but a slave's oath is counted worthless. The slaves may be the only important witnesses to a given act, but under only one condition can they testify. With the consent of their master they may testify *under torture*. It is a critical moment at this hearing when a litigant who is confident of his case proudly announces, "I challenge my enemy to put my slaves under torture"; or the other, attacking first, cries out, "I demand that my enemy submit his slaves to torture." Theoretically the challenged party may refuse, practically a refusal is highly dangerous. "If his slaves didn't know something bad, why were they kept silent?" the jury will ask. So the rack is brought forth. The wretched menials are stretched upon it. One must hope that often the whole process involves more show of cruelty than actual brutality. What now the slaves gasp out between their twists and howls is duly taken down as "important evidence," and goes into the record.[1]

117. The Athenian Jury Courts. — A convenient interval has elapsed since one of these preliminary hearings. To-day has been set for the actual trial before a member of the archons in the "Green" court. Ariston, a wealthy olive farmer, is suing Lamachus, an exporter of the Peiræus, for failing to account for the proceeds of a cargo of olives lately shipped to Naxos. To follow the trial in entirety we should have been at the courthouse at first dawn. Then we would have seen the jurymen come grumbling in, some from the suburbs, attended by link boys. These jurors represent a large fraction of the whole Athenian people. There are about six thousand in all. Pretty nearly every citizen above thirty years of age can give in his name as desiring jury duty; but naturally it is the elderly and the indolent who most prefer the service. One thousand of the six act as mere substitutes; the rest serve as often as the working of a complicated system of drawing by lot assigns them to sit as jurors on a particular case. It is well there are five thousand always thus available, for Athenian juries are very large; 201, 401, 501, 1001 are numbers heard of, and sometimes even greater.[2] The more important the case, the larger the jury; but *Ariston* v. *Lamachus* is only a commonplace affair; 401 jurors are quite enough. Even with that "small court," the audience which the pleaders now have to address will seem huge to any latter-day lawyer who is accustomed

[1] Athenian opinion was on the whole in favor of receiving as valid testimony the evidence extorted thus from slaves by mere animal fear. Antiphon the orator speaks of how truth may be wrung from slaves by torture; " by which they are compelled to speak the truth though they must die for it afterward [at the hands of the master they have incriminated], for the present necessity is to each stronger than the future." This has been well called one of the few cases of extreme *stupidity* on the part of the Athenians.

[2] The odd unit was no doubt added to prevent a tie.

to his "twelve men in a box"; and needless to say, quite different methods must be used in dealing with such a company.

Each "dicast" (to use the proper name) has a boxwood tablet to show at the entrance as his voucher to the Scythian police-archers on duty; he has also a special staff of the color of the paint on the door of the court room.[1] The chamber itself is not especially elegant; a long line of hard benches rising in tiers for the dicasts, and facing these a kind of pulpit for the presiding magistrates, with a little platform for the orators, a small altar for the preliminary sacrifice, and a few stools for attendants and witnesses complete the simple furnishings. There are open spaces for spectators, though no seats; but there will be no lack of an audience today, for the rumor has gone around, "Hypereides has written Ariston's argument." The chance to hear a speech prepared by that famous oration-monger is enough to bring every dicast out early, and to summon a swarm of loiterers up from the not distant Agora.

118. The Juryman's Oath. — The dicasts are assumed to approach their duty with all due solemnity. They have sworn to vote according to the laws of Athens, never to vote for a repudiation of debts, nor to restore political exiles, nor to receive bribes for their votes, nor take bribes in another's behalf, nor let anybody even tempt them with such proffers. They are to hear both sides impartially and vote strictly according to the merits of the case : and the oath winds up awfully — "Thus do I invoke Zeus, Poseidon, and Demeter to smite with destruction me and my house if I violate any of these obligations, but if I keep them I pray for many blessings." [2]

---

[1] Each court room had its distinguishing color. There were about ten regular court rooms, besides some for special tribunals; *e.g.* the Areopagus for the trial of homicides.

[2] We have not the exact text of all the dicasts' oath, but we can reproduce it fairly completely from Demosthenes's *Oration against Timocrates.*

119. Opening the Trial. The Plaintiff's Speech. — The oath
is admirable, but the dicasts are not in a wholly juridical
state of mind. Just before the short sacrifice needful to
commence proceedings, takes place, old Zenosthenes on the
second row nudges his neighbor : "I don't like the looks of
that Lamachus. He can't be honest, and gird his chiton
that way. I shall vote against him." "And I — my wife
knows his wife, and — " The archon rises. The crier bids
"silence!" The proceedings begin : but all through the
hearing there is whispering and nudging along the jurors'
benches. The litigants are quite aware of the situation and
are trying their best to win some advantage therefrom.

Ariston is the first to speak. He has taken great pains
with the folds of his himation and the trim of his beard this
morning. He must be thoroughly genteel, but avoid all appearance of being a dandy. In theory every man has to
plead his own case in Athens, but not every man is an
equally good orator. If a litigant is very inept, he can
simply say a few words, then step aside with "My friend so-
and-so will continue my argument"; and a readier talker
will take his place.[1] Ariston, however, is a fairly clever
speaker. Having what he conceives a good case, he has ob-
tained the indirect services of Hypereides, one of the first
of the younger orators of Athens. Hypereides has written
a speech which he thinks is suitable to the occasion, Ariston
has memorized it, and delivers it with considerable gusto.
He has solid evidence, as is proved from time to time when
he stops to call, "Let the clerk read the testimony of this
or that." There often is a certain hum of approbation from
the dicasts when he makes his points. He continues
bravely, therefore, ever and anon casting an eye upon the
clepsydra near at hand, a huge water-clock which, something

[1] These "friends," however, were never regular professional advocates;
it would have been ruinous to let the jury get the impression that an
orator was being directly hired to speak to them.

like an hour glass, marks off the time allotted him. Some of his arguments seem to have nothing to do with the alleged embezzlement. He vilifies his opponent: calls Lamachus's mother coarse names, intimates that as a boy he had no decent schooling, charges him with cowardice in the recent Mantinea campaign in which he served, hints that he has quarreled with his relatives. On the other hand, Ariston grandiloquently praises *himself* as well born, well educated, an honorable soldier and citizen, a man any Athenian would be glad to consider a friend. It is very plain all these personalia delight the jury.[1] When Ariston's "water has run out" and he concludes his speech, there is a loud murmur of applause running along the benches of the dicasts.

120. The Defendant's Speech. Demonstrations by the Jury. — It is now Lamachus's turn. He also has employed a professional speech-writer (*logographos*) of fame, Isæus, to prepare his defense. But almost at the outset he is in difficulties. Very likely he has a bad case to begin with. He makes it worse by a shrill, unpleasant voice and ungainly gestures. Very soon many dicasts are tittering and whispering jibes to their companions. The evidence does not seem to prove his contentions. As his harangue proceeds, the presiding archon (who has really very little control of the dicasts) is obliged "to remind the gentlemen of the jury that they have taken solemn oath to hear both sides of the question."

Lamachus fights doggedly on. Having put in all his real arguments, he takes refuge also in blackguarding his opponent. Did Ariston get his wealth honestly? was not his father a rascally grain dealer who starved the people? Yet there is still more impatience among the dicasts.

[1] For the depths of personal insult into which Greek litigants could descend there is no better instance than Demosthenes's (otherwise magnificent) *Oration on the Crown*, wherein he castigates his foe Æschines.

Lamachus now uses his last weapon. Upon the pleader's stand clamber his five young children clad in black mourning garments. They all weep together, and when not wiping their eyes, hold out their hands like religious suppliants, toward the dicasts.[1]

"Ah! Gentlemen of the jury," whines their father, "if you are moved by the voices of your lambs at home, pity these here. Acquit me for *their* sakes. Do not find against me and plunge these innocent darlings into want and misery, by impoverishing their father."

Appeals like this have swayed more than one jury during the last year, but the fates are all against Lamachus. From a back bench comes a dreaded shout that is instantly caught up by the front tiers also:

"*Katába! Katába!* — Go down! Go down!"

Lamachus hesitates. If he obeys, he loses all the rest of his defense. If he continues now, he enrages many of the dicasts, who will be absolutely sure to find against him. The presiding archon vainly rises, and tries to say something about "fair play." Useless. The uproar continues. Like a flock of scared doves Lamachus and all his five children flee incontinently from the tribune, amid ironical cheers and laughter.

121. The First Verdict. — There is silence at length. "The dicasts will proceed to vote," announces the court crier. The huge urns (one of bronze, one of wood) with narrow mouths are passed among the benches. Each juror has two round bronze disks, one solid, one with a hole bored in the middle. The solid acquit, the pierced ones convict. A juror drops the ballot he wishes to count into the bronze urn; the other goes into the wooden urn. The bronze

---

[1] For such an appeal to an Athenian dicastery, see Aristophanes's *Wasps*. The pertinent passages are quoted in *Readings in Ancient History*, vol. I, p. 238–40.

urn is carried to the archon, and there is an uneasy hush
while the 401 ballots are counted by the court officers. As
expected, more than 300 dicasts vote that Ariston is entitled to damages against Lamachus as an embezzler.

122. The Second and Final Verdict. — Ariston is smiling;
his friends are congratulating him, but the trial is by no
means over. If Lamachus had been found guilty of something for which the law provided an absolute fixed penalty,
this second part of the proceedings could be omitted. But
here, although the jury has said *some* damage or penalties
are due, it has still to fix the amount. Ariston has now to
propose to the dicasts a sum which he thinks is adequate
to avenge his wrongs and losses; Lamachus can propose a
smaller sum and try to persuade the court that it is entirely
proper. Each side must act warily. Athenian jurors are
fickle folk. The very men who have just howled down
Lamachus may, in a spasm of repentance, vote for absurdly
low damages. Again, Lamachus must not propose anything
obviously inadequate, otherwise the jurors who have just
voted against him may feel insulted, and accept Ariston's
estimate.[1] Ariston therefore says that he deserves at least
a talent. Lamachus rejoins that half a talent is more than
ample, even conceding Ariston's alleged wrongs. The arguments this time are shorter and more to the point. Then
comes the second balloting. A second time a majority
(smaller this time, but enough) is in favor of Ariston. The
better cause has conquered; and there is at least this advantage to the Athenian legal system, there will be no appeal
nor tedious technicalities before a "higher court." The verdict of the dicastery is final.

[1] Undoubtedly Socrates would have escaped with his life, if (after his
original condemnation) he had proposed a real penalty to the jury, instead
of an absurdly small fine. The only alternative for the dicasts was to accept
the proposition of his opponents, — in his case death.

123. The Merits and Defects of the Athenian Courts.—
No doubt injustice is sometimes done. Sometimes it is the
honest man who hears the dreaded "*Kataba!*" Sometimes
the weeping children have their intended effect. Sometimes
it is the arguments about "My opponent's scoundrelly ancestry" which win the verdict. At the same time, your Athenian dicast is a remarkably shrewd and acute individual.
He can distinguish between specious rhetoric and a real
argument. He is probably honestly anxious to do justice.
In the ordinary case where his personal interests or prejudices
do not come into play, the decision is likely to match with
justice quite as often perhaps as in the intricate court system
of a great republic many centuries after the passing of
Athens.

Certain features of some Athenian trials have not explained
themselves in the example just witnessed. To prevent
frivolous or blackmailing litigation it is provided that, if the
plaintiff in a suit gets less than one fifth of the ballots in his
favor (thus clearly showing he had no respectable case), he
is liable to a heavy fine or, in default thereof, exile. Again,
we have not waited for the actual closing scene—the dicasts
each giving up his colored staff as a kind of voucher to
the court officers, and in return getting his three obols (9
cents) daily jury fee, which each man claps promptly in his
cheek, and then goes off home to try the case afresh at the
family supper.

124. The Usual Punishments in Athens.—Trials involving
murder or manslaughter come before the special court of
Areopagus, and cannot well be discussed here, but most
other criminal cases are tried before the dicasts in much
the same way as a civil trial. When the law does not have
a set penalty, the jury virtually has to sentence the defendant after convicting him, choosing between one of two
proposed penalties. Greek courts can inflict death, exile,

fines, but almost never imprisonment. There is no "penitentiary" or "workhouse" in Athens; and the only use for a jail is to confine accused persons whom it is impossible to release on bail before their trial. The Athens city jail ("The House," as it is familiarly called — *Oikēma*) is a very simple affair, an open building, carelessly guarded and free to visitors all through the daylight. The inmates have to be kept in heavy fetters, otherwise they would be sure to take flight; and indeed escapes from custody are somewhat common.

125. The Heavy Penalty of Exile. — An Athenian will regard locking a criminal up for a term of years as a very foolish and expensive proceeding. If he has nothing wherewith to pay a round fine, why, simply send him into exile. This penalty is direful indeed to a Greek. The exile has often no protector, no standing in the courts of the foreign city, no government to avenge any outrage upon him. He can be insulted, starved, stripped, nay, murdered, often with impunity. Worse still, he is cut off from his friends with whom all his life is tied up; he is severed from the guardian gods of his childhood, — "*the* City," the city of his birth, hopes, longings, exists no more for him. If he dies abroad, he is not sure of a decent funeral pyre; and meanwhile his children may be hungering at home. So long as the Athenians have this tremendous penalty of exile at their disposal, they do not feel the need of penitentiaries.

126. The Death Penalty at Athens. — There are also the stocks and whipping posts for meting out summary justice to irresponsible offenders. When the death penalty is imposed (and the matter often lies in the discretion of the dicasts), the criminal, if of servile or Barbarian blood, may be put to death in some hideous manner and his corpse tossed into the Barathron, a vile pit on the northwest side of Athens, there to be dishonored by the kites and crows.

The execution of Athenian citizens, however, is extremely humane. The condemned is given a cup of poisonous hemlock juice and allowed to drink it while sitting comfortably among his friends in the prison. Little by little his body grows numb; presently he becomes senseless, and all is over without any pain.[1] The friends of the victim are then at liberty to give his body a suitable burial.

An Athenian trial usually lasts all day, and perhaps we have been able to witness only the end of it. It may well happen, however, that we cannot attend a dicastery at all. This day may be one which is devoted to a meeting of the public assembly, and duty summons the jurors, not to the court room, but to the Pnyx. This is no loss to us, however. We welcome a chance to behold the Athenian Ecclesia in action.

[1] No one can read the story of the death of Socrates in the prison, as told by Plato in the *Phædo*, without feeling (aside from the noble philosophical setting) how much more humane were such executions by hemlock than is the modern gallows or electric chair.

CHAPTER XVI.

THE ECCLESIA OF ATHENS.

127. The Rule of Democracy in Athens. — The Ecclesia, or Public Assembly, of Athens is something more than the chief governmental organ in the state. It is the great leveling engine which makes Athens a true democracy, despite the great differences in wealth between her inhabitants, and the marked social pretentions of "the noble and the good" — the educated classes. At this time Athens is profoundly wedded to her democratic constitution. Founded by Solon and Clisthenes, developed by Themistocles and Pericles, it was temporarily overthrown at the end of the Peloponnesian War; but the evil rule then of the "Thirty Tyrants" has proved a better lesson on the evils of oligarchic rule than a thousand rhetoricians' declamations upon the advantages of the "rule of the many" as against the "rule of the few." Attica now acknowledges only one Lord — *King Demos* — "King Everybody" — and until the coming of bondage to Macedon there will be no serious danger of an aristocratic reaction.

128. Aristocracy and Wealth. Their Status and Burdens. — True, there are old noble families in Athens, — like the Alcmæonidæ whereof Pericles sprang, and the Eumolpidæ who supply the priests to Demeter, the Earth Mother. But these great houses have long since ceased to claim anything but *social* preëminence. Even then one must take pains not to assume airs, or the next time one is litigant before the dicastery, the insinuation of "an undemocratic, oligarchic manner of life" will win very many adverse votes among the jury. Nobility and wealth are only allowed to assert themselves in Athens when justified by an extraordinary amount of public service and public generosity.

Xenophon in his *Memorabilia* makes Socrates tell Critobulus, a wealthy and self-important individual, that he is really so hampered by his high position as to be decidedly poor. "You are obliged," says Socrates, "to offer numerous and magnificent sacrifices; you have to receive and entertain sumptuously a great many strangers, and to feast [your fellow] citizens. You have to pay heavy contributions towards the public service, keeping horses and furnishing choruses in peace times and in war bearing the expense of maintaining triremes and paying the special war taxes; and if you fail to do all this, they will punish you with as much severity as if you were caught stealing their money."

129. Athenian Society Truly Democratic up to a Certain Point. — Wealth, then, means one perpetual round of public services and obligations, sweetened perhaps with a little empty praise, an inscription, an honorary crown, or best of all, an honorary statue "to the public benefactor" as the chief reward. On the other hand one may be poor and be a thoroughly self-respecting, nay, prominent citizen. Socrates had an absurdly small invested fortune and the gods knew that he did little enough in the way of profitable labor.[1] He had to support his wife and three children upon this income. He wore no chiton. His himation was always an old one, unchanged from summer to winter. He seems to have possessed only one pair of good sandals all his life. His rations were bread and water, save when he was invited out. Yet this man was welcome in the "very best society."

---

[1] Socrates's regular income from invested property seems to have been only about $12 per year. It is to be hoped his wife, Xanthippe, had a little property of her own!

Alcibiades, leader of the fast, rich set, and many more of
the gilded youth of Athens dogged his heels. One meets
not the slightest evidence that his poverty ever prevented
him from carrying his philosophic message home to the
wealthy and the noble. There is no snobbishness, then, in
this Athenian society. Provided a man is not pursuing a
base mechanic art or an ignoble trade, provided he has a real
message to convey,— whether in literature, philosophy, or
statecraft,—there are no questions " who was your father?"
or "what is your income?"[1] Athens will hear him and
accept his best. For this open-mindedness — almost unique
in ancient communities — one must thank King Demos and
his mouthpiece, the Ecclesia.

Athenians are intensely proud of their democracy. In
Æschylus's *Persians*, Atossa, the Barbarian queen, asks
concerning the Athenians :—

" Who is the lord and shepherd of their flock ? "

Very prompt is the answer :—

"They are not slaves, they bow to no man's rule."

Again in Euripides's *Suppliants* there is this boast touching
Athens :—

" No will of one
Holdeth this land : it is a city and free.
The whole folk year by year, in parity of service is our king."

130. The Voting Population of Athens. — Nevertheless when
we ask about this " whole folk," and who the voters are, we
soon discover that Athens is very far from being a pure
democracy. The multitudes of slaves are of course without
votes, and so is the numerous class of the important, cultivated, and often wealthy metics. To get Athenian citizenship is notoriously hard. For a stranger (say a metic who

[1] Possibly the son of a man whose parents notoriously had been slaves
in Athens would have found many doors closed to him.

had done some conspicuous public service) to be given the franchise, a special vote must be passed by the Ecclesia it-self; even then the new citizen may be prosecuted as un-deserving before a dicastery, and disfranchised. Again, only children both of whose parents are free Athenian citizens can themselves be enrolled on the carefully guarded lists in the deme books. The status of a child, one of whose parents is a metic, is little better than a bastard.[1]

Under these circumstances the whole number of voters is very much less than at a later day will appear in American communities of like population. Before the Peloponnesian War, when the power of Athens was at its highest point, there were not less than 30,000 full citizens and possibly as many as 40,000. But those days of imperial power are now ended. At present Athens has about 21,000 citizens, or a few more. It is impossible, however, to gather all these in any single meeting. A great number are farmers living in the remote villages of Attica; many city dwellers also will be too busy to think the 3-obol (9-cent) fee for attendance worth their while.[2] Six thousand seems to be a good num-ber for ordinary occasions and no doubt much business can be despatched with less, although this is the legal quorum set for most really vital matters. Of course a great crisis, *e.g.* a declaration of war, will bring out nearly every voter whose farm is not too distant.

131. Meeting Times of the Ecclesia. — Four times in

---

[1] Of course women were entirely excluded from the Ecclesia, as from all other forms of public life. The question of "woman's rights" had been agitated just enough to produce comedies like Aristophanes's *Par-liament of Women*, and philosophical theories such as appear in Plato's *Republic*.

[2] Payment for attendance at the Pnyx seems to have been introduced about 390 B.C. The original payment was probably only one obol, and then from time to time increased. It was a sign of the relative decay of political interest in Athens when it became needful thus to reward the commonalty for attendance at the Assembly.

every prytany [1] the Ecclesia must be convened for ordinary business, and oftener if public occasion requires. Five days' notice has to be given of each regular meeting, and along with the notice a placard announcing the proposals which are to come up has to be posted in the Agora. But if there is a sudden crisis, formalities can be thrown to the winds; a sudden bawling of the heralds in the streets, a great smoky column caused by burning the traders' flimsy booths in the Agora,— these are valid notices of an extraordinary meeting to confront an immediate danger.

If this has been a morning when the Ecclesia has been in session, nothing unusual has occurred at first in the busy Agora, except that the jury courts are hardly in action, and a bright flag is whipping the air from the tall flagpole by the Pnyx (the Assembly Place). Then suddenly there is a shouting through the Agora. The clamor of traffic around the popular flower stalls ceases; everybody who is not a slave or metic (and these would form a large fraction of the crowd of marketers) begins to edge down toward one end of the Agora. Presently a gang of Scythian police-archers comes in sight. They have a long rope sprinkled with red chalk wherewith they are "netting" the Agora. The chalk will leave an infallible mark on the mantle of every tardy citizen, and he who is thus marked as late at the meeting will lose his fee for attendance, if not subject himself to a fine. So there is a general rush away from the Agora and down one of the various avenues leading to the Pnyx.

132. The Pnyx (Assembly Place) at Athens. — The Pnyx is an open space of ground due west from the Acropolis.

---

[1] "A prytany" was one tenth of a year, say 35 or 36 days, during which time the 50 representatives of one of the ten Athenian tribes then serving as members of the Council of 500 (each tribe taking its turn) held the presidency of the Council and acted as a special executive committee of the government. There were thus at least 40 meetings of the Ecclesia each year, as well as the extraordinary meetings.

It originally sloped gently away towards the northeast, but
a massive retaining wall had been built around it, in an
irregular semicircle, and the space within filled with solidly
packed earth sloping inwards, making a kind of open air
auditorium. It is a huge place, 394 feet long, and 213
feet at the widest. The earthen slope is entirely devoid of
seats; everybody casts himself down sprawling or on his
haunches, perhaps with an old himation under him. Directly
before the sitters runs a long ledge hewn out of the rock,
forming, as it were, the "stage" side of the theater.
Here the rock has been cut away, so as to leave a sizable
stone pulpit standing forth. with a small flight of steps on
each side. This is the *Bema*, the orator's stand, whence
speak the "demagogues,"[1] the molders of Athenian public
opinion. In front of the Bema there is a small portable
altar for the indispensable sacrifices. In the rear of the
Bema are a few planks laid upon the rock. Here will sit
the fifty *Prytanes* in charge of the meeting. There is a
handsome chair for the presiding officer upon the Bema itself. These are all the furnishings of the structure wherein
Athens makes peace and war, and orders her whole civil
and foreign policy. The Hellenic azure is the only roof
above her sovran law makers. To the right, as the orators
stand on the Bema, they can point toward the Acropolis
and its glittering temples; to the left towards the Peiræus,
and the blue sea with the inevitable memories of glorious
Salamis. Surely it will be easy to fire all hearts with
patriotism!

133. The Preliminaries of the Meeting. — Into this space
the voters swarm by hundreds — all the citizens of Athens,
from twenty years and upward, sufficiently interested to
come. At each crude entrance stands a corps of watchful

---

[1] A "demagogue" (= people-leader) might well be a great statesman,
and not necessarily a cheap and noisy politician.

lexiarchs and their clerks, checking off those present and turning back interlopers. As the entering crowds begin to thin, the entrance ways are presently closed by wicker hurdles. The flag fluttering on high is struck. The Ecclesia is ready for action.

Much earlier than this, the farmers and fishermen from the hill towns or from Salamis have been in their places, grumbling at the slowness of the officials. People sit down where they can; little groups and clans together, wedged in closely, chattering up to the last minute, watching every proceeding with eyes as keen as cats'. All the gossip left over from the Agora is disposed of ere the prytanes — proverbially late — scramble into their seats of honor. The police-archers move up and down, enforcing a kind of order. Amid a growing hush a sucking pig is solemnly slaughtered by some religious functionary at the altar, and the dead victim carried around the circuit of the Pnyx as a symbolic purification of the audience.

"Come inside the purified circuit," enjoins a loud herald to the little groups upon the edge.[1]

Then comes a prayer invoking the gods' favor upon the Athenians, their allies, and this present meeting in particular, winding up (the herald counts this among the chief parts of his duty) with a tremendous curse on any wretch who should deceive the folk with evil counsel. After this the real secular business can begin. Nothing can be submitted to the Ecclesia which has not been previously considered and matured by the Council of 500. The question to be proposed is now read by the herald as a "*Pro-bouleuma*" — a suggested ordinance by the Council. Vast as is the audience, the acoustic properties of the Pnyx are excel-

---

[1] Aristophanes's *Acharnians* (ll. 50 ff.) gives a valuable picture of this and other proceedings at the Pnyx, but one should never forget the poet's exaggerations for comedy purposes, nor his deliberate omission of matters likely to be mere tedious detail to his audience.

ient, and all public officers and orators are trained to
harangue multitudes in the open air, so that the thousands
get every word of the proposition.

134. Debating a Proposition. — "Resolved by the Boule,
the tribe Leontis holding the prytany, and Heraclides
being clerk, upon the motion of Timon the son of Timon
the Eleusinian,[1] that" — and then in formal language it is
proposed to increase the garrison of the allied city of Byzantium by 500 hired Arcadian mercenaries, since the king of
Thrace is threatening that city, and its continued possession
is absolutely essential to the free import of grain into
Attica.

There is a hush of expectancy; a craning of necks.

"Who wishes to speak?" calls the herald.

After a decent pause Timon, the mover of the measure,
comes forward. He is a fairly well-known character and
commands a respectable faction among the Demos. There
is some little clapping, mixed with jeering, as he mounts the
Bema. The president of the prytanes — as evidence that
he has now the right to harangue — hands him a myrtle
wreath which he promptly claps on his head, and launches
into his argument. Full speedily he has convinced at least
a large share of the audience that it was sheer destruction
to leave Byzantium without an efficient garrison. Grain
would soon be at famine prices if the town were taken, etc.,
etc. The only marvel is that the merciful gods have averted
the disaster so long in the face of such neglect. — Why had
the board of strategi, responsible in such matters, neglected
this obvious duty? [Cheers intermixed with catcalls.]
This was not the way the men who won Marathon had dealt
with dangers, nor later worthies like Nicias or Thrasybulus.

---

[1] This seems to have been the regular form for beginning a *probouleuma*
although nearly all our information comes from the texts of proposals
after they have been made formal decrees by the sovran Demos.

[More cheers and catcalls.] He winds up with a splendid invocation to Earth, Sky, and Justice to bear witness that all this advice is given solely with a view to the weal of Athens.

"He had Isocrates teach him how to launch that peroration," mutters a crabbed old citizen behind his peak-trimmed beard, as Timon descends amid mingled applause and derision.

"Very likely; Iphicrates is ready to answer him," replies a fellow.

"Who wishes to speak?" the herald demands again. From a place directly before the Bema a well-known figure, the elderly general, Iphicrates, is rising. At a nod from the president, he mounts the Bema and assumes the myrtle. He has not Timon's smooth tones nor oratorical manner. He is a man of action and war, and no tool of the Agora coteries. A salvo of applause greets him. Very pithily he observes that Byzantium will be safe enough if the city will only be loyal to the Athenian alliance. Athens needs all her garrisons nearer home. Timon surely knows the state of the treasury. Is he going to propose a special tax upon his fellow countrymen to pay for those 500 mercenaries? [Loud laughter and derisive howls directed at Timon.] Athens needs to keep her strength for *real* dangers; and those are serious enough, but not at Byzantium. At the next meeting he and the other strategi will recommend — etc., etc. When Iphicrates quits the Bema there is little left of Timon's fine " Earth, Sky, and Justice."

135. Voting at the Pnyx. — But other orators follow on both sides. Once Timon, egged on by many supporters, tries to gain the Bema a second time, but is told by the president that one cannot speak twice on the same subject. Once the derision and shouting becomes so violent that the president has to announce, "Unless there is silence I must adjourn the meeting." Finally, after an unsuccessful effort to amend the proposal, by reducing the garrison at Byzantium to 250, the movers of the measure realize that the votes will probably be against them. They try to break up the meeting.

"I hear thunder!" "I feel rain!" they begin shouting, and such ill omens, if really in evidence, would be enough to force an adjournment; but the sky is delightfully clear. The president simply shrugs his shoulders; and now the Pnyx is fairly rocking with the yell, "A vote! A vote!"

The president rises. Taking the vote in the Ecclesia is a very simple matter when it is a plain question of "yes" or "no" on a proposition.[1]

"All who favor the *probouleuma* of Timon will raise the right hand!"

A respectable but very decided minority shows itself.

"Those who oppose."

The adverse majority is large. The morning is quite spent. There is a great tumult. Men are rising, putting on their himatia, ridiculing Timon; while the herald at a nod from the president declares the Ecclesia adjourned.

136. The Ecclesia as an Educational Instrument. — Timon and his friends retire crestfallen to discuss the fortunes of war. They are not utterly discouraged, however. The Ecclesia is a fickle creature. What it withholds to-day it may grant to-morrow. Iphicrates, whose words have carried such weight now, may soon be howled down and driven from the Bema much as was the unfortunate litigant in the jury court. Still, with all its faults, the Ecclesia is the great school for the adults of Athens. All are on terms of perfect equality. King Demos is not the least respecter of wealth and family. Sophistries are usually

---

[1] When an *individual* had to be voted for, then ballots were used.

penetrated in a twinkling by some coarse expletive from a remote corner of the Pnyx. Every citizen understands the main issues of the public business. *He is part of the actual working government,* not once per year (or less often) at the ballot box, but at least forty times annually; and dolt he would be, did he not learn at least all the superficialities of statecraft. He may make grievous errors. He may be misled by mob prejudice or mob enthusiasm; but he is not likely to persist in a policy of crass blundering very long. King Demos may indeed rule a fallible human monarchy, but it is thanks to him, and to his high court held at the Pnyx, that Athens owes at least half of that sharpness of wit and intelligence which is her boast.

CHAPTER XVII.

THE AFTERNOON AT THE GYMNASIA.

137. The Gymnasia. Places of General Resort. — The market is thinning after a busy day; the swarms of farmer-hucksters with their weary asses are trudging homeward; the schoolrooms are emptying; the dicasteries or the Ecclesia, as the case may be, have adjourned. Even the slave artisans in the factories are allowed to slacken work. The sun, a ball of glowing fire, is slowly sinking to westward over the slopes of Ægaleos; the rock of the Acropolis is glowing as if in flame; intense purple tints are creeping over all the landscape. The day is waning, and all Athenians who can possibly find leisure are heading towards the suburbs for a walk, a talk, and refreshment of soul and body at the several Gymnasia.

Besides various private establishments and small " wrestling schools " for the boys, there are three great public Gymnasia at Athens, — the Lyceum to the east of the town; the Cynosarges [1] to the southward; and last, but not at all least, the Academy. This is the handsomest, the most famous, the most characteristic. We shall do well to visit it.

138. The Road to the Academy. — We go out toward the northwest of the city, plunging soon into a labyrinth of garden walls, fragrant with the fruit and blossoms within, wander amid dark olive groves where the solemn leaves of

[1] The Cynosarges was the only one of these freely opened to such Athenians as had non-Athenian mothers. The other two were reserved for the strictly "full citizens."

158

the sacred trees are talking sweetly; and presently mount
a knoll by some suburban farm buildings, then look back to
find that slight as is the elevation, here is a view of marvelous beauty across the city, the Acropolis, and the
guardian mountains. From the rustling ivy coverts come
the melodious notes of birds. We are glad to learn that
this is the suburb of Colonus, the home of Sophocles the
tragedian, and here is the very spot made famous in the re-
nowned chorus of his *Œdipous at Colonus*. It is too early, of
course, to enjoy the nightingale which the poet asserts sings
often amid the branches, but the scene is one of marvelous
charm. We are not come, however, to admire Colonus.
The numerous strollers indicate our direction. Turning
a little to the south, we see, embowered amid the olive
groves which line the unseen stream of the Cephissos, a
wall, and once beyond it find ourselves in a kind of spacious
park combined with an athletic establishment. This is the
Academy, — founded by Hipparchus, son of Peisistratus
the tyrant, but given its real embellishments and beauty by
Cimon, the son of Miltiades the victor of Marathon.

139. The Academy. — The Academy is worthy of the
visit. The park itself is covered with olive trees and more
graceful plane trees. The grass beneath us is soft and
delightful to the bare foot (and nearly everybody, we
observe, has taken off his sandals). There are marble and
bronze statues skilfully distributed amid the shrubbery
—shy nymphs, peeping fauns, bold satyrs. Yonder is a
spouting fountain surmounted by a noble Poseidon with his
trident; above the next fountain rides the ocean car of
Amphitrite. Presently we come to a series of low buildings. Entering, we find them laid out in a quadrangle with
porticoes on every side, somewhat like the promenades
around the Agora. Inside the promenades open a series of
ample rooms for the use of professional athletes during

stormy weather, and for the inevitable bathing and anointing with oil which will follow all exercise. This great square court formed by the "gymnasium" proper is swarming with interesting humanity, but we pass it hastily in order to depart by an exit on the inner side and discover a second more conventionally laid out park. Here to right and to left are short stretches of soft sand divided into convenient sections for wrestling, for quoit hurling, for javelin casting, and for jumping; but a loud shout and cheering soon draw us onward. At the end of this park we find the stadium; a great oval track, 600 feet (a *stadium*) for the half circuit, with benches and all the paraphernalia for a foot race. The first contests have just ended. The racers are standing, panting after their exertions, but their friends are talking vehemently. Out in the sand, near the statue of Hermes (the patron god of gymnasia) is a dignified and self-conscious looking man in a purple-edged chiton — the gymnasiarch, the official manager of the Academy. While he waits to organize a second race we can study the visitors and habitués of the gymnasium.

140. The Social Atmosphere and Human Types at the Academy. — What the Pnyx is to the political life of Athens, this the Academy and the other great gymnasia are to its social and intellectual as well as its physical life. Here in daily intercourse, whether in friendly contest of speed or brawn, or in the more valuable contest of wits, the youth of Athens complete their education after escaping from the rod of the schoolmaster. Here they have daily lessons on the mottoes, which (did such a thing exist) should be blazoned on the coat of arms of Greece, as the summing up of all Hellenic wisdom: —

"Know thyself,"
and again: —
"Be moderate."

Precept, example, and experience teach these truths at
the gymnasia of Athens. Indeed, on days when the
Ecclesia is not in session, when no war is raging, and they
are not busy with a lawsuit, many Athenians will spend
almost the whole day at the Academy. For whatever are
your interests, here you are likely to find something to
engross you.

It must be confessed that not everybody at the Academy
comes here for physical or mental improvement. We see
a little group squatting and gesticulating earnestly under an
old olive tree — they are obviously busy, not with philosophic theory, but with dice. Again, two young men pass us
presenting a curious spectacle. They are handsomely
dressed and over handsomely scented, but each carries carefully under each arm a small cock; and from time to time
they are halted by friends who admire the birds. Clearly
these worthies' main interests are in cockfighting; and
they are giving their favorites "air and exercise" before
the deadly battle, on which there is much betting, at the
supper party that night. Also the shouting and rumbling
from a distance tells of the chariot course, where the sons
of the more wealthy or pretentious families are lessening
their patrimonies by training a "two" or a "four" to con-
tend at the Isthmian games or at Olympia.

141. Philosophers and Cultivated Men at the Gymnasia. —
All these things are true, and Athens makes full display
here of the usual crop of knaves or fools. Nevertheless this
element is in the minority. Here a little earlier or a little
later than our visit (for just now he is in Sicily) one could
see Plato himself — walking under the shade trees and ex-
pounding to a little trailing host of eager-eyed disciples the
fundamental theories of his ideal Commonwealth. Here are
scores of serious bearded faces, and heads sprinkled with
gray, moving to and fro in small groups, discussing in me-

*l*odious Attic the philosophy, the poetry, the oration, which has been partly considered in the Agora this morning, and which will be further discussed at the symposium to-night. Everything is entirely informal. Even white-haired gentlemen do not hesitate to cast off chiton and himation and spring around nimbly upon the sands, to "try their distance" with the quoits, or show the young men that they have not forgotten accuracy with the javelin, or even, against men of their own age, to test their sinews in a mild wrestling bout. It is undignified for an old man to attempt hard feats beyond his advanced years. No one expects any great proficiency from most of those present. It is enough to attempt gracefully, and to laugh merrily if you do not succeed. Everywhere there is the greatest good nature, and even frolicking, but very little of the really boisterous.

142. The Beautiful Youths at the Academy. — Yet the majority of the visitors to the Academy have an interest that is not entirely summed up in proper athletics, or in the baser sports, or in philosophy. Every now and then a little whisper runs among the groups of strollers or athletes : "There he goes ! — a new one ! How beautiful !" — and there is a general turning of heads.

A youth goes by, his body quite stripped, and delicately bronzed by constant exposure to the sun. His limbs are graceful, but vigorous and straight, his chest is magnificently curved. He lifts his head modestly, yet with a proud and easy carriage. His hair is dark blonde; his profile very "Greek" — nose and forehead joining in unbroken straight line. A little crowd is following him; a more favored comrade, a stalwart, bearded man, walks at his side. No need of questioning now whence the sculptors of Athens get their inspiration. This happy youth, just out of the schoolroom, and now to be enrolled as an armed ephebus, will be the model soon for some immortal bronze or marble.

Fortunate is he, if his humility is not ruined by all the admiration and flattery; if he can remember the injunctions touching "modesty," which master and father have repeated so long; if he can remember the precept that true beauty of body can go only with true beauty of soul. Now at least is his day of hidden or conscious pride. All Athens is commending him. He is the reigning toast, like the "belle" of a later age. Not the groundlings only, but the poets, rhetoricians, philosophers, will gaze after him, seek an introduction, compliment him delicately, give themselves the pleasure of making him blush deliciously, and go back to their august problems unconsciously stimulated and refreshed by this vision of "the godlike."[1]

143. The Greek Worship of Manly Beauty. — The Greek worship of the beautiful masculine form is something which the later world will never understand. In this worship there is too often a coarseness, a sensual dross, over which a veil is wisely cast. But the great fact of this worship remains: to the vast majority of Greeks "beauty" does not imply a delicate maid clad in snowy drapery; it implies a perfectly shaped, bronzed, and developed youth, standing forth in his undraped manhood for some hard athletic battle. This ideal possesses the national life, and affects the entire Greek civilization. Not beauty in innocent weakness, but beauty in resourceful strength — before this beauty men bow down.[2]

[1] For pertinent commentary on the effect of meeting a beautiful youth upon very grave men, see, e.g., Plato's *Charmides* (esp. 155 a) and *Lysis* (esp. 206 d). Or better still in Xenophon's *Symposium* (I. 9), where we hear of the beautiful youth Autolycus, "even as a bright light at night draws every eye, so by *his* beauty drew on him the gaze of all the company [at the banquet]. Not a man was present who did not feel his emotions stirred by the sight of him."

[2] Plato (*Republic*, p. 402) gives the view of enlightened Greek opinion when he states, "There can be no fairer spectacle than that of a man who

It is this masculine type of beauty, whether summed up in a physical form or translated by imagery into the realm of the spirit, that Isocrates (a very good mouthpiece for average enlightened opinion) praises in language which strains even his facile rhetoric. "[Beauty] is the first of all things in majesty, honor, and divineness. Nothing devoid of beauty is prized; the admiration of virtue itself comes to this, that of all manifestations of life, virtue is the most beautiful. The supremacy of beauty over all things can be seen in our own disposition toward it, and toward them. Other things we merely seek to attain as we need them, but beautiful things inspire us with love, *love* which is as much stronger than *wish* as its object is better. To the beautiful alone, as to the gods, we are never tired of doing homage; delighting to be their slaves rather than to be the rulers of others."

Could we put to all the heterogeneous crowd in the wide gymnasium the question, "What things do you desire most?" the answer "To be physically beautiful" (not "handsome" merely, but "beautiful") would come among the first wishes. There is a little song, very popular and very Greek. It tells most of the story.

> The best of gifts to mortal man is health ;
> The next the bloom of beauty's matchless flower;
> The third is blameless and unfraudful wealth ;
> The fourth with friends to speed youths' joyous hour.[1]

Health and physical beauty thus go before wealth and the passions of friendship, — a true Greek estimate !

combines the possession of *moral* beauty in his soul, with *outward* beauty of body, corresponding and harmonizing with the former, because the same great pattern enters into both."

[1] Translation by Milman. The exact date of this Greek poem is uncertain, but its spirit is entirely true to that of Athens at the time of this sketch.

144. The Detestation of Old Age. — Again, we are quick to learn that this "beauty" is the beauty of youth. It is useless to talk to an Athenian of a "beautiful old age." Old age is an evil to be borne with dignity, with resignation if needs be, to be fought against by every kind of bodily exercise; but to take satisfaction in it? — impossible. It means a diminishing of those keen powers of physical and intellectual enjoyment which are so much to every normal Athenian. It means becoming feeble, and worse than feeble, ridiculous. The physician's art has not advanced so far as to prevent the frequent loss of sight and hearing in even moderate age. No hope of a future renewal of noble youth in a happier world gilds the just man's sunset. Old age must, like the untimely passing of loved ones, be endured in becoming silence, as one of the fixed inevitables; but it is gloomy work to pretend to find it cheerful. Only the young can find life truly happy. Euripides in *The Mad Heracles* speaks for all his race: —

> Tell me not of the Asian tyrant,
>   Or of palaces plenished with gold;
> For such bliss I am not an aspirant,
>   If *youth* I might only behold: —
> Youth that maketh prosperity higher,
> And ever adversity lighter.[1]

145. The Greeks unite Moral and Physical Beauty. — But here at the Academy, this spirit of beautiful youth, and the "joy of life," is everywhere dominant. All around us are the beautiful bodies of young men engaged in every kind of graceful exercise. When we question, we are told that current belief is that in a great majority of instances there is a development and symmetry of mind corresponding to the glory of the body. It is contrary to all the prevalent

[1] Mahaffy, translator. Another very characteristic lament for the passing of youth is left us by the early elegiac poet Mimnermus.

notions of the reign of "divine harmony" to have it otherwise. The gods abhor all gross contradictions! Even now
men will argue over a strange breach of this rule; — why
did heaven suffer Socrates to have so beautiful a soul set in
so ugly a body? — Inscrutable are the ways of Zeus!

However, we have generalized and wandered enough.
The Academy is a place of superabounding activities. Let
us try to comprehend some of them.

146. The Usual Gymnastic Sports and their Objects. —
Despite all the training in polite conversation which young
men are supposed to receive at the gymnasium, the object
of the latter is after all to form places of athletic exercise.
The Athenians are without most of those elaborate field
games such as later ages will call "baseball" and "foot-
ball"; although, once learned, they could surely excel in
these prodigiously. They have a simple "catch" with
balls, but it hardly rises above the level of a children's pas-
time. The reasons for these omissions are probably, first,
because so much time is devoted to the "palæstra" exercises; secondly, because military training eats up about all
the time not needed for pure gymnastics.

The "palæstra" exercises, taught first at the boys' training establishments and later continued at the great gymnasia, are nearly all of the nature of latter-day "field
sports." They do not depend on the costly apparatus of
twentieth century athletic halls; and they accomplish their
ends with extremely simple means. The aim of the in-
structor is really twofold — to give his pupils a body fit
and apt for war (and we have seen that to be a citizen
usually implies being a hoplite), and to develop a body
beautiful to the eye and efficient for civil life. The naturally beautiful youth can be made more beautiful; the
naturally homely youth can be made at least passable under
the care of a skilful gymnastic teacher.

147. Professional Athletes: the Pancration. — Athletics, then, are a means to an end and should not be tainted with professionalism. True, as we wander about the Academy we see heavy and over brawny individuals whose " beauty " consists in flattened noses, mutilated ears, and mouths lacking many teeth, and who are taking their way to the remote quarter where boxing is permitted. Here they will wind hard bull's hide thongs around their hands and wrists, and pummel one another brutally, often indeed (if in a set contest) to the very risk of life. These men are obviously professional athletes who, after appearing with some success at the "Nemea," are in training for the impending "Pythia" at Delphi. A large crowd of youths of the less select kind follows and cheers them; but the better public opinion frowns on them. They are denounced by the philosophers. Their lives no less than their bodies "are not beautiful" — *i.e.* they offend against the spirit of harmony inherent in every Greek. Still less are they in genteel favor when, the preliminary boxing round being finished, they put off their boxing thongs and join in the fierce *Pancration*, a not unskilful combination of boxing with wrestling, in which it is not suffered to strike with the knotted fist, but in which, nevertheless, a terrible blow can be given with the bent fingers. Kicking, hitting, catching, tripping, they strive together mid the "*Euge! Euge!*—Bravo! Bravo!" of their admirers until one is beaten down hopelessly upon the sand, and the contest ends without harm. Had it been a real Pancration, however, it would have been desperate business, for it is quite permissible to twist an opponent's wrist, and even to break his fingers, to make him give up the contest. Therefore it is not surprising that the Pancration, even more than boxing, is usually reserved for professional athletes.

148. Leaping Contests. — But near at hand is a more pleasing contest. Youths of the ephebus age are practicing leap-

ing. They have no springboard, no leaping pole, but only
a pair of curved metal dumb-bells to aid them. One after
another their lithe brown bodies, shining with the fresh
olive oil, come forward on a lightning run up the little
mound of earth, then fly gracefully out across the soft
sands. There is much shouting and good-natured rivalry.
As each lad leaps, an eager attendant marks his distance
with a line drawn by the pickaxe. The lines gradually
extend ever farther from the mound. The rivalry is keen.
Finally, there is one leap that far exceeds the rest.[1] A merry
crowd swarms around the blushing victor. A grave middle-
aged man takes the ivy crown from his head, and puts it
upon the happy youth. " Your father will take joy in you,"
he says as the knot breaks up.

149. Quoit Hurling. — Close by the leapers is another
stretch of yellow sand reserved for the quoit throwers.
The contestants here are slightly older, — stalwart young
men, who seem, as they fling the heavy bronze discus, to be
reaching out eagerly into the fulness of life and fortune
before them. Very graceful are the attitudes. Here it was
the sculptor Miron saw his " Discobolus " which he immor-
talized and gave to all the later world; "stooping down to
take aim, his body turned in the direction of the hand which
holds the quoit, one knee slightly bent as though he meant
to vary the posture and to rise with the throw." [2] The caster,
however, does not make his attempt standing. He takes a
short run, and then the whole of his splendid body seems to
spring together with the cast.

150. Casting the Javelin. — The range of the quoit hurlers
in turn seems very great, but we cannot delay to await the

---

[1] If the data of the ancients are to be believed, the Greeks achieved
records in leaping far beyond those of any modern athletes, but it is
impossible to rely on data of this kind.

[2] The quotation is from Lucian (Roman Imperial period).

issue. Still elsewhere in the Academy they are hurling the javelin. Here is a real martial exercise, and patriotism as well as the natural athletic spirit urges young men to excel. The long light lances are being whirled at a distant target with remarkable accuracy ; and well they may, for every contestant has the vision of some hour when he may stand on the poop of a trireme and hear the dread call, "All hands repel boarders," or need all his darts to break up the rush of a pursuing band of hoplites.

151. Wrestling. — The real crowds, however, are around the wrestlers and the racers. Wrestling in its less brutal form is in great favor. It brings into play all the muscles of a man; it tests his resources both of mind and body finely. It is excellent for a youth and it fights away old age. The Greek language is full of words and allusions taken from the wrestler's art. The palæstras for the boys are called " the wrestling school " par excellence. It is no wonder that now the ring on the sands is a dense one and constantly growing. Two skilful amateurs will wrestle. One — a speedy rumor tells us — is, earlier and later in the day, a rising comic poet ; the other is not infrequently heard on the Bema. Just at present, however, they have forgotten anapests and oratory. A crowd of cheering, jesting friends thrusts them on. Forth they stand, two handsome, powerful men, well oiled for suppleness, but also sprinkled with fine sand to make it possible to get a fair grip in the contest.

For a moment they wag their sharp black beards at each other defiantly, and poise and edge around. Then the poet, more daring, rushes in, and instantly the two have grappled — each clutching the other's left wrist with his right hand. The struggle that follows is hot and even, until a lucky thrust from the orator's foot lands the poet in a sprawling heap; whence he rises with a ferocious grin and renews the contest. The second time they both fall together. "A tie!" calls the long-gowned friend who acts as umpire, with an officious flourish of his cane.

The third time the poet catches the orator trickily under the thigh, and fairly tears him off the ground; but at the fourth meeting the orator slips his arm in decisive grip about his opponent's waist and with a mighty wrench upsets him.

"Two casts out of three, and victory!"

Everybody laughs good-naturedly. The poet and the orator go away arm in arm to the bathing house, there to have another good oiling and rubbing down by their slaves, after removing the heavily caked sand from their skin with the strigils. Of course, had it been a real contest in the "greater games," the outcome might have been more serious; for the rules allow one to twist a wrist, to thrust an arm or foot into the foeman's belly, or (when things are desperate) to dash your forehead — bull fashion — against your opponent's brow, in the hope that his skull will prove weaker than yours.

152. Foot Races. — The continued noise from the stadium indicates that the races are still running; and we find time to go thither. The simple running match, a straight-away dash of 600 feet, seems to have been the original contest at the Olympic games ere these were developed into a famous and complicated festival; and the runner still is counted among the favorites of Greek athletics. As we sit upon the convenient benches around the academy stadium we see at once that the track is far from being a hard, well-rolled "cinder path"; on the contrary, it is of soft sand into which the naked foot sinks if planted too firmly, and upon it the most adept "hard-track" runner would at first pant and flounder helplessly. The Greeks have several kinds of foot races, but none that are very short. The

shortest is the simple *stadium* (600 feet), a straight hard
dash down one side of the long oval; then there is the
"double course" (*diaulos*) down one side and back; the
"horse race"—twice clear around (2400 feet); and lastly
the hard-testing "long course" (*dolichos*) which may vary
in length according to arrangement, — seven, twelve, twenty,

THE RACE IN ARMOR.

or even twenty-four stadia, we are told; and it is the last
(about three miles) that is one of the most difficult contests
at Olympia.

At this moment a party of four hale and hearty men still
in the young prime are about to compete in the "double
race." They come forward all rubbed with the glistening
oil, and crouch at the starting point behind the red cord
held by two attendants. The gymnasiarch stands watch-
fully by, swinging his cane to smite painfully whoever, in
over eagerness, breaks away before the signal. All is
ready; at his nod the rope falls. The four fly away together, pressing their elbows close to their sides, and going
over the soft sands with long rhythmic leaps, rather than
with the usual rapid running motion. A fierce race it is,
amid much exhortation from friends and shouting. At
length, as so often, — when speeding back towards the

stretched cord, — the rearmost runner suddenly gathers amazing speed, and, flying with prodigious leaps ahead of his rivals, is easily the victor. His friends are at once about him, and we hear the busy tongues advising, "You must surely race at the Pythia; the Olympia; etc."

This simple race over, a second quickly follows: five heavy, powerful men this time, but they are to run in full hoplite's armor — the ponderous shield, helmet, cuirass, and greaves. This is the exacting "Armor Race" (*Hoplito-dromos*), and safe only for experienced soldiers or professional athletes.[1] Indeed, the Greeks take all their foot races very seriously, and there are plenty of instances when the victor has sped up to the goal, and then dropped dead before the applauding stadium. There are no stop watches in the Academy; we do not know the records of the present or of more famous runners; yet one may be certain that the "time" made, considering the very soft sand, has been exceedingly fast.

153. The Pentathlon : the Honors paid to Great Athletes. — We have now seen average specimens of all the usual athletic sports of the Greeks. Any good authority will tell us, however, that a truly capable athlete will not try to specialize so much in any one kind of contest that he cannot do justice to the others. As an all around well-trained man he will try to excel in the *Pentathlon*, the "five contests." Herein he will successfully join in running, javelin casting, quoit throwing, leaping, and wrestling.[2] As the contest proceeds the weaker athletes will be

---

[1] It was training in races like these which enabled the Athenians at Marathon to "charge the Persians on the run" (Miltiades' orders), all armored though they were, and so get quickly through the terrible zone of the Persian arrow fire.

[2] The exact order of these contests, and the rules of elimination as the games proceeded, are uncertain — perhaps they varied with time and place.

eliminated; only the two fittest will be left for the final
trial of strength and skill. Fortunate indeed is "he who
overcometh" in the Pentathlon. It is the crown of athletic
victories, involving, as it does, no scanty prowess both of
body and mind. The victor in the Pentathlon at one of
the great Pan-Hellenic games (Olympian, Pythian, Isthmian,
or Nemean) or even in the local Attic contest at the Panathenæa is a marked man around Athens or any other Greek
city. Poets celebrate him; youths dog his heels and try to
imitate him; his kinsfolk take on airs; very likely he is
rewarded as a public benefactor by the government. But
there is abundant honor for one who has triumphed in *any*
of the great contests; and even as we go out we see people
pointing to a bent old man and saying, "Yes; he won the
quoit hurling at the Nemea when Ithycles was archon." [1]

. . . The Academy is already thinning. The beautiful
youths and their admiring "lovers" have gone homeward.
The last race has been run. We must hasten if we would
not be late to some select symposium. The birds are more
melodious than ever around Colonus; the red and golden
glow upon the Acropolis is beginning to fade; the night is
sowing the stars; and through the light air of a glorious
evening we speed back to the city.

[1] This would make it 398 B.C. The Athenians dated their year by the
name of their "first Archon" (*Archon eponymos*).

CHAPTER XVIII.

ATHENIAN COOKERY AND THE SYMPOSIUM.

154. Greek Meal Times. — The streets are becoming empty.
The Agora has been deserted for hours. As the warm balmy
night closes over the city the house doors are shut fast, to
open only for the returning master or his guests, bidden
to dinner. Soon the ways will be almost silent, to be disturbed, after a proper interval, by the dinner guests returning homeward. Save for these, the streets will seem those
of a city of the dead: patrolled at rare intervals by the
Scythian archers, and also ranged now and then by cutpurses
watching for an unwary stroller, or miscreant roisterers
trolling lewd songs, and pounding on honest men's doors as
they wander from tavern to tavern in search of the lowest
possible pleasures.

We have said very little of eating or drinking during our
visit in Athens, for, truth to tell, the citizens try to get
through the day with about as little interruption for food
and drink as possible. But now, when warehouse and gymnasium alike are left to darkness, all Athens will break its
day of comparative fasting.

Roughly speaking, the Greeks anticipate the latter-day
"Continental" habits in their meal hours. The custom of
Germans and of many Americans in having the heartiest
meal at noonday would never appeal to them. The hearty
meal is at night, and no one dreams of doing any serious
work after it. When it is finished, there may be pleasant
discourse or varied amusements, but never real business;

and even if there are guests, the average dinner party breaks
up early. Early to bed and early to rise, would be a maxim
indorsed by the Athenians.

Promptly upon rising, our good citizen has devoured a
few morsels of bread sopped in undiluted wine; that has
been to him what "coffee and rolls" will be to the French-
man, — enough to carry him through the morning business,
until near to noon he will demand something more satisfying. He then visits home long enough to partake of a
substantial déjeuner (*ariston*, first breakfast = *akratisma*).
He has one or two hot dishes — one may suspect usually
warmed over from last night's dinner — and partakes of some
more wine. This *ariston* will be about all he will require
until the chief meal of the day — the regular dinner (*deîpnon*)
which would follow sunset.

155. Society desired at Meals. — The Athenians are a gregarious sociable folk. Often enough the citizen must dine
alone at home with "only" his wife and children for company, but if possible he will invite friends (or get himself
invited out). Any sort of an occasion is enough to excuse
a dinner-party, — a birthday of some friend, some kind of
family happiness, a victory in the games, the return from,
or the departure upon, a journey : — all these will answer;
or indeed a mere love of good fellowship. There are innumerable little eating clubs; the members go by rotation
to their respective houses. Each member contributes either
some money or has his slave bring a hamper of provisions.
In the fine weather picnic parties down upon the shore are
common.[1] "Anything to bring friends together" — in the
morning the Agora, in the afternoon the gymnasium, in the
evening the symposium — that seems to be the rule of
Athenian life.

[1] Such excursions were so usual that the literal expression "Let us
banquet at the shore" (σήμερον ἀκτάσωμεν) came often to mean simply
"Let us have a good time."

However, the Athenians seldom gather to eat for the mere sake of animal gorging. They have progressed since the Greeks of the Homeric Age. Odysseus[1] is made to say to Alcinoüs that there is nothing more delightful than sitting at a table covered with bread, meat, and wine, and listening to a bard's song; and both Homeric poems show plenty of gross devouring and guzzling. There is not much of this in Athens, although Bœotians are still reproached with being voracious, swinish "flesh eaters," and the Greeks of South Italy and Sicily are considered as devoted to their fare, though of more refined table habits. Athenians of the better class pride themselves on their light diet and moderation of appetite, and their neighbors make considerable fun of them for their failure to serve satisfying meals. Certain it is that the typical Athenian would regard a twentieth century *table d'hôte* course dinner as heavy and unrefined, if ever it dragged its slow length before him.

156. The Staple Articles of Food. — However, the Athenians have honest appetites, and due means of silencing them. The diet of a poor man is indeed simple in the extreme. According to Aristophanes his meal consists of a cake, bristling with bran for the sake of economy, along with an onion and a dish of sow thistles, or of mushrooms, or some other such wretched vegetables; and probably, in fact, that is about all three fourths of the population of Attica will get on ordinary working days, always with the addition of a certain indispensable supply of oil and wine.

Bread, oil, and wine, in short, are the three fundamentals of Greek diet. With them alone man can live very healthfully and happily; without them elaborate vegetable and meat dishes are poor substitutes. Like latter-day Frenchmen or Italians with their huge loaves or macaroni, *bread* in one form or another is literally the staff of life to the

[1] *Odyssey*, IX. 5–10.

Greek. He makes it of wheat, barley, rye, millet, or spelt, but preferably of the two named first. As a rule the wheat flour alone is baked up into loaves. The barley meal is kneaded (not baked) and eaten raw or half raw as a sort of porridge. Of wheat loaves there are innumerable shapes on sale in the Agora, — slender rolls, convenient loaves, and also huge loaves needing two or three bushels of flour, exceeding even those made in a later day in Normandy. At every meal the amount of bread or porridge consumed is enormous; there is really little else at all substantial. Persian visitors to the Greeks complain that they are in danger of rising from the table hungry.

But along with the inevitable bread goes the inevitable *olive oil*. No latter-day article will exactly correspond to it. First of all it takes the place of butter as the proper condiment to prevent the bread from being tasteless.[1] It enters into every dish. The most versatile cook will be lost without it. Again, at the gymnasium we have seen its great importance to the athletes and bathers. It is therefore the Hellenic substitute for soap. Lastly, it fills the lamps which swing over every dining board. It takes the place of electricity, gas, or petroleum. No wonder Athens is proud of her olive trees. If she has to import her grain, she has a surplus for export of one of the three great essentials of Grecian life.

The third inevitable article of diet is *wine*. No one has dreamed of questioning its vast desirability under almost all circumstances. Even drunkenness is not always improper. It may be highly fitting, as putting one in a "divine frenzy," partaking of the nature of the gods. Musæus the semi-mythical poet is made out to teach that the reward of virtue will be something like perpetual intoxication in the next

---

[1] There was extremely little cow's butter in Greece. Herodotus (iv. 2) found it necessary to explain the process of "cow-cheese-making" among the Scythians.

world. Æschines the orator will, ere long, taunt his opponent Demosthenes in public with being a "water drinker";
and Socrates on many occasions has given proof that he
possessed a very hard head. Yet naturally the Athenian
has too acute a sense of things fit and dignified, too noble
a perception of the natural harmony, to commend drunkenness on any but rare occasions. Wine is rather valued as
imparting a happy moderate glow, making the thoughts
come faster, and the tongue more witty. Wine raises the
spirits of youth, and makes old age forget its gray hairs.
It chases away thoughts of the dread hereafter, when one
will lose consciousness of the beautiful sun, and perhaps
wander a "strengthless shade" through the dreary underworld.

There is a song attributed to Anacreon, and nearly
everybody in Athens approves the sentiment: —

> Thirsty earth drinks up the rain,
> Trees from earth drink that again ;
> Ocean drinks the air, the sun
> Drinks the sea, and him, the moon.
> Any reason, canst thou think,
> I should thirst while all these drink? [1]

157. Greek Vintages. — All Greeks, however, drink their
wine so diluted with water that it takes a decided quantity
to produce a "reaction." The average drinker takes three
parts water to two of wine; if he is a little reckless the
ratio is four of water to three of wine; equal parts "make
men mad" as the poet says, and are probably reserved for
very wild dinner parties. As for drinking pure wine no
one dreams of the thing — it is a practice fit for Barbarians.
There is good reason, however, for this plentiful use of
water. In their original state Greek wines were very
strong, perhaps almost as alcoholic as whisky, and the

[1] Translation from Von Falke's *Greece and Rome.*

Athenians have no Scotch climate to excuse the use of such stimulants.[1]

No wine served in Athens, however, will appeal to a later-day connoisseur. It is all mixed with resin, which perhaps makes it more wholesome, but to enjoy it then becomes an acquired taste. There are any number of choice vintages, and you will be told that the local Attic wine is not very desirable, although of course it is the cheapest. Black wine is the strongest and sweetest; white wine is the weakest; rich golden is the driest and most wholesome. The rocky isles and headlands of the Ægean seem to produce the best vintage — Thasos, Cos, Lesbos, Rhodes, all boast their grapes; but the best wine beyond a doubt is from Chios.[2] It will fetch a mina ($18) the "metreta," i.e. nearly 50 cents per quart. At this same time you can buy a "metreta" of common Attic wine for four drachmæ (72 cents), or say two cents per quart. The latter — when one considers the dilution — is surely cheap enough for the most humble.

158. Vegetable Dishes. — Provided with bread, oil, and wine, no Athenian will long go hungry; but naturally these are not a whole feast. As season and purse may afford they will be supplanted by such vegetables as beans (a staple article), peas, garlic, onions, radishes, turnips, and asparagus; also with an abundance of fruits, — besides figs (almost a fourth indispensable at most meals), apples, quinces, peaches,

[1] There was a wide difference of opinion as to the proper amount of dilution. Odysseus (*Odyssey*, IX. 209) mixed his fabulously strong wine from Maron in Thrace with twenty times its bulk of water. Hesiod abstemiously commended three parts of water to one of wine. Zaleucus, the lawgiver of Italian Locri, established the death penalty for drinking unmixed wine save by physicians' orders (*Athenæus*, X. 33).

[2] Naturally certain foreign vintages had a demand, just because they were foreign. Wine was imported from Egypt and from various parts of Italy. It was sometimes mixed with sea water for export, or was made aromatic with various herbs and berries. It was ordinarily preserved in great earthern jars sealed with pitch.

pears, plums, cherries, blackberries, the various familiar nuts, and of course a plenty of grapes and olives. The range of selection is in fact decidedly wide : only the twentieth century visitor will miss the potato, the lemon, and the orange ; and when he pries into the mysteries of the kitchen a great fact at once stares him in the face. The Greek must dress his dishes without the aid of sugar. As a substitute there is an abundant use of the delicious Hymettus honey, — "fragrant with the bees," — but it is by no means so full of possibilities as the white powder of later days. Also the Greek cook is usually without fresh cow's milk, and most goat's milk probably takes its way to cheese. No morning milk carts rattle over the stones of Athens.

159. Meat and Fish Dishes. — Turning to the meat dishes, we at once learn that while there is a fair amount of farm poultry, geese, hares, doves, partridges, etc., on sale in the market, there is extremely little fresh beef or even mutton, pork, and goat's flesh. It is quite expensive, and counted too hearty for refined diners. The average poor man in fact hardly tastes flesh except after one of the great public festivals ; then after the sacrifice of the "hecatomb" of oxen, there will probably be a distribution of roast meat to all the worshipers, and the honest citizen will take home to his wife an uncommon luxury — a piece of roast beef. But the place of beef and pork is largely usurped by most excellent fish. The waters of the Ægean abound with fish. The import of salt fish (for the use of the poor) from the Propontis and Euxine is a great part of Attic commerce. A large part of the business at the Agora centers around the fresh fish stalls, and we have seen how extortionate and insolent were the fishmongers. Sole, tunny, mackerel, young shark, mullet, turbot, carp, halibut, are to be had, but the choicest regular delicacies are the great Copaic eels from Bœotia ; these, "roasted on the coals and wrapped in beet leaves," are a dish fit for the Great King. Lucky is the host who has them for his dinner party. Oysters and mussels too are in demand, and there is a considerable sale of snails, "the poor man's salad," even as in present-day France.

Clearly, then, if one is not captious or gluttonous, there should be no lack of good eating in Athens, despite the reputation of the city for abstemiousness. Let us pry therefore into the symposium of some good citizen who is dispensing hospitality to-night.

160. Inviting Guests to a Dinner Party. —

> Who loves thee, him summon to thy board;
> Far off be he who hates.

This familiar sentiment of Hesiod, one Prodicus, a well-to-do gentleman, had in mind when he went to the Agora this morning to arrange for a dinner party in honor of his friend Hermogenes, who was just departing on a diplomatic mission to the satrap of Mysia. While walking along the Painted Porch and the other colonnades he had no difficulty in seeing most of the group he intended to invite, and if they did not turn to greet him, he would halt them by sending his slave boy to run and twitch at their mantles, after which the invitation was given verbally. Prodicus, however, deliberately makes arrangements for one or two more than those he has bidden. It will be entirely proper for his guests to bring friends of their own if they wish; and very likely some intimate whom he has been unable to find will invite himself without any bidding.

At the Agora Prodicus has had much to do. His house is a fairly large and well-furnished one, his slaves numerous and handy, but he has not the cook or the equipment for a really elaborate symposium. At a certain quarter on the great square he finds a contractor who will supply all the extra appointments for a handsome dinner party — tables, extra lamps, etc. Then he puts his slave boy to bawling out:

"Who wants an engagement to cook a dinner?"

This promptly brings forward a sleek, well-dressed fellow whose dialect declares that he is from Sicily, and who asserts he is an expert professional cook.   Prodicus engages him and has a conference with him on the profound question of "whether the tunnies or the mullets are better to-day, or will there be fresh eels?"   This point and similar minor matters settled, Prodicus makes liberal purchases at the fish and vegetable stalls, and his slaves bear his trophies homeward.

161. Preparing for the Dinner. The Sicilian Cook. — All that afternoon the home of Prodicus is in an uproar.   The score of slaves show a frantic energy.   The aula is cleaned and scrubbed: the serving girls are busy hanging festoons of leaves and weaving chaplets.   The master's wife — who does not dream of actually sharing in the banquet — is nevertheless as active and helpful as possible; but especially she is busy trying to keep the peace between the old house servants and the imported cook.   This Sicilian is a notable character.   To him cookery is not a handicraft: it is the triumph, the quintessence of all science and philosophy.   He talks a strange professional jargon, and asserts that he is himself learned in astronomy — for that teaches the best seasons, *e.g.* for mackerel and haddock; in geometry, — that he might know how a boiler or gridiron should be set to the best advantage; in medicine, that he might prepare the most wholesome dishes.   In any case he is a perfect tyrant around the kitchen, grumbling about the utensils, cuffing the spit-boy, and ever bidding him bring more charcoal for the fire and to blow the bellows faster.[1]

By the time evening is at hand Prodicus and his house

[1] The Greeks seem to have cooked over a rather simple open fireplace with a wood or charcoal fire.   They had an array of cooking utensils, however, according to all our evidence, elaborate enough to gladden a very exacting modern *chef*.

are in perfect readiness. The bustle is ended; and the
master stands by the entrance way, clad in his best and
with a fresh myrtle wreath, ready to greet his guests. No
ladies will be among these. Had there been any women
invited to the banquet, they would surely be creatures of no
very honest sort; and hardly fit, under any circumstances,
to darken the door of a respectable citizen. The mistress
and her maids are "behind the scenes." There may be a
woman among the hired entertainers provided, but for a refined Athenian lady to appear at an ordinary symposium is
almost unthinkable.[1]

162. The Coming of the Guests. — As each guest comes, he
is seen to be elegantly dressed, and to wear now, if at no
other time, a handsome pair of sandals.[2] He has also taken
pains to bathe and to perfume himself. As soon as each
person arrives his sandals are removed in the vestibule by
the slaves and his feet are bathed. No guest comes alone,
however: every one has his own body servant with him,
who will look after his footgear and himation during the
dinner, and give a certain help with the serving. The
house therefore becomes full of people, and will be the scene
of remarkable animation during the next few hours.

Prodicus is not disappointed in expecting some extra
visitors. His guest of honor, Hermogenes, has brought along
two, whom the host greets with the polite lie: "Just in time
for dinner. Put off your other business. I was looking for
you in the Agora and could not find you."[3] Also there
thrusts in a half genteel, half rascally fellow, one Palladas,

---

[1] In marriage parties and other strictly family affairs women were
allowed to take part; and we have an amusing fragment of Menander as
to how, on such rare occasions, they monopolized the conversation.

[2] Socrates, by way of exception to his custom, put on some fine sandals
when he was invited to a banquet.

[3] It is with such a white fib that the host Agathon salutes Aristodemus,
Socrates's companion, in Plato's *Symposium*.

who spends all his evenings at dinner parties, being willing to be the common butt and jest of the company (having indeed something of the ability of a comic actor about him) in return for a share of the good things on the table. These "Parasites" are regular characters in Athens, and no symposium is really complete without them, although often their fooleries cease to be amusing.[1]

163. The Dinner Proper. — The Greeks have not anticipated the Romans in their custom of making the standard dinner party nine persons on three couches, — three guests on each. Prodicus has about a dozen guests, two on a couch. They "lie down" more or less side by side upon the cushioned divans, with their right arms resting on brightly striped pillows and the left arms free for eating. The slaves bring basins of water to wash their hands, and then beside each couch is set a small table, already garnished with the first course, and after the casting of a few bits of food upon the family hearth fire, — the conventional "sacrifice" to the house gods, — the dinner begins.

Despite the elaborate preparations of the Sicilian cook, Prodicus offers his guests only two courses. The first consists of the substantial dishes — the fish, the vegetables, the meat (if there is any). Soups are not unknown, and had they been served might have been eaten with spoons; but Athens like all the world is innocent of forks, and fingers take their place. Each guest has a large piece of soft bread on which he wipes his fingers from time to time and presently

---

[1] Of these "Parasites" or "Flies" (as owing to their migratory habits they were sometimes called), countless stories were told, whereof the following is a sample: There was once a law in Athens that not over thirty guests were to be admitted to a marriage feast, and an officer was obliged to count all the guests and exclude the superfluous. A "fly" thrust in on one occasion, and the officer said: "Friend, you must retire. I find one more here than the law allows." "Dear fellow," quoth the "fly," "you are utterly mistaken, as you will find, if you will kindly count again — only *beginning with me.*"

casts it upon the floor.[1] When this first course is finished, the tables are all taken out to be reset, water is again poured over the hands of the guests, and garlands of flowers are passed. The use of garlands is universal, and among the guests, old white headed and bearded Sosthenes will find nothing more undignified in putting himself beneath a huge wreath of lilies than an elderly gentleman of a later day will find in donning the "conventional" dress suit. The conversation, — which was very scattering at first, — becomes more animated. A little wine is now passed about. Then back come the tables with the second course — fruits, and various sweetmeats and confectionery with honey as the staple flavoring. Before this disappears a goblet of unmixed wine is passed about, and everybody takes a sip: "To the Good Genius," they say as the cup goes round.

164. Beginning the Symposium. — Prodicus at length gives a nod to the chief of his corps of servers.

"Bring in the wine!" he orders. The slaves promptly whisk out the tables and replace them with others still smaller, on which they set all kinds of gracefully shaped beakers and drinking bowls. More wreaths are distributed, also little bottles of delicate ointment. While the guests are praising Prodicus's nard, the servants have brought in three huge "mixing bowls" (*craters*) for the wines which are to furnish the main potation.

So far we have witnessed not a symposium, but merely a dinner; and many a proper party has broken up when the last of the dessert has disappeared; but, after all, the drinking bout is the real crown of the feast. It is not so much the wine as the things that go with the wine that are so delightful. As to what these desirable condiments are, opinions differ. Plato (who is by no means too much of a philosopher to be a real man of the world) says in his

---

[1] Napkins were not used in Greece before Roman days.

Protagoras that mere conversation is *the* thing at a symposium. "When the company are real gentlemen and men
of education, you will see no flute girls nor dancing girls nor
harp girls; they will have no nonsense nor games, but will be
content with one another's conversation."[1] But this ideal,
though commended, is not always followed in decidedly
intellectual circles.   Xenophon[2] shows us a select party
wherein Socrates participated, in which the host has been
fain to hire in a professional Syracusian entertainer with two
assistants, a boy and a girl, who bring their performance to
a climax by a very suggestive dumb-show play of the story of
Bacchus and Ariadne.   Prodicus's friends, being solid, somewhat pragmatic men — neither young sports nor philosophers — steer a middle course.   There is a flute girl present,
because to have a good symposium without some music is
almost unimaginable; but she is discreetly kept in the background.

165. The Symposiarch and his Duties. — "Let's cast for
our Symposiarch!" is Prodicus's next order, and each guest
in turn rattles the dice box.   Tychē (Lady Fortune) gives
the presidency of the feast to Eunapius, a bright-eyed,
middle-aged man with a keen humor, but a correct sense of
good breeding.   He assumes command of the symposium;
takes the ordering of the servants out of Prodicus's hands,
and orders the wine to be mixed in the craters with proper
dilution.   He then rises and pours out a libation from each
bowl "to the Olympian Gods," "to the Heroes," and "t
Zeus the Saviour," and casts a little incense upon the altar
The guests all sing a *Pœan*, not a warrior's charging song
this time, but a short hymn in praise of the Wine-God
some lilting catch like Alcæus's

[1] Plato again says (*Politicus*, 277 *b*), "To intelligent persons, a living
being is more truly delineated by language and discourse than by any
painting or work of art."

[2] In his *Symposium* — which is far less perfect as literature than
Plato's, but probably corresponds more to the average instance.

In mighty flagons hither bring
The deep red blood of many a vine,
That we may largely quaff and sing
The praises of the God of wine.

166. Conversation at the Symposium. — After this the symposium will proceed according to certain general rules which it is Eunapius's duty to enforce; but in the main a "program" is something to be avoided. Everybody must feel himself acting spontaneously and freely. He must try to take his part in the conversation and neither speak too seldom nor too little. It is not "good form" for two guests to converse privately among themselves, nor for anybody to dwell on unpleasant or controversial topics. Aristophanes has laid down after his way the proper kind of things to talk about.[1] "[Such as] 'how Ephudion fought a fine pancratium with Ascondas though old and gray headed, but showing great form and muscle.' This is the talk usual among refined people [or again] 'some manly act of your youth; for example, how you chased a boar or a hare, or won a torch race by some bold device.' [Then when fairly settled at the feast] straighten your knees and throw yourself in a graceful and easy manner upon the couch. Then make some observations upon the beauty of the appointments, look up at the ceiling and praise the tapestry of the room."

As the wine goes around, tongues loosen more and more. Everybody gesticulates in delightful southern gestures, but does not lose his inherent courtesy. The anecdotes told are often very egoistic. The first personal pronoun is used extremely often, and "I" becomes the hero of a great many exploits. The Athenian, in short, is an adept at praising himself with affected modesty, and his companions listen good-humoredly, and retaliate by praising themselves.

[1] *Wasps*, 1174–1564.

167. Games and Entertainments. — By the time the craters are one third emptied the general conversation is beginning to be broken up. It is time for various standard diversions. Eunapius therefore begins by enjoining on each guest in turn to sing a verse in which a certain letter must not appear, and in event of failure to pay some ludicrous forfeit. Thus the bald man is ordered to begin to comb his hair; the lame man (halt since the Mantinea campaign), to stand up and dance to the flute player, etc. There are all kinds of guessing of riddles — often very ingenious as become the possessors of " Attic salt." Another diversion is to compare every guest present to some mythical monster, a process which infallibly ends by getting the " Parasite " likened to Cerberus, the Hydra, or some such dragon, amid the laughter of all the rest. At some point in the amusement the company is sure to get to singing songs : — " Scolia " — drinking songs indeed, but often of a serious moral or patriotic character, whereof the oft-quoted song in praise of Harmodius and Aristogeiton the tyrant-slayers is a good example.[1] No "gentleman" will profess to be a public singer, but to have a deep, well-trained voice, and to be able to take one's part in the symposium choruses is highly desirable, and some of the singing at Prodicus's banquet is worth hearing.

Before the evening is over various games will be ordered in, especially the *cottabus*, which is in great vogue. On the top of a high stand, something like a candelabrum, is balanced rather delicately a little saucer of brass. The players stand at a considerable distance with cups of wine. The game is to toss a small quantity of wine into the balanced saucer so smartly as to make the brass give out a clear ringing sound, and to tilt over upon its side.[2] Much shouting,

---

[1] Given in *Readings in Ancient History*, Vol. I, p. 117, and in many other volumes.

[2] This was the simplest form of the *cottabus* game; there were numerous elaborations, but our accounts of them are by no means clear.

merriment, and a little wagering ensues.   While most of the company prefer the cottabus, two, who profess to be experts, call for a gaming board and soon are deep in the " game of towns " — very like to latter-day " checkers," played with a board divided into numerous squares.   Each contestant has thirty colored stones, and the effort is to surround your opponent's stones and capture them.   Some of the company, however, regard this as too profound, and after trying their skill at the cottabus betake themselves to the never failing chances of dice.   Yet these games are never suffered (in refined dinner parties) to banish the conversation.   That after all is the center, although it is not good form to talk over learnedly of statecraft, military tactics, or philosophy. If such are discussed, it must be with playful abandon, and a disclaimer of being serious; and even very grave and gray men remember Anacreon's preference for the praise of " the glorious gifts of the Muses and of Aphrodite " rather than solid discussions of " conquest and war."

168. Going Home from the Feast : Midnight Revellers. — At length the oil lamps have begun to burn dim.   The tired slaves are yawning.   Their masters, despite Prodicus's intentions of having a very proper symposium, have all drunk enough to get unstable and silly.   Eunapius gives the signal.   All rise, and join in the final libation to Hermes.   " Shoes and himation, boy," each says to his slave, and with thanks to their host they all fare homeward.

Such will be the ending to an extremely decorous feast. With gay young bloods present, however, it might have degenerated into an orgy; the flute girl (or several of them) would have contributed over much to the " freedom "; and when the last deep crater had been emptied, the whole company would have rushed madly into the street, and gone whirling away through the darkness, — harps and

flutes sounding, boisterous songs pealing, red torches
tossing. Revellers in this mood would be ready for anything. Perhaps they would end in some low tavern at the
Peiræus to sleep off their liquor; perhaps their leader
would find some other Symposium in progress, and after
loud knockings, force his way into the house, even as did
the mad Alcibiades, who (once more to recall Plato) thrust
his way into Agathon's feast, staggering, leaning on a flute
girl, and shouting "Where's Agathon!" Such an inroad
would be of course the signal for more and ever more hard
drinking. The wild invaders might make themselves completely at home, and dictate all the proceedings: the end
would be even as at Agathon's banquet, where everybody
but Socrates became completely drunken, and lay prone
on the couches or the floor. One hopes that the honest
Prodicus has no such climax to his symposium.

. . . At length the streets grow quiet. Citizens sober or
drunken are asleep: only the vigilant Scythian archers
patrol the ways till the cocks proclaim the first gray of
dawn.

CHAPTER XIX

COUNTRY LIFE AROUND ATHENS

169. Importance of his Farm to an Athenian. — We have followed the doings of a typical Athenian during his ordinary activities around the city, but for the average gentleman an excursion outside the town is indispensable at least every two or three days, and perhaps every day. He must visit his farm; for his wealth and income are probably tied up there, rather than in any unaristocratic commercial and manufacturing enterprises. Homer's "royal" heroes are not ashamed to be skilful at following the plow[1]: and no Athenian feels that he is contaminating himself by "trade" when he supervises the breeding of sheep or the raising of onions. We will therefore follow in the tracks of certain well-to-do citizens, when we turn toward the Itonian gate sometime during the morning, while the Agora is still in a busy hum, even if thus we are curtailing our hypothetical visits to the Peiræus or to the bankers.

170. The Country by the Ilissus: the Greeks and Natural Beauty. — Our companions are on horseback (a token of tolerable wealth in Athens), but the beasts amble along not too rapidly for nimble grooms to run behind, each ready to aid his respective master. Once outside the gate the regular road swings down to the south towards Phalerum; we, however, are in no great haste and desire to see as much as possible. The farms we are seeking lie well north of the

---

[1] See Odysseus's boasts, *Odyssey*, XVIII. 360 et passim. The gentility of farming is emphasized by a hundred precepts from Hesiod.

city, but we can make a delightful circuit by skirting the
city walls with the eastern shadow of the Acropolis behind
us, and going at first northeast, along the groves and leafy
avenues which line the thin stream of the Ilissus,[1] the
second " river " of Athens.

Before us through the trees came tantalizing glimpses of
the open country running away towards shaggy gray
Hymettus. Left to itself the land would be mostly arid
and seared brown by the summer sun; but everywhere the
friendly work of man is visible. One can count the little
green oblong patches, stretching even up the mountain side,
marked with gleaming white farm buildings or sometimes
with little temples and chapels sacred to the rural gods.
Once or twice also we notice a plot of land which seems
one tangled waste of trees and shrubbery. This is a sacred
temenos, an inviolate grove, set apart to some god; and
within the fences of the compound no mortal dare set foot
under pain of direful sacrilege and pollution.

Following a kind of bridle path, however, we are soon
amid the groves of olive and other trees, while the horses
plod their slow way beside the brook. Not a few citizens
going or coming from Athens meet us, for this is really one
of the parks and breathing spaces of the closely built city.
The Athenians and Greeks in general live in a land of such
natural beauty that they take this loveliness as a matter
of course. Very seldom do their poets indulge in deliberate
descriptions of " beautiful landscapes "; but none the less
the fair things of nature have penetrated deeply into their
souls. The constant allusions in Homer and the other
masters of song to the great storm waves, the deep shades
of the forest, the crystal brooks, the pleasant rest for wan-
derers under the shade trees, the plains bright with spring

---

[1] The Ilissus, unlike its sturdier rival, the Cephisus, ran dry during the
summer heats; but there was enough water along its bed to create a dense
vegetation.

flowers, the ivy twining above· a grave, the lamenting nightingale, the chirping cicada, tell their own story; men seldom describe at length what is become warp and woof of their inmost lives.   The mere fact that the Greeks dwell *constantly* in such a beautiful land, and have learned to love it so intensely, makes frequent and set descriptions thereto seem trivial.

171. Plato's Description of the Walk by the Ilissus. — Nevertheless occasionally this inborn love of the glorious outer world must find its expression, and it is of these very groves along the Ilissus that we have one of the few "nature pieces" in Athenian literature.   As the plodding steeds take their way let us recall our Plato — his *Phædrus*, written probably not many years before this our visit.

Socrates is walking with Phædrus outside the walls, and urges the latter : " Let us go to the Ilissus and sit down in some quiet spot."   " I am fortunate," answers Phædrus, " in not having my sandals on, and. as you never have any, we may go along the brook and cool our feet.   This is the easiest way, and at midday is anything but unpleasant." He adds that they will go on to the tallest plane tree in the distance, "where are shade and gentle breezes, and grass whereon we may either sit or lie. . . .   The little stream is delightfully clear and bright.   I can fancy there might well be maidens playing near [according to the local myth of Boreas's rape of Orithyia]."   And so at last they come to the place, when Socrates says : " Yes indeed, a fair and shady resting place it is, full of summer sounds and scents.   There is the lofty and spreading plane tree, and the agnus castus, high and clustering in the fullest blossom and the greatest fragrance, and the stream which flows beneath the plane tree is deliciously cool to the feet.   Judging by the ornaments and images [set] about, this must be a spot sacred to Achelous and the Nymphs; moreover there is a sweet breeze

and the grasshoppers are chirruping; and the greatest
charm of all is the grass like a pillow, gently sloping to the
head." [1]

172. The Athenian Love of Country Life. — So the two
friends had sat them down to delve in delightful profundi-
ties; but following the bridle path, the little brook and its
groves end for us all too soon. We are in the open country
around Athens, and the fierce rays of Helios beat strongly
on our heads. We are outside the city, but by no means
far from human life. Farm succeeds farm, for the land
around Athens has a goodly population to maintain, and
there is a round price for vegetables in the Agora. Truth
to tell, the average Athenian, though he pretends to love the
market, the Pnyx, the Dicasteries, and the Gymnasia, has a
shrewd hankering for the soil, and does not care to spend
more time in Athens than necessary. Aristophanes is full
of the contrasts between " country life " and " city life " and
almost always with the advantage given the former. Says
his Strepsiades (in *The Clouds*), " A country life for me —
dirty, untrimmed, lolling around at ease, and just abounding in bees and sheep and oil cake." His Dicæopolis
(*Acharnians*) voices clearly the independence of the farmer:
"How I long for peace.[2] I'm disgusted with the city; and
yearn for my own farm which never bawled out [as in the
markets] 'buy my coals' or 'buy my vinegar' or 'oil,' or
knew the word 'buy,' but just of itself produced everything."
And his Trygæus (in *The Peace*) states the case better yet:
"Ah! how eager I am to get back into the fields, and break
up my little farm with the mattock again . . . [for I re-
member] what kind of a life we had there; and those cakes
of dried fruits, and the figs, and the myrtles, and the sweet

---

[1] Jewett, translator; slightly altered.
[2] *I.e.* the end of the Peloponnesian War, which compelled the farming
population to remove inside the walls.

new wine, and the violet bed next to the well, and the olives we so long for!"

There is another reason why the Athenians rejoice in the country. The dusty streets are at best a poor playground for the children, the inner court of the house is only a respectable prison for the wife. In the country the lads can enjoy themselves; the wife and the daughters can roam about freely with delightful absence of convention. There will be no happier day in the year than when the master says, "Let us set out for the farm."

173. Some Features of the Attic Country. — Postponing our examination of Athenian farmsteads and farming methods until we reach some friendly estate, various things strike us as we go along the road. One is the skilful system of irrigation, — the numerous watercourses drawn especially from the Cephisus, whereby the agriculturists make use of every possible scrap of moisture for the fields, groves, and vineyards. Another is the occasional olive tree we see standing, gnarled and venerable, but carefully fenced about; or even (not infrequently) we see fences only with but a dead and utterly worthless stump within. Do not speak lightly of these "stumps," however. They are none the less "moriai" — sacred olive trees of Athena, and carefully tended by public wardens.[1] Contractors are allowed to take the fruit

---

[1] Athenians loved to dwell on the "divine gift" of the olive. Thus Euripides sang (*Troades*, 799) : —

> In Salamis, filled with the foaming
>   Of billows and murmur of bees,
> Old Telamon stayed from his roaming
>   Long ago, on a throne of the seas,
> Looking out on the hills olive laden,
>   Enchanted, where first from the earth
> The gray-gleaming fruit of the Maiden
>   Athena had birth.
>   — MURRAY, translator.

The hero Telamon was reputed an uncle of Achilles and one of the early kings of Salamis.

of the live trees under carefully regulated conditions; but no one is allowed to remove the stumps, much less hew down a living tree. An offender is tried for "impiety" before the high court of the Areopagus, and his fate is pretty surely death, for the country people, at least, regard their sacred trees with a fanatical devotion which it would take long to explain to a stranger.

Also upon the way one is pretty sure to meet a wandering beggar — a shrewd-eyed, bewhiskered fellow. He carries, not a barrel organ and monkey, but a blinking tame crow

ITINERANT PIPER WITH HIS DOG.

perched on his shoulder, and at every farmstead he halts to whine his nasal ditty and ask his dole.

> Good people, a handful of barley bestow
> On the child of Apollo, the sleek sable crow;
> Or a trifle of wheat, O kind friends, give; —
> Or a wee loaf of bread that the crow may live.

It is counted good luck by the housewife to have a chance to feed a "holy crow," and the owner's pickings are goodly. By the time we have left the beggar behind us we are at the farm whither our excursion has been tending.

174. An Attic Farmstead. — We are to inspect the landed estate of Hybrias, the son of Xanthippus. It lies north of Athens on the slopes of Anchesmus, one of the lesser hills

which roll away toward the marble-crowned summits of
Pentelicus. Part of the farm lands lie on the level ground
watered by the irrigation ditches; part upon the hillsides,
and here the slopes have been terraced in a most skilful
fashion, in order to make the most of every possible inch of
ground, and also to prevent any of the precious soil from
being washed down by the torrents of February and March.
The owner is a wealthy man, and has an extensive establishment; the farm buildings — once whitewashed, but now
for the most part somewhat dirty — wander away over a
large area. There are wide courts, deep in manure, surrounded by barns; there are sties, haymows, carefully closed
granaries, an olive press, a grain mill, all kinds of stables
and folds, likewise a huge irregularly shaped house wherein
are lodged the numerous slaves and the hired help. The
general design of this house is the same as of a city house
— the rooms opening upon an inner court, but naturally its
dimensions are ampler, with the ampler land space.

Just now the courtyard is a noisy and animated sight.
The master has this moment ridden in, upon one of his pe-
riodic visits from Athens; the farm overseer has run out to
meet him and report, and half a dozen long, lean hunting
dogs — Darter, Roarer, Tracker, Active, and more [1] — are
dancing and yelping, in the hope that their owner will
order a hare hunt. The overseer is pouring forth his
usual burden of woe about the inefficient help and the lack
of rain, and Hybrias is complaining of the small spring crop
— "Zeus send us something better this summer!" While
these worthies are adjusting their troubles we may look
around the farm.

175. Plowing, Reaping, and Threshing. — Thrice a year
the Athenian farmer plows, unless he wisely determines

[1] For an exhaustive list of names for Greek dogs, see Xenophon's
curious *Essay on Hunting*, ch. VII, § 5.

to let his field lie fallow for the nonce; and the summer plowing on Hybrias's estate is now in progress. Up and down a wide field the ox team is going.[1] The plow is an extremely primitive affair — mainly of wood, although over the sharpened point which forms the plowshare a plate of iron has been fitted. Such a plow requires very skilful handling to cut a good furrow, and the driver of the team has no sinecure.

WOMEN POUNDING MEAL.

In a field near by, the hinds are reaping a crop of wheat which was late in ripening.[2] The workers are bending with semicircular sickles over their hot task; yet they form a merry, noisy crowd, full of homely "harvest songs," nominally in honor of Demeter, the Earth Mother, but ranging upon every conceivable rustic topic. Some laborers are cutting the grain, others, walking behind, are binding into sheaves and piling into clumsy ox wains. Here and there a sheaf is standing, and we are told that this is left "for luck," as an offering to the rural Field Spirit; for your farm hand is full of superstitions. Also amid the workers a youth is passing with a goodly jar of cheap wine, to which the harvesters make free to run from time to time for refreshment.

Close by the field is the threshing floor. More laborers

[1] Mules were sometimes used for drawing the plow, but horses, it would seem, never.

[2] The regular time for reaping the October-sown wheat was May or June.

— not a few bustling country lasses among them — are
spreading out the sheaves with wooden forks, a little at a
time, in thin layers over this circular space, which is paved
with little cobblestones. More oxen and a patient mule are
being driven over it — around and around — until every
kernel is trodden out by their hoofs. Later will come the
tossing and the winnowing ; and, when the grain has been
thoroughly cleaned, it will be stored in great earthern jars
for the purpose of sale or against the winter.

176. Grinding at the Mill. — Nearer the farmhouses
there rises a dull grinding noise. It is the mill preparing the flour for the daily baking, for seldom — at least
in the country — will a Greek grind flour long in advance
of the time of use. There the round upper millstone is
being revolved upon an iron pivot against its lower mate and
turned by a long wooden handle. Two nearly naked slave
boys are turning this wearily — far pleasanter they consider
the work of the harvesters, and very likely this task is set
them as a punishment. As the mill revolves a slave girl
pours the grain into a hole in the center of the upper millstone. As the hot, slow work goes on, the two toilers chant
together a snatch from an old mill song, and we catch the
monotonous strain : —

> Grind, mill, grind,
> For Pittacus did grind —
> Who was king over great Mytilene.

It will be a long time before there is enough flour for the
day. The slaves can at least rejoice that they live on a
large farm. If Hybrias owned a smaller estate, they would
probably be pounding up the grain with mortar and pestle
— more weary yet.

177. The Olive Orchards. — We, at least, can leave them to
their work, and escape to the shade of the orchards and the

vineyards. Like every Athenian farmer, Hybrias has an
olive orchard. The olives are sturdy trees. They will
grow in any tolerable soil and thrive upon the mountain
slopes up to as far as 1800 feet above sea level. They are
not large trees, and their trunks are often grotesquely
gnarled, but there is always a certain fascination about the
wonderful shimmer of their leaves, which flash from gray

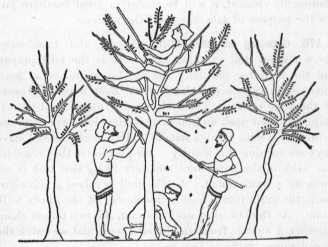

GATHERING THE OLIVE HARVEST.

to silver-white in a sunny wind. Hybrias has wisely
planted his olives at wide intervals, and in the space between the ground has been plowed up for grain. Olives
need little care. Their harvest comes late in the autumn,
after all the other crops are out of the way. They are
among the most profitable products of the farm, and the
owner will not mind the poor wheat harvest "if only the
olives do well." [1]

[1] The great drawback to olive culture was the great length of time required to mature the trees — sixteen years. The destruction of the trees,

178. The Vineyards. — The fig orchard forms another great part of the farm, but more interesting to strangers are the vineyards. Some of the grapes are growing over pointed stakes set all along the upland terraces; a portion of the vineyards, however, is on level ground. Here a most picturesque method has been used for training the vines. Tall and graceful trees have been set out — elm, maple, oak, poplar. The lower limbs of the trees have been cut away and up their trunks and around their upper branches now swing the vines in magnificent festoons. The growing vines have sprung from tree to tree. The warm breeze has set the rich clusters — already turning purple or golden — swaying above our heads. The air is filled with brightness, greenery, and fragrance. The effect of this "vineyard grove" is magical.

179. Cattle, Sheep, and Goats. — There is also room in the orchards for apples, pears, and quinces, but there is nothing distinctive about their culture. If we are interested in cattle, however, we can spend a long time at the barns, or be guided out to the upland pasture where Hybrias's flocks and herds are grazing. Horses are a luxury. They are almost never used in farm work, and for riding and cavalry service it is best to import a good courser from Thessaly; no attempt, therefore, is made to breed them here. But despite the small demand for beef and butter a good many cattle are raised; for oxen are needed for the plowing and carting, oxhides have a steady sale, and there is a regular call for beeves for the hecatombs at the great public sacrifices. Sheep are in greater acceptance. Their wool is of large importance to a land which knows comparatively little of cotton. They can live on scanty pastur-

e.g. in war by a ravaging invader, was an infinitely greater calamity than the burning of the standing grain or even of the farmhouses. Probably it was the ruin of their olive trees which the Athenians mourned most during the ravaging of Attica in the Peloponnesian War.

age where an ox would starve. Still more in favor are goats. Their coarse hair has a thousand uses. Their flesh and cheese are among the most staple articles in the Agora. Sure-footed and adventurous, they scale the side of the most unpromising crags in search of herbage and can sometimes be seen perching, almost like birds, in what seem utterly

inaccessible eyries. Thanks to them the barren highlands of Attica are turned to good account, — and between goat raising and bee culture an income can sometimes be extracted from the very summits of the mountains. As for the numerous swine, it is enough to say that they range under Hybrias's oak forest and fatten

RURAL SACRIFICE TO A WOODEN STATUE OF DIONYSUS.

on the acorns, although their swineherd, wrapped in a filthy sheepskin, is a far more loutish and ignoble fellow than the " divine Eumæus " glorified in the *Odyssey*.

180. The Gardens and the Shrine. — Did we wish to linger, we could be shown the barnyard with its noisy retinue of hens, pheasants, guinea fowl, and pigeons; and we would be asked to admire the geese, cooped up and being gorged for fattening, or the stately peacocks preening their splendors. We would also hear sage disquisitions from the "oldest inhabitants " on the merits of fertilizers, especially on the uses of mixing seaweed with manure, also we would be told of the almost equally important process of burying a toad in a sealed jar in the midst of a field to save the corn from the crows and the field mice. Hybrias laughs at such superstitions — "but what can you say to the rustics?" Hybrias himself will display with more refined pride the gardens used by his wife and children when they come out from Athens, — a fountain feeding a delightful rivulet; myrtles, roses, and pomegranate trees shedding their perfumes, which are mingled with the odors from the beds of hyacinths, violets, and asphodel. In the center of the gardens rises a chaste little shrine with a marble image and an altar, always covered with flowers or fruit by the mistress and her women. "To Artemis," reads the inscription, and one is sure that the virgin goddess takes more pleasure in this fragrant temple than in many loftier fanes.[1]

We are glad to add here our wreaths ere turning away from this wholesome, verdant country seat, and again taking our road to Athens.

---

[1] For the description of a very beautiful and elaborate country estate, with a temple thereon to Artemis, see Xenophon's *Anabasis*, bk. V. 3.

CHAPTER XX.

THE TEMPLES AND GODS OF ATHENS.

181. Certain Factors in Athenian Religion. — We have seen the Athenians in their business and in their pleasure, at their courts, their assemblies, their military musters, and on their peaceful farms ; yet one great side of Athenian life has been almost ignored — the religious side. A " Day in Athens " spent without taking account of the gods of the city and their temples would be a day spent with almost half-closed eyes.[1]

It is far easier to learn how the Athenians arrange their houses than how the average man among them adjusts his attitude toward the gods. While any searching examina-tion of the fundamentals of Greek cultus and religion is here impossible, two or three facts must, nevertheless, be kept in mind, if we are to understand even the *outward* side of this Greek religion which is everywhere in evidence about us.

First of all we observe that the Greek religion is a religion of purely natural growth. No prophet has initiated it, or claimed a new revelation to supplement the older views. It has come from primitive times without a visible break even down to the Athens of Plato. This explains at once why so many time-honored stories of the Olympic deities are very gross, and why the gods seem to give countenance

[1] No attempt is made in this discussion to enumerate the various gods and demigods of the conventional mythology, their regular attributes, etc. It is assumed the average history or manual of mythology gives sufficient information.

to moral views which the best public opinion has long since
called scandalous and criminal. The religion of Athens, in
other words, may justly claim to be judged by its best, not
by its worst; by the morality of Socrates, not of Homer.

Secondly, this religion is not a church, nor a belief, but is
part of the government. Every Athenian is born into accepting the fact that Athena Polias is the divine warder of
the city, as much as he is born into accepting the fact that
it is his duty to obey the strategi in battle. To repudiate
the gods of Athens, e.g. in favor of those of Egypt,
is as much iniquity as to join forces against the Athenians
if they are at war with Egypt; — the thing is sheer trea-
son, and almost unthinkable. For countless generations
the Athenians have worshipped the " Ancestral Gods."
They are proud of them, familiar with them; the gods
have participated in all the prosperity of the city. Athena
is as much a part of Attica as gray Hymettus or white-
crowned Pentelicus; and the very fact that comedians, like
Aristophanes, make good-natured fun of the divinities indicates that " they are members of the family."

Thirdly, notice that this religion is one mainly of outward reverence and ceremony. There is no " Athenian
church "; nobody has drawn up an " Attic creed " — " I believe in Athena, the City Warder, and in Demeter, the Earth
Mother, and in Zeus, the King of Heaven, etc." Give
outward reverence, participate in the great public sacrifices,
be careful in all the minutiæ of private worship, refrain
from obvious blasphemies — you are then a sufficiently pious
man. What you *believe* is of very little consequence. Even
if you privately believe there are no gods at all, it harms no
one, provided your outward conduct is pious and moral.

182. What constitutes " Piety " in Athens. — Of course
there have been some famous prosecutions for " impiety."
Socrates was the most conspicuous victim; but Socrates

was a notable worshipper of the gods, and certainly all the charges of his being an "atheist" broke down. What he was actually attacked with was "corrupting the youth of Athens," *i.e.* giving the young men such warped ideas of their private and public duties that they ceased to be moral and useful citizens. But even Socrates was convicted only with difficulty[1]; a generation has passed since his death. Were he on trial at present, a majority of the jury would probably be with him.

The religion of Athens is something very elastic, and really every man makes his own creed for himself, or — for paganism is almost never dogmatic — accepts the outward cultus with everybody else, and speculates at his leisure on the nature of the deity. The great bulk of the uneducated are naturally content to accept the old stories and superstitions with unthinking credulity. It is enough to know that one must pray to Zeus for rain, and to Hermes for luck in a slippery business bargain. There are a few philosophers who, along with perfectly correct outward observance, teach privately that the old Olympian system is a snare and folly. They pass around the daring word which Xenophanes uttered as early as the sixth century B.C.: —

> One God there is, greatest of gods and mortals,
> Not like to man is he in mind or in body.
> All of him sees, all of him thinks, and all of him hearkens.

This, of course, is obvious pantheism, but it is easy to cover up all kinds of pale monotheism or pantheism under vague references to the omnipotence of "Zeus."

183. The Average Athenian's Idea of the Gods. — The average intelligent citizen probably has views midway be-

---

[1] It might be added that if Socrates had adopted a really worldly wise line of defense, he would probably have been acquitted, or subjected merely to a mild pecuniary penalty.

tween the stupid rabble and the daring philosophers.   To
him the gods of Greece stand out in full divinity, honored
and worshipped because they are protectors of the good,
avengers of the evil, and guardians of the moral law.
They punish crime and reward virtue, though the punishment may tarry long.   They demand a pure heart and a
holy mind of all that approach them, and woe to him who
wantonly defies their eternal laws.   This is the morality
taught by the master tragedians, Æschylus and Sophocles,
and accepted by the best public opinion at Athens; for the
insidious doubts cast by Euripides upon the reality of any
divine scheme of governance have never struck home.   The
scandalous stories about the domestic broils on Olympus, in
which Homer indulges, only awaken good-natured banter.
It is no longer proper — as in Homeric days — to pride oneself on one's cleverness in perjury and common falsehood.
Athenians do not have twentieth century notions about
the wickedness of lying, but certain it is the gods do not
approve thereof.   In short, most of the better class of
Athenians are genuinely "religious"; nevertheless they
have too many things in this human world to interest them
to spend overmuch time in adjusting their personal concepts
of the deity to any system of theology.

184. Most Greeks without belief in Immortality. — Yet one
thing we must add.   This Greek religious morality is built
up without any clear belief in a future life.   Never has the
average Hellene been able to form a satisfactory conception
of the soul's existence, save dwelling within a mortal body
and under the glorious light of belovèd Helios.   To Homer
the after life in Hades was merely the perpetuation of the
shadows of departed humanity, " strengthless shades " who
live on the gloomy plains of asphodel, feeding upon dear
memories, and incapable of keen emotions or any real mental or physical progress or action.   Only a few great sinners

like Tantalus, doomed to eternal torture, or favored beings like Menelaus, predestined to the "Blessed Isles," are
ordained to any real immortality. As the centuries advanced, and the possibilities of this terrestrial world grew
ever keener, the hope of any future state became ever
more vague. The fear of a gloomy shadow life in Hades
for the most part disappeared, but that was only to confirm
the belief that death ends all things.

> Where'er his course man tends,
> Inevitable death impends,
> And for the worst and for the best,
> Is strewn the same dark couch of rest.[1]

So run the lines of a poet whose name is forgotten, but
who spoke well the thought of his countrymen.

True there has been a contradiction of this gloomy theory.
The "Orphic Mysteries," those secret religious rites which
have gained such a hold in many parts of Greece, including
Athens, probably hold out an earnest promise to the "initiates" of a blessed state for them hereafter. The doctrine
of a real elysium for the good and a realm of torment for
the evil has been expounded by many sages. Pindar, the
great bard of Thebes, has set forth the doctrine in a glowing
ode.[2] Socrates, if we may trust the report Plato gives of
him, has spent his last hours ere drinking the hemlock, in
adducing cogent, philosophic reasons for the immortality of
the soul. All this is true, — and it is also true that these
ideas have made no impression upon the general Greek consciousness. They are accepted half-heartedly by a relatively
few exceptional thinkers. Men go through life and face
death with no real expectation of future reward or punishment, or of reunion with the dear departed. If the gods

[1] Milman, translator.
[2] Quoted in *Readings in Ancient History*, vol. I, pp. 261–262, and
in many works in Greek literature.

are angry, you escape them at the grave; if the gods are
friendly, all they can give is wealth, health, honor, a hale
old age, and prosperity for your children. The instant
after death the righteous man and the robber are equal.
This fundamental deduction from the Greek religion must
usually, therefore, be made — it is a religion for *this world
only*. Let us see what are its usual outward operations.

185. The Multitude of Images of the Gods. — Gods are
everywhere in Athens. You cannot take the briefest walk
without being reminded that the world is full of deities.
There is a "Herm"[1] by the main door of every house, as
well as a row of them across the Agora. At many of the
street crossings are little shrines to Hecate; or statues of
Apollo Agyieus, the street guardian; or else a bay tree
stands there, a graceful reminder of this same god, to which
it is sacred. In every house there is the small altar whereon
garlands and fruit offerings are daily laid to Zeus Herkeios, and another altar to Hestia. On one or both of these
altars a little food and a little wine are cast at every meal.
All public meetings or court sessions open with sacrifice;
in short, to attempt any semi-important public or private
act without inviting the friendly attention of the deity is
unthinkable. To a well-bred Athenian this is second instinct; he considers it as inevitable as the common courtesies
of speech among gentlemen. Plato sums up the current
opinion well, "All men who have any decency, in the
attempting of matters great or small, always invoke divine
aid."[2]

[1] A stone post about shoulder high, surmounted by a bearded head.
Contrary to modern impression, the average Greek did not conceive of
Hermes as a beautiful youth. He was a grave, bearded man. The youth-
ful aspect came through the manipulation of the Hermes myths by the
master sculptors — *e.g.* Praxiteles.

[2] *Timæus*, p. 27 c

186. Greek Superstition. — In many cases, naturally, piety runs off into crass superstition. The gods, everybody knows, frequently make known future events by various signs. He who can understand these signs will be able to adjust his life accordingly and enjoy great prosperity. Most educated men take a sensible view of "omens," and do not let them influence their conduct absurdly. Some, however, act otherwise. There is, for instance, Laches, one of the guests at Prodicus's feast. He lives in a realm of mingled hopes and fears, although he is wealthy and well-educated.[1] He is all the time worried about dreams, and paying out money to the sharp and wily "seer" (who counts him his best client) for "interpretations." If a weasel crosses his path, he will not walk onward until somebody else has gone before him, or until he has thrown three stones across the road. He is all the time worrying about the significance of sudden noises, meteors, thunder; especially he is disturbed when he sees birds flying in groups or towards unlucky quarters of the heavens.[2] Laches, however, is not merely religious — although he is always asking "which god shall I invoke now?" or "what are the omens for the success of this enterprise?" His own associates mock him as being superstitious, and say they never trouble themselves about omens save in real emergencies. Still it is "bad luck" for any of them to stumble over a threshold, to meet a hare suddenly, or especially to find a snake (the companion of the dead) hidden in the house.

187. Consulting Omens. — Laches's friends, however, all regularly consult the omens when they have any important enterprise on hand — a voyage, a large business venture, a

---

[1] See Theophratus's character, "*The Superstitious Man.*"

[2] The birds of clearest omen were the great birds of prey — hawks, "Apollo's swift messengers," and eagles, "the birds of Zeus." It was a good omen if the birds flew from left to right, a bad omen if in the reverse direction.

marriage treaty, etc. There are several ready ways, not
expensive; the interpreters are not priests, only low-born
fellows as a rule, whose fees are trifling. You can find out
about the future by casting meal upon the altar fire and
noticing how it is burned, by watching how chickens pick
up consecrated grain,[1] by observing how the sacrificial smoke
curls upward, etc. The best way, however, is to examine
the entrails of the victim after a sacrifice. Here everything
depends on the shape, size, etc., of the various organs, especially of the liver, bladder, spleen, and lungs, and really
expert judgment by an experienced and high-priced seer is
desirable. The man who is assured by a reliable seer, " the
livers are large and in fine color," will go on his trading
voyage with a confident heart.

188. The Great Oracles. — Assuredly there is a better way
still to read the future; at least so Greeks of earlier ages
have believed. Go to one of the great oracles, whereof that
of Apollo at Delphi is the supreme, but not the unique, example. Ask your question in set form from the attendant
priests, not failing to offer an elaborate sacrifice and to bestow all the "gifts" (golden tripods, mixing bowls, shields,
etc.) your means will allow. Then (at Delphi) wait silent
and awe-stricken while the lady Pythia, habited as a young
girl, takes her seat on a tripod over a deep cleft in the
rock, whence issues an intoxicating vapor. She inhales
the gas, sways to and fro in an ecstasy, and now, duly "inspired," answers in a somewhat wild manner the queries
which the priest will put in behalf of the suppliants. Her
incoherent words are very hard to understand, but the
priest duly "interprets" them, i.e. gives them to the suppliant in the form of hexameter verses. Sometimes the

[1] A very convenient way, — for it was a good sign if the chickens ate
eagerly and one could always get a fair omen by keeping the fowls hungry
a few hours ere " putting the question " 1

meaning of these verses is perfectly clear. Very often they are truly "Delphic," with a most dubious meaning—as, in that oft-quoted instance, when the Pythia told Crœsus if he went to war with Cyrus, "he would destroy a mighty monarchy," and lo, he destroyed his own!

Besides Delphi, there are numerous lesser oracles, each with its distinctive method of "revelation." But there is none, at least of consequence, within Attica, while a journey to Delphi is a serious and highly expensive undertaking. And as a matter of fact Delphi has partially lost credit in Athens. In the great Persian War Delphi unpatriotically "medized"—gave oracles friendly to Xerxes and utterly discouraging to the patriot cause. Then after this conviction of false prophesy, the oracle fell, for most of the time, into the hands of Sparta, and was obviously very willing to "reveal" things only in the Lacedæmonian interest. Hellenes generally and the Spartans in particular have still much esteem for the utterances of the Pythia, but Athenians are not now very partial to her. Soon will come the seizure of Delphi by the Phocians and the still further discrediting of this once great oracle.

189. Greek Sacrifices. — The two chief elements of Greek worship, however, are not consideration of the future, but sacrifice and prayer. Sacrifices in their simple form, as we have seen, take place continually, before every routine act. They become more formal when the proposed action is really important, or when the suppliant wishes to give thanks for some boon, or, at rarer intervals, to desire purification from some offense. There is no need of a priest for the simpler sacrifices. The father of the family can pour out the libation, can burn the food upon the altar, can utter the prayer for all his house; but in the greater sacrifices a priest is desirable, not as a sacred intermediary betwixt god and man, but as an expert to advise the worshipper what are the competent rites, and to keep him from ignorantly angering heaven by unhappy words and actions.[1]

Let us witness a sacrifice of this more formal kind, and while so doing we can tread upon the spot we have seemed in a manner to shun during our wanderings through Athens, the famous and holy Acropolis.

190. The Route to the Acropolis. — Phormion, son of Cresphontes, has been to Arcadia, and won the pentathlon in some athletic contests held at Mantinea. Although not equal to a triumph in the "four great Panhellenic contests," it was a most notable victory. Before setting out he vowed a sheep to Athena the Virgin if he conquered. The goddess was kind, and Phormion is very grateful. While the multitudes are streaming out to the Gymnasia, the young athlete, brawny and handsome, surrounded by an admiring coterie of friends and kinsmen, sets out for the Acropolis.

Phormion's home is in the "Ceramicus," the so-called "potters' quarter." His walk takes him a little to the west of the Agora, and close to the elegant temple of Hephæstos,[2] but past this and many other fanes he hastens. It was not the fire god which gave him fair glory at Mantinea. He goes onward until he is forced to make a detour to the left, at the craggy, rough hill of Areopagus which rises before him. Here, if time did not press, he might have tarried to pay respectful reverence before a deep fissure cleft in the side of the rock. In front of this fissure stands a little altar. All Phormion's company look away as they pass the spot, and they mutter together "Be propitious, O Eumenides!" (literally, Well-minded Ones). For like true Greeks

---

[1] There were almost no hereditary priesthoods in Attica (outside the Eumolpidæ connected with the mystical cult of Eleusis). Almost anybody of good character could qualify as a priest with due training, and there was little of the sacrosanct about the usual priestly office.

[2] This temple, now called the *Theseum*, is the only well preserved ancient temple in modern Athens.

they delight to call foul things with fair and propitious names; and that awful fissure and altar are sacred to the Erinyes (Furies), the horrible maidens, the trackers of guilt, the avengers of murder; and above their cave, on these rude

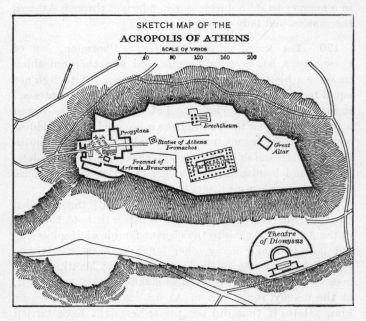

SKETCH MAP OF THE
ACROPOLIS OF ATHENS

rocks, sits the august court of the Areopagus when it meets as a "tribunal of blood" to try cases of homicide.

Phormion's party quicken their steps and quit this spot of ill omen. Then their sight is gladdened. The whole glorious Acropolis stands out before them.

191. The Acropolis of Athens. — Almost every Greek city has its own formidable citadel, its own *acropolis*, — for "citadel" is really all this word conveys. Corinth boasts of its "Acro-Corinthus," Thebes of its "Cadmeia," — but *the* Acropolis is in Athens. The later world will care little for any other, and the later world will be right. The Athenian stronghold has long ceased to be a fortress, though still it rises steep and strong. It is now one vast temple compound, covered with magnificent buildings. Whether considered as merely a natural rock commanding a marvelous view, or as a consecrated museum of sculpture and architecture, it deserves its immortality. We raise our eyes to *the Rock* as we approach it.

The Acropolis dominates the plain of Athens. All the city seems to adjust itself to the base of its holy citadel. It lifts itself as tawny limestone rock rising about 190 feet above the adjacent level of the town.[1] In form it is an irregular oval with its axis west and east. It is about 950 feet long and 450 feet at its greatest breadth. On every side but the west the precipice falls away sheer and defiant, rendering a feeble garrison able to battle with myriads.[2] To the westward, however, the gradual slope makes a natural pathway always possible, and human art has long since shaped this with convenient steps. Nestling in against the precipice are various sanctuaries and caves; *e.g.* on the northwestern side, high up the slope beneath the precipice, open the uncanny grottoes of Apollo and of Pan. On the southern side, close under the very shadow of the citadel, is the temple of Asclepius, and, more to the southeast, the great open theater of Dionysus has been scooped out of the rock, a place fit to contain an audience of some 15,000.[3]

[1] It is nearly 510 feet above the level of the sea.

[2] Recall the defense which the Acropolis was able to make against Xerxes's horde, when the garrison was small and probably ill organized, and had only a wooden barricade to eke out the natural defenses.

[3] The stone seats of this theater do not seem to have been built till about 340 B.C. Up to that time the surface of the ground sloping back to the Acropolis seems simply to have been smoothed off, and probably covered with temporary wooden seats on the days of the great dramatic festivals.

So much for the bare "bones" of the Acropolis; but now under the dazzling sunshine how it glitters with indescribable splendor! Before us as we ascend a whole succession of buildings seem lifting themselves, not singly, not in hopeless confusion, but grouped admirably together by a kind of wizardry, so that the harmony is perfect, — each visible, brilliant column and pinnacle, not merely flashing its own beauty, but suggesting another greater beauty just behind.

192. The Use of Color upon Athenian Architecture and Sculptures. — While we look upward at this group of temples and their wealth of sculpture, let us state now something we have noticed during all our walks around Athens, but have hitherto left without comment. Every temple and statue in Athens is not left in its bare white marble, as later ages will conceive is demanded by "Greek architecture" and statuary, but is decked in brilliant color — "painted," if you will use an almost unfriendly word. The columns and gables and ceilings of the buildings are all painted. Blue, red, green, and gold blaze on all the members and ornaments. The backgrounds of the pediments, metopes, and frieze are tinted some uniform color on which the sculptured figures in relief stand out clearly. The figures themselves are tinted or painted, at least on the hair, lips, and eyes. Flesh-colored warriors are fighting upon a bright red background. The armor and horse trappings on the sculptures are in actual bronze. The result is an effect indescribably vivid. Blues and reds predominate: the flush of light and color from the still more brilliant heavens above adds to the effect. Shall we call it garish? We have learned to know the taste of Athenians too well to doubt their judgment in matters of pure beauty. And they are right. *Under an Athenian sky* temples and statues almost demand a wealth of color which in a somber clime would seem intolerable. The brilliant lines of the Acropolis buildings are the just answer of the Athenian to the brilliancy of Helios.

193. The Chief Buildings on the Acropolis. — And now to ascend the Acropolis. We leave the discussion of the details of the temples and the sculpture to the architects and archæologists. The whole plateau of the Rock is covered with religious buildings, altars, statues. We pass through the Propylæa, the worthy rival of the Parthenon behind, a magnificent portal, with six splendid Doric columns facing us; and as we go through them, to right and to left open out equally magnificent columned porticoes.[1] As we emerge from the Propylæa the whole vision of the sacred plateau bursts upon us simultaneously. We can notice only the most important of the buildings. At the southwestern point of the Acropolis on the angle of rock which juts out beyond the Propylæa is the graceful little temple of the " Wingless Victory," built in the Ionic style. The view commanded by its bastion will become famous throughout the world. Behind this, nearer the southern side, stands the less important temple of Artemis Braurōnia. Nearer the center and directly before the entrance rises a colossal brazen statue — " monstrous," many might call its twenty-six feet of height, save that a master among masters has cast the spell of his genius over it. This is the famous Athena Promachos,[2] wrought by Phidias out of the spoils of Marathon. The warrior goddess stands in full armor and rests upon her mighty lance. The gilded lance tip gleams so dazzlingly we may well believe the tale that sailors use it for a first landmark as they sail up the coast from Cape Sunium.

[1] That to the north was the larger and contained a kind of picture gallery.

[2] Athena Foremost in Battle.

Looking again upon the complex of buildings we single
out another on the northern side: an irregularly shaped
temple, or rather several temples joined together, the Erechtheum, wherein is the sanctuary of Athena Polias (the
revered "City Warden"), the ancient wooden statue, gro-
tesque, beloved, most sacred of all the holy images in
Athens. And here on the southern side of this building is
the famous Caryatid porch; the "Porch of the Maidens,"
which will be admired as long as Athens has a name. But
our eyes refuse to linger long on any of these things. Behind the statue of the Promachos, a little to the southern
side of the plateau, stands the Parthenon — the queen jewel
upon the crown of Athens.

194. The Parthenon.—Let others analyze its sculptures and
explain the technical reasons why Ictinus and Callicrates,
the architects, and Phidias, the sculptor, created here the
supreme masterpiece for the artistic world. We can state
only the superficialities. It is a noble building by mere
size; 228 feet measure its side, 101 feet its front. Forty-six
majestic Doric columns surround it; they average thirty-
four feet in height, and six feet three inches at the base.
All these facts, however, do not give the soul of the Parthenon. Walk around it slowly, tenderly, lovingly. Study
the elaborate stories told by the pediments, — on the east
front the birth of Athena, on the west the strife of Athena
and Poseidon for the possession of Athens. Trace down
the innumerable lesser sculptures on the " metopes " under
the cornice, — showing the battles of the Giants, Centaurs,
Amazons, and of the Greeks before Troy; finally follow
around, on the whole inner circuit of the body of the temple,
the frieze,[1] showing in bas-relief the Panathenaic procession,
with the beauty, nobility, and youth of Athens marching in

---

[1] This, of course, is on the outside wall of the " cella," but inside the
surrounding colonnade.

glad festival; comprehend that these sculptures will never be surpassed in the twenty-four succeeding centuries; that here are supreme examples for the artists of all time, — and *then*, in the face of this final creation, we can realize that the Parthenon will justify its claim to immortality.

One thing more. There are hardly any straight lines in the Parthenon. To the eye, the members and the steps of the substructure may seem perfectly level; but the measuring rod betrays marvelously subtle curves. As nature abhors right angles in her creations of beauty, so have these Greeks. Rigidity, unnaturalness, have been banished. The Parthenon stands, not merely embellished with inimitable sculptures, but perfectly adjusted to the natural world surrounding.[1]

We have seen only the exterior of the Parthenon. We must wait now ere visiting the interior, for Phormion is beginning his sacrifice.

195. A Sacrifice on the Acropolis. — Across the sacred plateau advances the little party. As it goes under the Propylæa a couple of idle temple watchers[2] give its members a friendly nod. The Acropolis rock itself seems deserted, save for a few worshippers and a party of admiring Achæan visitors who are being shown the glories of the Parthenon.[3] There seems to be a perfect labyrinth of statues of gods, heroes, and departed worthies, and almost as many altars, great and small, placed in every direction.

[1] It was an inability to discover and execute these concealed curves which give certain of the older modern imitations of the Parthenon their unpleasant impressions of hardness and rigidity.

[2] The most important function of these watchers seems to have been to prevent dogs from entering the Acropolis. Probably they were inefficient old men favored with sinecure offices.

[3] The Acropolis seems to have become a great " show place " for visitors to Athens soon after the completion of the famous temples.

Phormion leads his friends onward till they come near to the wide stone platform somewhat in the rear of the Parthenon. Here is the "great altar" of Athena, whereon the "hecatombs" will be sacrificed, even a hundred oxen or more,[1] at some of the major public festivals; and close beside it stands also a small and simple altar sacred to Athena Parthenos, Athena the Virgin. Suitable attendants have been in readiness since dawn waiting for worshippers. One of Phormion's party leads behind him a bleating white lamb "without blemish."[2] It is a short matter now to bring the firewood and the other necessaries. The sacrifice takes place without delay.

First a busy "temple sweeper" goes over the ground around the altar with a broom; then the regular priest, a dignified gray-headed man with a long ungirt purple chiton, and a heavy olive garland, comes forward bearing a basin of holy water. This basin is duly passed to the whole company as it stands in a ring, and each in turn dips his hand and sprinkles his face and clothes with the lustral water. Meantime the attendant has placed another wreath around the head of the lamb. The priest raises his hand.

"Let there be silence," he commands (lest any unlucky word be spoken); and in a stillness broken only by the auspicious twittering of the sparrows amid the Parthenon gables, he takes barley corns from a basket, and sprinkles them on the altar and over the lamb. With his sacred knife he cuts a lock of hair from the victim's head and casts it on

[1] We know by an inscription of 169 oxen being needed for a single Athenian festival.

[2] This was a very proper creature to sacrifice to a great Olympian deity like Athena. Goats were not suitable for her, although desirable for most of the other gods. It was unlawful to sacrifice swine to Aphrodite. When propitiating the gods of the underworld, — Hades, Persephone, etc., — a *black* victim was in order. Poor people could sacrifice doves, cocks, and other birds.

the fire. Promptly now the helper comes forward to complete the sacrifice. Phormion and his friends are a little
anxious. Will the lamb take fright, hang back, and have
to be dragged to its unwilling death? The clever attendant
has cared for that. A sweet truss of dried clover is lying
just under the altar. The lamb starts forward, bleating joyously. As it bows its head[1] as if consenting to its fate,
the priest stabs it dexterously in the neck with his keen
blade. The helper
claps a bowl under
the neck to catch the
spurting blood. A
flute player in readi-
ness, but hitherto
silent, suddenly
strikes up a keen
blast to drown the
dying moans of the
animal. Hardly has
the lamb ceased to
struggle before the
priest and the helper
have begun to cut
it up then and there.
Certain bits of the

SACRIFICING A PIG.

fat and small pieces from each limb are laid upon the altar,
and promptly consumed. These are the goddess's peculiar
portion, and the credulous at least believe that she, though
unseen, is present to eat thereof; certainly the sniff of the
burning meat is grateful to her divine nostrils. The priest
and the helper are busy taking off the hide and securing the
best joint — these are their "fees" for professional services.
All the rest will be duly gathered up by Phormion's body

[1] If a larger animal — an ox — failed to bow its head auspiciously, the
omen could be rectified by suddenly splashing a little water in the ears.

servant and borne home, — for Phormion will give a fine feast on "sacred mutton" that night.[1]

Meantime, while the goddess's portion burns, Phormion approaches the altar, bearing a shallow cup of unmixed wine, and flings it upon the flame.

"Be propitious, O Lady," he cries, "and receive this my drink offering." [2]

The sacrifice is now completed.   The priest assures Phormion that the entrails of the victim foretokened every possible favor in future athletic contests — and this, and his insinuating smile, win him a silver drachma to supplement his share of the lamb.   Phormion readjusts the chaplet upon his own head, and turns towards the Parthenon.   After the sacrifice will come the prayer.

*   *   *   *   *   *   *

196. The Interior of the Parthenon and the Great Image of Athena. — The whole Acropolis is the home of Athena.   The other gods harbored thereon are only her inferior guests. Upon the Acropolis the dread goddess displays her many aspects.   In the Erechtheum we worship her as Athena Polias, the ancient guardian of the hearths and homes of the city.   In the giant Promachos, we see her the leader in war, — the awful queen who went with her fosterlings to the deadly grappling at Marathon and at Salamis; in the little temple of "Wingless Victory" [3] we see her as Athena the Victorious, triumphant over Barbarian and Hellenic foe; but in the Parthenon we adore her in her purest conception —

[1] As already suggested (page 180) a sacrifice (public, or, if on a large scale, private) was about the only occasion on which Athenians tasted beef, pork, or mutton.

[2] The original intention of this libation at the sacrifice was very clearly to provide the gods with wine to "wash down" their meat.

[3] The term "Wingless Victory" (*Nikē Apteros*) has reference to a special type and aspect of Athena, not to the goddess *Nikē* (Victory) pure and simple.

the virgin queen, now chaste and calm, her battles over, the pure, high incarnation of all "the beautiful and the good" that may possess spirit and mind, — the sovran intellect, in short, purged of all carnal, earthy passion. It is meet that such a goddess should inhabit such a dwelling as the Parthenon.[1]

Phormion passes under the eastern porch, and does not forget (despite the purification before the sacrifice) to dip the whisk broom, lying by the door, in the brazen laver of holy water and again to sprinkle himself. He passes out of the dazzling sunlight into a chamber that seems at first to be lost in a vast, impenetrable gloom. He pauses and gazes upward; above him, as little by little his eyes get their adjustment, a faint pearly light seems streaming downward. It is coming through the translucent marble slabs of the roof of the great temple.[2] Then out of the gloom gleam shapes, objects, — a

ATHENA PARTHENOS.
"Varvakeion Model" of the great Athena of Phidias.

[1] There was still another aspect in which Athena was worshipped on the Acropolis. She had a sacred place (*temenos*), though without a temple, sacred to her as *Athena Erganē* — Athena Protectress of the Arts.

[2] This seems to be the most reasonable way to assume that the *cella* of the Parthenon was lighted, in view of the danger, in case of open skylights, of damage to the holy image by wind and rain.

face. He catches the glitter of great jewels and of massy gold, as parts of the rich garments and armor of some vast image. He distinguishes at length a statue, — the form of a woman, nearly forty feet in height. Her left hand rests upon a mighty shield; her right hand holds a winged "Victory," itself of nigh human size. Upon her breast is the awful ægis, the especial breastplate of the high gods. Around the foot of her shield coils a serpent. Upon her head is a mighty helmet. And all the time that these things are becoming manifest, evermore clearly one beholds the majestic face, — sweetness without weakness, intellectuality without coldness, strength mingled justly with compassion. This is the Athena Parthenos, the handiwork of Phidias.[1]

We will not heap up description. What boots it to tell that the arms and vesture of this "chryselephantine" statue are of pure gold; that the flesh portions are of gleaming ivory; that Phidias has wrought the whole so nobly together that this material, too sumptuous for common artists, becomes under his assembling the perfect substance for the manifestation of deity?

. . . Awestruck by the vision, though often he has seen it, Phormion stands long in reverent silence. Then at length, casting a pinch of incense upon the brazier, constantly smoking before the statue, he utters his simple prayer.

197. Greek Prayers. — Greek prayers are usually very pragmatic. "Who," asks Cicero, who can speak for both Greeks and Romans in this particular, "ever thanked the gods that he was a good man? Men are thankful for riches,

---

[1] Of this statue no doubt there could be said what Dion Chrysostomos said of the equally famous "Zeus" erected by Phidias at Olympia. "The man most depressed with woes, forgot his ills whilst gazing on the statue, so much light and beauty had Phidias infused within it." Besides the descriptions in the ancient writers we get a clear idea of the general type of the Athena Parthenos from recently discovered statuettes, especially the "Varvakeion" model (40½ inches high). This last is cold and lifeless as a work of art, but fairly accurate as to details.

honor, safety. . . . We beg of the sovran God [only] what makes us safe, sound, rich and prosperous." [1] Phormion is simply a very average, healthy, handsome young Athenian. While he prays he stretches his hands on high, as is fitting to a deity of Olympus.[2] His petition runs much as follows : —

" Athena, Queen of the Ægis, by whatever name thou lovest best,[3] give ear.

" Inasmuch as thou dids't heed my vow, and grant me fair glory at Mantinea, bear witness I have been not ungrateful. I have offered to thee a white sheep, spotless and undefiled. And now I have it in my mind to attempt the pentathlon at the next Isthmia at Corinth. Grant me victory even in that ; and not one sheep but five, all as good as this to-day, shall smoke upon thine altar. Grant also unto me, my kinsmen and all my friends, health, riches and fair renown."

A pagan prayer surely ; and there is a still more pagan epilogue. Phormion has an enemy, who is not forgotten.

" And oh! gracious, sovran Athena, blast my enemy Xenon, who strove to trip me foully in the foot race. May his wife be childless or bear him only monsters ; may his whole house perish ; may all his wealth take flight ; may his friends forsake him ; may war soon cut him off, or may he die amid impoverished, dishonored old age. If this my sacrifice has found favor in thy sight, may all these evils come upon him unceasingly. And so will I adore thee and sacrifice unto thee all my life." [4]

---

[1] Cicero, De Nat. Deor. ii. 36.

[2] In praying to a deity of the lower world the hands would be held down. A Greek almost never knelt, even in prayer. He would have counted it degrading.

[3] This formula would be put in, lest some favorite epithet of the divinity be omitted.

[4] Often a curse would become a real substitute for a prayer; e.g. at Athens, against a rascally and traitorous general, a solemn public curse would be pronounced at evening by all the priests and priestesses of the

The curse then is a most proper part of a Greek prayer! Phormion is not conscious of blasphemy. He merely follows invariable custom.

It is useless to expect "Christian sentiments" in the fourth century B.C., yet perhaps an age should be judged, not by its average, but by its best. Athenians can utter nobler prayers than those of the type of Phormion. Xenophon makes his model young householder Ischomenus pray nobly "that I may enjoy health and strength of body, the respect of my fellow citizens, honorable safety in times of war, and wealth honestly increased." [1]

There is a simple little prayer also which seems to be a favorite with the farmers. Its honest directness carries its own message.

"Rain, rain, dear Zeus, upon the fields of the Athenians and the plains." [2]

Higher still ascends the prayer of Socrates, when he begs for "the good" merely, leaving it to the wise gods to determine what "the good" for him may be; and in one prayer, which Plato puts in Socrates's mouth, almost all the best of Greek ideals and morality seems uttered. It is spoken not on the Acropolis, but beside the Ilissus at the close of the delightful walk and chat related in the *Phædrus*.

"Beloved Pan, and all ye other gods who haunt this place, give me the beauty of the inward soul, and may the outward and the inward man be joined in perfect harmony. May I reckon the wise to be wealthy, and may I have such a quantity of gold as none but the temperate can carry. Anything more? — That prayer, I think, is enough for me."

city, each shaking in the air a red cloth in token of the bloody death to which the offender was devoted.

[1] Xenophon, *The Economist*, xi, p. 8.

[2] It was quoted later to us by the Emperor Marcus Aurelius, who adds, "In truth, we ought not to pray at all, or we ought to pray in this simple and noble fashion."

Phormion and his party are descending to the city to spend the evening in honest mirth and feasting, but we are fain to linger, watching the slow course of the shadows as they stretch across the Attic hills. Sea, sky, plain, mountains, and city are all before us, but we will not spend words upon them now. Only for the buildings, wrought by Pericles and his mighty peers, we will speak out our admiration. We will gladly confirm the words Plutarch shall some day say of them, " Unimpaired by time, their appearance retains the fragrance of freshness, as though they had been inspired by an eternally blooming life and a never aging soul." [1]

[1] Plutarch wrote this probably after 100 A.D., when the Parthenon had stood for about five and a half centuries.

CHAPTER XXI.

THE GREAT FESTIVALS OF ATHENS.

198. The Frequent Festivals at Athens. — Surely our "Day in Athens" has been spent from morn till night several times over, so much there is to see and tell. Yet he would be remiss who left the city of Athena before witnessing at least several of the great public festivals which are the city's noble pride. There are a prodigious number of religious festivals in Athens.[1] They take the place of the later "Christian Sabbath" and probably create a somewhat equal number of rest days during the year, although at more irregular intervals. They are far from being "Scotch Sundays," however. On them the semi-riotous "joy of life" which is part of the Greek nature finds its fullest, ofttimes its wildest, expression. They are days of merriment, athletic sports, great civic spectacles, chorals, public dances.[2] To complete our picture of Athens we must tarry for a swift cursory glance upon at least three of these fête days of the city of Pericles, Sophocles, and Phidias.

199. The Eleusinia. — Our first festival is the Eleusinia, the festival of the Eleusinian mysteries. It is September, the "19th of Boēdromiōn," the Athenians will say. Four

[1] In Gulick (*Life of the Ancient Greeks*, pp. 304–310) there is a valuable list of Attic festivals. The Athenians had over thirty important religious festivals, several of them, *e.g.*, the Thesmorphoria (celebrated by the women in honor of Demeter), extending over a number of days.

[2] It is needless to point out that to the Greeks, as to many other ancient peoples, — for example, the Hebrews, — *dancing* often had a religious significance and might be a regular part of the worship of the gods.

228

days have been spent by the "initiates" and the "candidates" in symbolic sacrifices and purifications.[1] On one of these days the arch priest, the "Hierophant," has preached a manner of sermon at the Painted Porch in the Agora setting forth the awfulness and spiritual efficacy of these Mysteries, sacred to Demeter the Earth Mother, to her daughter Persephone, and also to the young Iacchus, one of the many incarnations of Dionysus, and who is always associated at Eleusis with the divine " Mother and Daughter."   The great cry has gone forth to the Initiates — " To the Sea, ye Mystæ! " and the whole vast multitude has gone down to bathe in the purifying brine.

Now on this fifth day comes the sacred procession from Athens across the mountain pass to Eleusis.   The participants, by thousands, of both sexes and of all ages, are drawn up in the Agora ere starting.   The Hierophant, the "Torchbearer," the " Sacred Herald," and the other priests wear long flowing raiment and high mitres like Orientals. They also, as well as the company, wear myrtle and ivy chaplets and bear ears of corn and reapers' sickles.   The holy image of Iacchus is borne in a car, the high priests marching beside it; and forth with pealing shout and chant they go, — down the Ceramicus, through the Dipylon gate, and over the hill to Eleusis, twelve miles away.

200. The Holy Procession to Eleusis. — Very sacred is the procession, but not silent and reverential.   It is an hour when the untamed animal spirits of the Greeks, who after all are a young race and who are gripped fast by natural instinct, seem uncurbed.   Loud rings the "orgiastic" cry, " *Iacchë! Iacchë! evoë!* "

---

[1] Not all Athenians were among the " initiated," but it does not seem to have been hard to be admitted to the oaths and examination which gave one participation in the mysteries. About all a candidate had to prove was blameless character. Women could be initiated as well as men.

There are wild shouts, dances, jests, songs,[1] postures. As the marchers pass the several sanctuaries along the road there are halts for symbolic sacrifices. So the multitude slowly mounts the long heights of Mount Ægaleos, until — close to the temple of Aphrodite near the summit of the pass — the view opens of the broad blue bay of Eleusis, shut in by the isle of Salamis, while to the northward are seen the green Thrasian plain, with the white houses of Eleusis town[2] near the center, and the long line of outer hills stretching away to Megara and Bœotia.

The evening shadows are falling, while the peaceful army sweeps over the mountain wall and into Eleusis. Every marcher produces a torch, and bears it blazing aloft as he nears his destination. Seen in the dark from Eleusis, the long procession of innumerable torches must convey an effect most magical.

201. The Mysteries of Eleusis. — What follows at Eleusis ? The " mysteries " are " mysteries " still ; we cannot claim initiation and reveal them. There seem to be manifold sacrifices of a symbolic significance, the tasting of sacred " portions " of food and drink — a dim foreshadowing of the Christian sacrament of the Eucharist ; especially in the great hall of the Temple of the Mystæ in Eleusis there take place a manner of symbolic spectacles, dramas perhaps one may call them, revealing the origin of Iacchus, the mystical union of Persephone and Zeus, and the final joy of Demeter.

This certainly we can say of these ceremonies. They seem to have afforded to spiritually minded men a sense of

---

[1] We do not possess the official chant of the Mystæ used on their march to Eleusis. Very possibly it was of a swift riotous nature like the Bacchinals' song in Euripides's *Bacchinals* (well translated by Way or by Murray).

[2] This was about the only considerable town in Attica outside of Athens.

remission of personal sin which the regular religion could never give; they seem also to have conveyed a fair hope of immortality, such as most Greeks doubted. Sophocles tells thus the story : "Thrice blessed are they who behold these mystic rites, ere passing to Hades' realm. They alone have life there. For the rest all things below are evil." [1] And in face of imminent death, perhaps in hours of shipwreck, men are wont to ask one another, "Have you been initiated at Eleusis ? "

202. The Greater Dionysia and the Drama. — Again we are in Athens in the springtime: "The eleventh of Elaphebolion" [March]. It is the third day of the Greater Dionysia. The city has been in high festival; all the booths in the Agora hum with redoubled life; strangers have flocked in from outlying parts of Hellas to trade, admire, and recreate ; under pretext of honoring the wine god, inordinate quantities of wine are drunk with less than the prudent mixture of water. There is boisterous frolicking, singing, and jesting everywhere. It is early blossom time. All whom you meet wear huge flower crowns, and pelt you with the fragrant petals of spring.[2]

So for two days the city has made merry, and now on the third, very early, "to the theater" is the word on every lip. Magistrates in their purple robes of office, ambassadors from foreign states, the priests and religious dignitaries, are all going to the front seats of honor. Ladies of gentle family, carefully veiled but eager and fluttering, are going with their maids, if the productions

---

[1] Sophocles, *Frag.* 719.

[2] Pindar (*Frag.* 75) says thus of the joy and beauty of this fête: " [Lo !] this festival is due when the chamber of the red-robed Hours is opened and odorous plants wake to the fragrant spring. Then we scatter on undying earth the violet, like lovely tresses, and twine roses in our hair; then sounds the voice of song, the flute keeps time, and dancing choirs resound the praise of Semele."

of the day are to be tragedies not comedies.[1] All the
citizens are going, rich and poor, for here again we meet
" Athenian democracy "; and the judgment and interest of
the tatter-clad fishermen seeking the general " two-obol "
seats may be almost as correct and keen as that of the
lordly Alcmæonid in his gala himation.

✓ **203. The Theater of Dionysus.** — Early dawn it is when
the crowds pour through the barriers around the Theater of
Dionysus upon the southern slope of the Acropolis. They
sit (full 15,000 or more) wedged close together upon rough
wooden benches set upon the hill slopes.[2] At the foot of
their wide semicircle is a circular space of ground, beaten
hard, and ringed by a low stone barrier. It is some ninety
feet in diameter. This is the *orchestra*, the " dancing place,"
wherein the chorus may disport itself and execute its
elaborate figures. Behind the orchestra stretches a kind of
tent or booth, the *skenē*. Within this the actors may retire
to change their costumes, and the side nearest to the audience is provided with a very simple scene, — some kind of
elementary scenery painted to represent the front of a
temple or palace, or the rocks, or the open country. This is
nearly the entire setting.[3] If there are any slight changes
of this screen, they must be made in the sight of the entire
audience. The Athenian theater has the blue dome of heaven
above it, the red Acropolis rock behind it. Beyond the

---

[1] It seems probable (on our uncertain information) that Athenian
ladies attended the moral and proper tragedies. It was impossible for
them to attend the often very coarse comedies. Possibly at the tragedies
they sat in a special and decently secluded part of the theater.

[2] These benches (before the stone theater was built in 340 B.C.) may be
imagined as set up much like the " bleachers " at a modern baseball park.
We know that ancient audiences wedged in very close.

[3] I think it is fairly certain that the classical Attic theater was without
any stage, and that the actors appeared on the same level as the chorus.
As to the extreme simplicity of all the scenery and properties there is not
the least doubt.

skenē one can look far away to the country and the hills.
The keen Attic imagination will take the place of the thousand arts of the later stage-setter.   Sophocles and his rivals,
even as Shakespeare in Elizabeth's England, can sound the
very depths and scale the loftiest heights of human passion,
with only a simulacrum of the scenery, properties, and me-

COMIC ACTORS DRESSED AS OSTRICHES.

chanical artifices which will trick out a very mean twentieth
century theater.

204. The Production of a Play. — The crowds are hushed
and expectant.   The herald, ere the play begins, proclaims
the award of a golden crown to some civic benefactor : a moment of ineffable joy to the recipient; for when is a true
Greek happier than when held up for public glorification ?
Then comes the summons to the first competing poet.

"Lead on your chorus."[1]   The intellectual feast of the
Dionysia has begun.

To analyze the Attic drama is the task of the philosopher
and the literary expert.   We observe only the superficialities.   There are never more than *three* speaking actors be-

[1] In the fourth century B.C. when the creation of original tragedies was
in decline, a considerable part of the Dionysia productions seem to have
been devoted to the works of the earlier masters, Æschylus, Sophocles,
and Euripides.

fore the audience at once. They wear huge masques, shaped to fit their parts. The wide mouthpieces make the trained elocution carry to the most remote parts of the theater. The actors wear long trailing robes and are mounted on high shoes to give them sufficient stature before the distant audience. When a new part is needed in the play, an actor retires into the booth, and soon comes forth with a changed masque and costume — an entirely new character. In such a costume and masque, play of feature and easy gesture is impossible; but the actors carry themselves with a stately dignity and recite their often ponderous lines with a grace which redeems them from all bombast. An essential part of the play is the chorus; indeed the chorus was once the main feature of the drama, the actors insignificant innovations. With fifteen members for the tragedy, twenty-four for the comedy,[1] old men of Thebes, Trojan dames, Athenian charcoal burners, as the case may demand — they sympathize with the hard-pressed hero, sing lusty choral odes, and occupy the time with song and dance while the actors are changing costume.

ACTOR IN COSTUME AS A FURY.

The audience follows all the philosophic reasoning of the

[1] In the "Middle" and "Later" comedy, so called, the chorus entirely disappears. The actors do everything.

tragedies, the often subtle wit of the comedies, with that
same shrewd alertness displayed at the jury courts of the
Pnyx. *"Authis! Authis!"* (again! again!) is the frequent
shout, if approving. Date stones and pebbles as well as
hootings are the reward of silly lines or bad acting. At
noon there is an interlude to snatch a hasty luncheon (perhaps without leaving one's seat). Only when the evening
shadows are falling does the chorus of the last play
approach the altar in the center of the orchestra for the
final sacrifice. A whole round of tragedies have been
given.[1] The five public judges announce their decision:
an ivy wreath to the victorious poet; to his *choregus* (the
rich man who has provided his chorus and who shares his
glory) the right to set up a monument in honor of the
victory. Home goes the multitude, — to quarrel over the
result, to praise or blame the acting, to analyze with
remarkable acuteness the poet's handling of religious, ethi-
cal, or social questions.

The theater, like the dicasteries and the Pnyx, is one of
the great public schools of Athens.

205. The Great Panathenaic Procession. — Then for the
last time let us visit Athens, at the fête which in its major
form comes only once in four years. It is the 28th of
Metageitniōn (August), and the eighth day of the Greater
Panathenæa, the most notable of all Athenian festivals.
By it is celebrated the union of all Attica by Theseus, as
one happy united country under the benign sway of mighty
Athena, — an ever fortunate union, which saved the land
from the sorrowful feuds of hostile hamlets such as have
plagued so many Hellenic countries. On the earlier days
of the feast there have been musical contests and gymnastic
games much after the manner of the Olympic games,

---

[1] Comedies, although given at this Dionysia, were more especially favored at the Lenæa, an earlier winter festival.

although the contestants have been drawn from Attica only.
There has been a public recital of Homer. Before a great
audience probably at the Pnyx or the Theater a rhapsodist
of noble presence — clad in purple and with a golden crown
— has made the Trojan War live again, as with his well-
trained voice he held the multitude spellbound by the music
of the stately hexameters.

Now we are at the eighth day. All Athens will march in
its glory to the Acropolis, to bear to the shrine of Athena
the sacred " peplos " — a robe specially woven by the noble
women of Athens to adorn the image of the guardian goddess.[1] The houses have opened; the wives, maids, and
mothers of gentle family have come forth to march in the
procession, all elegantly wreathed and clad in their best,
bearing the sacred vessels and other proper offerings. The
daughter of the " metics," the resident foreigners, go as
attendants of honor with them. The young men and the
old, the priests, the civil magistrates, the generals, all have
their places. Proudest of all are the wealthy and high-born
youths of the cavalry, who now dash to and fro in their
clattering pride. The procession is formed in the outer
Ceramicus. Amid cheers, chants, chorals, and incense smoke
it sweeps through the Agora, and slowly mounts the Acropolis. Center of all the marchers is the glittering peplos,
raised like a sail upon a wheeled barge of state — " the ship
of Athena." Upon the Acropolis, while the old peplos is
piously withdrawn from the image and the new one sub-
stituted, there is a prodigious sacrifice. A mighty flame
roars heavenward from the " great altar "; while enough
bullocks and kine have been slaughtered to enable every
citizen — however poor — to bear away a goodly mess of
roasted meat that night.

---

[1] Note that this robe was for the revered ancient and wooden image of
Athena Polias, not for the far less venerable statue of Athena Parthenos.

206. The View from the Temple of Wingless Victory. — We will not wait for the feasting but rather will take our way to the Temple of Wingless Victory, looking forth to the west of the Acropolis Rock.   So many things we see which we would fain print on the memory.   Behind us we have just left the glittering Parthenon, and the less august but hardly less beautiful Erechtheum, with its "Porch of the Maidens." To our right is the wide expanse of the roofs of the city and beyond the dark olive groves of Colonus, and the slopes of Ægaleos.   In the near foreground, are the red crags of Areopagus and the gray hill of the Pnyx.   But the eye will wander farther.   It is led away across the plainland to the bay of Phaleron, the castellated hill of Munychia, the thin stretch of blue water and the brown island seen across it — Salamis and its strait of the victory. Across the sparkling vista of the sea rise the headlands of Ægina and of lesser isles ; farther yet rise the lordly peaks of Argolis.   Or we can look to the southward.   Our gaze runs down the mountainous Attic coast full thirty miles to where Sunium thrusts out its haughty cape into the Ægean and points the way across the island-studded sea.

Evening is creeping on.   Behind us sounds the great pæan, the solemn chant to Athena, bestower of good to men.   As the sun goes down over the distant Argolic hills his rays spread a clear pathway of gold across the waters. Islands, seas, mountains far and near, are touched now with shifting hues, — saffron, violet, and rose, — beryl, topaz, sapphire, amethyst.   There will never be another landscape like unto this in all the world.   Gladly we sum up our thoughts in the cry of a son of Athens, Aristophanes, master of song, who loved her with that love which the land of Athena can ever inspire in all its children, whether its own by adoption or by birth : —

" *Oh, thou, our Athens!   Violet-crowned, brilliant, most enviable of cities!* "

INDEX

239

References are to pages.

References are to pages.

2790

WINGATE JUNIOR COLLEGE

P9-CEM-992

PRAISE FOR THE INCOMPARABLE
DOROTHY GARLOCK
AND HER PREVIOUS NOVEL
MOTHER ROAD

"Entertaining . . . engaging . . . spiced with Depression-era detail."

—*Publishers Weekly*

"Garlock's endearing characters and vividly depicted milieu will enchant her legions of readers. . . . A suspenseful romance."

—*Booklist*

"This special story shows a love that will overcome all odds. Let your imagination roam as you follow along Route 66 for a heartwarming experience that just won't quit."

—*Rendezvous*

"Colorful characters . . . a true picture of Oklahoma. . . . You will hate to see the book end."

—*Sunday Oklahoman*

"An exciting historical novel that fans will want to read . . . a murder mystery adds suspense . . . a panoramic view of a bygone America."

—*Midwest Book Review*

more . . .

"A wonderful look at life during the Depression, and at a road that led to a new life for many. The characters are great and true to life. *Mother Road* is a book that should definitely be added to your 'To Buy' list."
—TheRomanceReadersConnection.com

"Uplifting. . . . Dorothy Garlock writes about real people and real life."
—*Romantic Times*

"Take the opportunity to enjoy a well-told tale . . . highly recommended."
—RomRevToday.com

"A fascinating novel, with many twists and turns. . . . You'll have a hard time putting it down. I grew up alongside old Route 66, and any time the subject comes up, it gets my attention. . . .Take it from this old Okie, she got it right!"
—*Lebanon Daily Record* (MO)

"Delightful characters . . . a well-woven plotline. . . . I highly recommend *Mother Road*."
—MyShelf.com

Hope's Highway

BOOKS BY DOROTHY GARLOCK

DOROTHY GARLOCK

Hope's Highway

WARNER BOOKS

NEW YORK   BOSTON

This book is a work of historical fiction. In order to give a sense of the times, some names or real people or places have been included in the book. However, the events depicted in this book are imaginary, and the names of nonhistorical persons or events are the product of the author's imagination or are used fictitiously. Any resemblance of such nonhistorical persons or events to actual ones is purely coincidental.

If you purchase this book without a cover you should be aware that this book may have been stolen property and reported as "unsold and destroyed" to the publisher. In such case neither the author nor the publisher has received any payment for this "stripped book."

Copyright © 2004 by Dorothy Garlock
Excerpt from *Song of the Road* copyright © 2004 by Dorothy Garlock
All rights reserved. No part of this book may be reproduced in any form or by any electronic or mechanical means, including information storage and retrieval systems, without permission in writing from the publisher, except by a reviewer who may quote brief passages in a review.

Cover design by Diane Luger
Cover illustration by Wendell Minor

Warner Books

Time Warner Book Group
1271 Avenue of the Americas, New York, NY 10020
Visit our Web site at www.twbookmark.com

Printed in the United States of America

Originally published in trade paperback: January 2004
First Mass Market Paperback Printing: May 2004

10 9 8 7 6 5 4 3 2 1

ATTENTION CORPORATIONS AND ORGANIZATIONS:
Most WARNER books are available at quantity discounts with bulk purchase for educational, business, or sales promotional use. For information, please call or write: Special Markets Department, Warner Books, Inc. 135 W. 50th Street, New York, NY 10020-1393.
Telephone: 1-800-222-6747 Fax: 1-800-477-5925.

Dedicated with love to
ALEX (Hemmy) LEMON,
professor, poet, eligible bachelor.
And if he doesn't behave himself,
I'll tell his students how he got his nickname.

Hope's Highway

Rusty's song

What I See

I was alone on the Mother Road
Prospectin' for love like the Mother Lode.
I did not know that was what I sought.
I just knew that I hurt a lot.

They are blind who will not see,
None so blind as a man like me.

You were there, watchin' over me
With gentle touch and sweet sympathy,
With tender care like a gift so free,
You were there giving strength to me.

Now I know what you tried to share.
Now I see what was always there.
For my embrace you waited patiently
But I never saw what you meant to me.

They are blind who will not see,
None so blind as a man like me.

Come back, love, to my eager arms.
Come back, love, with your magic charms.
Give me love or I'll change to stone,
Give me hope or I'll die alone.

—F.S.I.

Prologue

1933
Hilton, Kansas

Brady STEPPED UP ONTO THE PORCH just as the door was shoved open. His brother came from the house carrying his wife, Becky. Her head lolled against his shoulder; blood covered her upper body and ran down the arm that swung limply. She was naked.

"Good Lord! What happened?" Brady croaked.

Although the brothers hadn't seen each other for six months, Brian, in his dazed state, seemed not in the least surprised to see him.

"I can't leave her in there with . . . him." Brian kissed Becky's forehead, cuddled her body close and stepped off the porch. Without another word he headed down the path to the barn. It was then that Brady saw the butt of a gun protruding from his brother's pocket.

"What happened?" Brady managed to say again. He

took a few running steps to follow his brother, then stopped. "Oh, Lord! Anna Marie—"

He dashed back up onto the porch and into the house. "Anna!" His voice was loud, as were the sounds of his boot heels on the bare floors as he hurriedly searched the rooms. He took the stairs two at a time to reach the bedrooms. The first one was empty, but the second one—

A man, naked except for his socks, lay sprawled on the blood-soaked bed. His male sex was still in its aroused state, his face destroyed. Brady paused only briefly in the doorway, then raced down the stairs. Satisfied that Anna Marie was not in the house, he ran toward the barn.

Brian sat weeping on a pile of hay in one of the stalls, Becky on his lap.

"I killed . . . my . . . Becky! Why did she do that in our bed? Why did she want to hurt me? What did I do wrong?"

"You didn't do anything wrong. She . . . Maybe he was forcing her—" Brady said the words certain they were not true.

"I killed . . . the son of a bitch and . . . I killed my Becky—" Brian lifted his right hand, the one holding the revolver, and pressed the cold tip to his head.

"Brian! For God's sake! Don't! Think of your little girl." Brady almost choked on his fear.

"She'll be better off . . . with you."

The cocking of the revolver split the silence in the barn. Brady caught his breath, then willed himself to start breathing again.

"Put down the gun, brother. Put it down and let's talk about it." Brady forced himself to speak calmly, though every nerve in his body was screaming.

"Tell Anna Marie I love her. Tell her I loved her

mama . . . and that I'm sorry." In a daze of pain and confusion, Brian hugged his wife's bloody body to him. "Go,
Brady. I don't want you to see this."

Too frightened to think clearly, Brady struggled for
words.

"Give me the gun, Brian! Please."

Cautiously and with much trepidation Brady inched
closer to his twin. His heart felt like a runaway train in his
chest.

"I just went crazy." Brian's tear-filled eyes pleaded for
understanding. "I loved her so much. It tore the heart
right out of me to see her with him like that." He rocked
back and forth, cradling his wife. He was laboring just to
breathe.

"We'll go out to Colorado, Brian. We'll leave here.
Just you and I and Anna Marie," Brady begged. "Put
down the gun so we can talk."

"The neighbors knew he was there. They tried to keep
me from goin' into the house. The sheriff will be here
soon. I don't deserve to live . . . don't want to live. Take
my little girl away from here . . . to where no one will
know her daddy killed her . . . mama . . ." The words
were hardly audible, scarcely more than a whisper.

"Oh, God, Brian, stop and think of what you're doing
to the child. Now, dammit to hell! Put down the gun!"

Brady had never felt so helpless in his life. *O Lord,
what can I do?* He was afraid to make a sudden move
while the barrel of the gun was pressed against his
brother's temple. He knew that there was a time when a
human being has taken all that he can endure, a time
when strength and logic were burned away. Was this the

moment for his brother, his twin, who had been closer to him than his mother?

Snatches of scenes from their lives together flashed before Brady's eyes.

The two of them, young boys of sixteen, standing beside the grave of their mother and then a year later beside that of their father, vowing always to take care of each other.

Working with a thrashing crew and later in the oil fields . . . always together.

Their first barn dance. How excited they had been! Brian had taken Becky. He had taken Lucy Waters.

Becky, her pink dress unbelted to hide her pregnancy, standing before the preacher, a proud and beaming Brian at her side.

The birth of little Anna Marie. Brian, smiling for days, blissfully unaware that Becky was not as happy with the child as he was.

Coming home from Colorado after receiving several letters from Brian and realizing that his brother was in a terrible state of depression. Arriving a day late.

Now, more terrified than he had ever been in his life, Brady moved closer to his brother, tears streaming unheeded down his cheeks. *Dear God, help me do and say the right thing.*

"What will I tell Anna Marie, Brian? Don't do this to your little girl . . . to me."

"You'd rather that she see me hang? I'll not put her through that." Brian's eyes were those of a man who was lost, beyond hope and willing to do anything just to make the pain go away.

"You'll not hang," Brady argued. "You'll still be alive in the pen and able to see Anna Marie."

Brian seemed not to hear him, but he harkened to the sound of a motorcar. His eyes darted to the doorway.

"It's the sheriff. Tell him to stay away! Go tell him!"

"I'll tell him. Give me the gun first."

"No! Do this for me, Brady. Go tell him."

"I'll tell him, but stay calm. Be careful with that gun. I'll be right back."

Brady ran to the front of the barn. The sheriff and his deputy were getting out of the car. And a small girl in a blue dress and white stockings was skipping down the street toward the house. Brady had just stepped out of the barn to tell the sheriff to head her off when he heard the cry.

"Becky! Becky!"

It was a sound Brady would remember until his dying day. It filled every crevice of the dimly lit barn and spilled over into the bright Kansas sunshine. It sent a shiver of terror all through him.

Boom!

Brady staggered. The sound of the gunshot brought physical pain so intense that it was scarcely to be borne.

"No!" he shouted, and ran back down the aisle toward his brother. "Oh, Brian, Brian—" The words burst from his throat as he gazed down at the body at his feet.

His beloved brother, his twin, was gone from him forever.

Brady turned and stumbled back to the barn door. He blinked in the brilliant sunlight as he saw his brother's child walking toward the front porch of the house.

"Anna," he shouted.

The little girl paused.

"Daddy! You're home!" With a happy smile on her little face she ran to Brady. He grabbed her up in his arms. "Uncle Brady! I thought you were Daddy"—she giggled—"till I saw your boots."

Holding her protectively close, Brady walked away from the house.

Chapter 1

SHE WAS ON HER WAY TO CALIFORNIA.

Margie couldn't help smiling. She would endure whatever came her way just to realize her dream of going to Hollywood, seeing the stars, and maybe, just maybe, getting a part in a movie. Not a big part. She'd never acted except in a high-school play, but everyone said she was so good she carried the performance.

Her father shifted the gears, the truck jerked and they moved down the dirt road to the highway designated as Route 66, the Mother Road, the highway that would take them all the way to California.

Margie said good-bye for the second time to Conway, Missouri, the town where she had been born and raised and where her dreams of being a movie star had made the long, lonely winter months tolerable.

She turned her thoughts to the events of the days following her father's surprising visit to the café where she worked.

"I'm goin' to California. You can come if you behave yourself," he had announced.

Margie had continued to swipe at the counter with a damp cloth. She was shocked . . . then angry at him for implying that she was in the habit of misbehaving. He had not spoken to her since her return to Conway last fall. She hadn't expected him to welcome her back with open arms or an offer of sympathy, but he could have come around to see if she was all right.

Now here he was inviting her to go with him to California, just weeks after his wife had run off and left him.

Irked by his remark, she couldn't let it go. "What do you mean, behave myself?"

"I ain't takin' ya if you're goin' to run off with every Tom, Dick or Harry that comes along."

"That wasn't what I did, and you know it." Margie kept her head down lest he see how much his words angered her. And how much they hurt.

"Well, are you comin' or not?"

"When are you leaving?"

"Thursday."

"That's day after tomorrow. What part of California?"

"Bakersfield."

"Why Bakersfield?"

"Because I want to. Are you comin' or not?" He inched toward the door, almost as if he couldn't wait to get away from her.

"I'll let you know tomorrow."

"Goddammit! I want to know now. You were eager enough to run off with that fly-by-night last summer."

"That's why I'm being cautious. That fly-by-night stole my money and left me stranded down in Oklahoma."

"I could of told you he was a no-good shyster. But you didn't ask me. You just took the bit in your teeth like you always do. I'm surprised you had enough sense to find your way back."

"You knew I was going with him. Everyone in town knew I was going. Why didn't you come tell me Ernie Harding wasn't dependable?"

" 'Cause you'd not of paid me no mind. That's why. You never did." He went to the door of the café. "Sundown tonight. If you're going, come out to the icehouse. If you're not there, I'll take Potter Jenkins or Mack Dertile."

That morning Margie had watched her father get into his truck. She knew that he would not take one of the town drunks. He had nothing but contempt for them and wouldn't give them an ice chip if they were dying of thirst.

Margie's father, Elmer Kinnard, was a short man with broad shoulders and arms thickened by years of lifting heavy blocks of ice. His light hair was thinning on top. For all his bluster Margie knew he wanted her to go because he lacked the confidence to make the trip alone.

Was he going to see Robert's family? He'd not cared anything for his son while he was growing up and hadn't seen him in years. Some of Robert's relatives on his mother's side had reported that he had done pretty well for himself in California real estate but had died a year ago of a heart attack. Margie guessed Elmer might have heard that his own wife, Goldie, had headed out there. If she had, she would soon discover that being married to Elmer wouldn't get her special treatment from his son's family.

Elmer had married Goldie six months earlier, just weeks after she had come to town to visit a cousin. She had set her cap for him. He appeared to be a good catch. Brazen, with sweet smiles and soft touches, she had cooked for him and cleaned his house while the whole town of Conway watched and wondered if she was going to hook him. She had.

At first, Elmer had been generous with Goldie. She was pretty, though a little plump. He had been flattered by her attention. After they had settled into marriage, his true tightfisted nature came to the fore. It was rumored that Goldie had become increasingly discontent with him and with their life in the small Missouri town. She left suddenly.

Elmer had never shown much interest in his only daughter. After her mother's death, Margie had gone to live with her maternal grandmother on the other side of the small town divided right down the middle by Route 66. She had never received a Christmas or a birthday present from him in all the years that followed, nor had he come to see her act in the school play or graduate from high school. And he usually avoided the café where she worked.

Margie's grandmother died the previous spring and left her a small inheritance. One hundred eighteen dollars seemed like a fortune, and Margie could see her dream of going to Hollywood becoming a reality. The dream, however, turned into a nightmare when the man she hired to take her stole her money, and she had to return to her old job at the diner in Conway. Because she was a good worker and the customers liked her, the owner was glad to have her back.

Bertha, the cook and wife of the owner, leaned in through the window that fronted the kitchen. "You're goin', ain't ya?"

"I want to."

"Then go, honey. There ain't nothin' here for ya. Go and see the sights before yo're tied down with babies and didies."

"Not much chance of that 'round here."

"Gettin' babies? Flitter! Let it be known ya want one and ever' horny man in the county would be here eatin' three squares a day and pinchin' yore cute little butt ever' time ya passed by."

"You and Harry have been awfully good to me. I don't know what I would have done if you hadn't given me my job back."

"You thinkin' Elmer wouldn'ta helped ya?"

"He never has."

"You've been good for us too, hon. It's why I don't want to see ya slingin' hash for the rest of yore life."

"I've always dreamed of going to Hollywood to see the stars."

"Yo're pretty enough to be one. Now, you'd better not tell Harry yo're leavin' until you know for sure Elmer's goin'. Be just like that rascal to get yore hopes up, then fizzle out."

"Rosemary wants to come back to work."

"Her old man broke her arm is the main reason ya got yore job back. She was good help."

"If I give notice and Papa changes his mind about going, I'd be out of a job."

"I heard he sold the icehouse."

"You did? Who'd he sell it to?"

"The bank. Who else has any money?"

"What do they want with it?"

"Who knows? I'd bet my bottom dollar that Goldie Kinnard didn't leave town broke. She might of got the bank to loan her money against the icehouse, and Elmer has to turn it over or pay the debt."

"He'd come out all right. One thing about my father, he knows how to hold on to his money. Grandma used to say that he saved ninety cents out of every dollar he made."

"Yeah, he's a skinflint. Ain't no doubt about that."

An hour before sunset Margie had walked the six blocks from the café to the icehouse. She was not a tall girl and was so slender as to appear fragile, yet she walked with her head up and back straight as if she were used to walking long distances. Her face was an oval frame for large light brown eyes, a straight nose and full, expressive lips. A barrette held her thick dark blond hair at the side. On first glance she did not seem a beautiful girl. But with a chin held high, bright interested eyes and lips that tilted at the corners in an almost constant smile, she nearly always got second and third glances.

As she approached the icehouse, her father came out onto the loading platform carrying a block of ice on his back, protected by his heavy leather shield. He eased the ice into a coaster wagon pulled by a barefoot boy, collected the money and stood waiting for her to say something.

"What car are you going in? Are you going to camp along the way?" Margie asked the questions as if continuing their earlier conversation.

"I'm goin' in my truck and I'm sure as hell not payin' the price for lodgin' from here to California. You figure you're too good to camp out?"

Margie ignored his sarcasm. "What do you expect of me?"

"I expect you to cook, tend the camp and keep your mouth shut."

"Where will I sleep?"

"In the truck."

You're so stingy even with your words. Is that why Goldie left you?

Pretending indifference so that he'd not know how eager she was to go with him, she let a long time elapse before she said anything more. As she waited, she thought about the times when she was younger that she had stood down the street and looked with longing at this building and wondered why her father didn't want her. She had dropped in on him once when she was twelve years old. His harsh words had sent her scurrying back to her grandmother, and she had never ventured near him again . . . until now.

"I heard you sold the icehouse."

"This is my last day."

"Will you miss it?"

"What do you care?"

"I don't."

There was silence while Elmer removed the leather

shield from his back and emptied the water from the pocket on the bottom.

"All right. I'll go with you." Margie blurted the words.

"I leave on Thursday."

"Do you need help getting the truck ready?"

"No. It's ready."

"Then why are you waiting until Thursday to go?"

"I got my reasons."

"Are you waiting to see if Goldie comes back so you won't have to take me?"

"I don't have to take you, girlie," he answered sharply.

"I'm not a girlie. I'm a grown woman, in case you haven't noticed. I'm twenty-three years old." Margie couldn't keep the bite out of her voice.

"Then you're old enough to keep your nose out of things that ain't none of your business," he said in the harsh voice she remembered from her childhood.

"I'm not foolish enough to quit my job until I'm sure that you're going. If I don't work, I don't eat." *And I sure can't depend on you for any help.*

"Quit. I'm leaving Thursday," he barked. Then he added, "Sunup." He went back into the icehouse before she could say anything more.

Margie couldn't remember ever having had a civil conversation with her father, and she was not upset over this one. She was too excited. She hardly felt her feet hitting the rough roadbed as she walked back to her rooming house to get ready for the trip and dream of Hollywood.

*   *   *

At sunup on Thursday Margie waited in front of the rooming house with everything she owned in a suitcase and a cardboard box.

It was the talk of the town that Elmer Kinnard was pulling up stakes and going to California. But the big news, a surprise to all, was that he was taking Margie with him. Nearly all the citizens of Conway knew Elmer and had done business with him. Most of them had watched his daughter grow up and wondered why it was that Elmer didn't seem to know that she was alive.

In a little corner of Margie's mind, as she waited, was the fear that her father might change his mind about taking her. As far as she knew, he had never been more than a hundred miles from Conway.

"Your papa not here yet?" The man who came out of the rooming house was the printer at the newspaper.

"Not yet. But he'll be along."

"Good-bye and good luck in California."

"Thank you."

A few minutes later a truck rounded the corner and stopped. It was the truck Elmer used to haul ice. The sturdy sides rose up a foot higher than the cab. A heavy tarp was stretched across the top and tied down. Extra tires were secured to the sides.

Elmer came to the back and, without a greeting of any kind, let down the tailgate and waited for Margie to lift her suitcase and then her box into the truck. He shoved them back under the tarp, raised the tailgate and fastened it.

"Let's go."

Now as the truck moved smoothly along the newly paved highway, Margie reflected on how little she knew about her father. She was reasonably sure that he wouldn't harm her, but she was also sure that she couldn't rely on him for protection. Harry and Bertha had seen to it that she would be able to protect herself. Before she left the café, Harry had given her a little pistol and taught her to load and shoot it.

"Ya can be sure of one thing, girl. If a man pushes himself on ya, he's goin' to do his damnedest to get in yore pants. Shoot the fucker, 'cause he won't leave ya alive to tell about it!" The pistol was tucked in her box, where it would be easy to get if she needed it.

Elmer Kinnard had never been an easy man to live with, and Margie wondered how he had managed to marry three women in his less than fifty years. His first wife died shortly after giving birth to Robert. Elmer turned the boy over to his wife's parents, which was understandable: He couldn't work and care for an infant. What was not understandable, however, was that after he had given the child away, he showed no more interest in him. In the early 1920s Robert went to California with his widowed grandmother, to live with her brother and his wife.

When Elmer was left with Margie, he turned her over to her grandmother. After he married Goldie, it was easy to see that he was fascinated with his new young wife. For a few months he was rather jovial in his quiet way, but it didn't last.

Now he was alone again.

Was he going to California thinking Goldie was there? Did he expect Robert's family to welcome him?

Miles passed in silence. Margie was content to gaze out the window and daydream. She was on her way again . . . to Hollywood. It was too good to be true. For years she had collected *Silver Screen* and several other movie magazines and thumbed through the pages until they were dog-eared.

She seldom had the chance to see a movie, but when she had, it had provided her with dreams for weeks. She was enchanted by the glamour of the stars. She imagined herself wearing the slinky evening gowns, feathery boas, beaded slippers and sparkling jewelry.

Most of all she dreamed of meeting a man like John Gilbert, George Raft or Ronald Colman who would sweep her off her feet and carry her away to a mansion surrounded by a big stone fence with an iron gate. There he would keep her for days and days making passionate love to her.

Back in 1926 she cried along with thousands of other fifteen-year-old girls when Rudolph Valentino died, and devoured all the news about the funeral and the mysterious woman who visited his tomb daily. Was she his secret lover, the love of his life? Had he loved—

"You got any money, girl?" Elmer asked, breaking into her daydreams.

"A little—and my name is Margie."

"I know what your name is. How much you got?"

"How much do you have?" she countered in the same tone of voice.

They were on their way. There was not much chance he would take her back. And if he stopped to put her out, she would reach for the pistol!

"If you got cash money, you'd best not carry it on you."

"It's safer on me than in my suitcase or my box."

"Do you think I'm goin' to steal it?"

"It was taken out of my suitcase before. I'm taking no chances this time."

Silence.

The pavement ended. They drove onto the gravel road and into the dust stirred up by a car ahead. Margie cranked up the window. She kept her nose pressed to the glass and watched the landscape go by. When they passed men working on the road, they slowed until they were barely creeping along, and Margie waved. Several of the men waved back.

It seemed to her that they traveled miles and miles before they came to the pavement again. What a relief it was to be off the gravel road and away from the dust. She rolled down the window again and breathed in the warm clean air.

Elmer resumed a speed of between twenty-five and thirty miles per hour. Her father was a good driver; she had to give him that. *But how was she going to endure weeks of confinement in this truck with this silent, cynical man?*

The sun was directly overhead when Elmer pulled the truck into a grove beside the road and stopped. Margie got out, stretched her arms and legs and looked around for a place to relieve herself. She found cover in a heavy stand of bushes amid the trees.

On the way back to the truck she stopped and watched her father pouring water from a bucket into the radiator. He was a puzzle to her and had been since she was old enough to know that he was not in the least like other girls' fathers. He was a neat-appearing man: clean-shaven, and he'd recently had a haircut. His overalls and shirt looked to be new. She knew that she would never *love* him, but she wished that she could *like* him.

Elmer dropped the tailgate, reached for a wooden box and dropped it on the ground. She took it to be an invitation to step up into the back of the truck. She was surprised at how compact and efficiently arranged it was. Close to the end on one side was a water barrel and next to it a cabinet with two doors. Tight against the cabinet was a small upright icebox fastened to the side of the truck. She didn't look, but was reasonably sure a small hole had been drilled in the bed of the truck beneath the icebox because there was no pan underneath to empty.

On the other side was a long bench piled high with bedding and boxes. Beneath it, she could see a camp stove and what appeared to be a small rolled-up pup tent. Across the front, next to the cab, her father had built in a heavy wooden box with a padlocked lid. On this was a thin pad.

Every foot of space in the truck bed had been utilized.

Margie looked at her father standing at the end of the truck and smiled to let him know how pleased she was with what he had done.

He grunted and walked away.

Chapter 2

FORTIFIED WITH A MEAT SANDWICH and with a fruit jar of water on the seat beside her, Margie silently watched the fields and farms they passed. She laughed aloud when she read the Burma-Shave sign: IF WIFEY SHUNS YOUR FOND EMBRACE—DON'T SHOOT THE ICEMAN—FEEL YOUR FACE. She glanced at Elmer, thinking that the jingle would surely bring a smile to his face, but he was staring straight ahead.

He appeared to be a bit nervous driving in the Springfield traffic. It made Margie wonder how he would handle the traffic in places like Oklahoma City and Amarillo.

In late afternoon she became aware that he was searching for something as they approached a side road. When they came to a corner where a three-sided log shed sat back from the road, he turned. They traveled for several minutes down a rutted path before pulling into a cleared area amid a stand of blackjack trees.

A truck somewhat like the one they were in was parked there. A man sat in a chair beside it with his hand on a big black dog. A woman tended a campfire. When Elmer stopped and stepped out of the cab, a man in overalls and wide-brimmed straw hat came from behind the raised hood of the truck to meet him.

"Howdy," he called. "Did you have any trouble finding the place?"

"No." Elmer moved away from the truck and stretched. "Came right to it."

The man shook hands with Elmer, then looked questioningly at Margie. When it became apparent to her that Elmer wasn't going to introduce her, Margie rounded the front of the truck and held out her hand.

"Hello. I'm Margie Kinnard. Elmer's daughter."

"Alvin Putman, little lady. I've known Elmer for a spell. Didn't even know he had a daughter. Come meet the wife. If we're goin' to be travelin' together, you'd better be gettin' acquainted. Grace will be downright glad to have a woman to visit with. Come on, Elmer," Alvin said when Elmer headed for the back of the truck. "You've not met my wife and son."

The woman, red-faced from bending over the fire, came toward Margie while wiping her hands on the apron tied around her waist. She had a pleasant smile. Mr. Putman introduced her with pride.

"My wife, Grace. Hon, this is Mr. Kinnard and his daughter, Margie."

Grace shook hands with Margie, then held her hand out to Elmer. "Alvin has told me about you, Mr. Kinnard, but he failed to mention that you had such a pretty daughter."

"Howdy do, ma'am."

"Come meet our son, Margie. Alvin and your pa will

want to chew the fat. Mr. Kinnard can meet Rusty later."
Grace took her hand and pulled her toward the man who
had been sitting beside the truck. He stood beside the
chair now, one hand on the back.

"Son, Mr. Kinnard brought his daughter. Her name is
Margie. Margie, our son, Rusty."

"Hello, Margie," he said softly.

"Hello." Margie held out her hand. Grace moved to
nudge the young man's arm. He lifted his hand. Margie
grasped it, suddenly realizing that Rusty was blind. Her
eyes went quickly to Grace, who was watching her
closely.

"She's about your age, Rusty. Pretty too. Blond hair,
brown eyes, not quite as tall as I am."

"Don't believe her," Margie said with a nervous laugh.
"I'm not pretty. I'm too skinny, my mouth is too big and
my hair looks like a haystack after a cyclone."

Rusty had a nice smile. It was hard for Margie to believe that the eyes that were turned toward her were not
seeing her. He was medium height, thin, and had on
striped overalls like his father wore. His thick dark
auburn hair fell across his forehead. He was clean-shaven
and, although not handsome, was nice-looking in a boy-
ish kind of way

"This is Blackie," Rusty said, bending down to scratch
the ears of a big black dog who watched her with dark intelligent eyes.

Margie laughed. "Hello, Blackie. It's not hard to figure
out how you got your name."

"Mother wanted to call him Whitey, but he wouldn't
answer to it."

"I don't blame you," Margie said to the dog. "Blackie

is a perfect name for you." She looked up to see that Rusty was still smiling. "How long have you had him?"

"Since he was a pup. About six years now."

"I've always wanted a dog, but I've never lived in a place where I could have one. See you later, Rusty. I'd better get back and help set up camp."

"Nice meeting you, Margie."

Grace walked back with her. "Rusty gets lonely for someone his own age to talk to," she said softly. "I'm glad you'll be traveling with us."

"Is he completely blind?"

"Almost. He sees shadows. He came down with a high fever when he was ten years old. We still don't know what it was. He plays the violin and the guitar and is terribly smart. I tell him something or read something to him and he never forgets it." Grace's hand clasped Margie's arm. "I don't want you to think he's a dummy."

"I didn't for a minute think he was a dummy."

"Some folks think that because he can't see, he can't hear. They'll talk to him real loud or ignore him. I hope the Lukers are as nice as you."

"Lukers?"

"Foley Luker, his wife and two kids. Didn't your pa tell you that we're going to travel in a caravan?"

"No. He's pretty close-mouthed."

"Mr. Luker was in the ice business too. That's how Alvin got to know him . . . and your pa. They hatched it up to travel together for safety reasons and to hang together when we get to California."

"I guess there is safety in numbers."

"We've heard that bad things can happen in a campground if you're alone."

"Are the Lukers to meet us here?"

"Alvin thought they would be here by now. I'd better get back and see to my pot of beans. My cousin made the trip to California two years ago. She wrote to tell me to cook up a mess of beans when I got a chance. When Alvin saw that pot of beans, he said there was enough gas there to blow us all the way to the west coast." Grace giggled, squeezed Margie's arm and left her laughing.

Grace had given Margie surprising news. Evidently her father had planned this trip to California with others who had been in the ice business. He had given considerable thought to making the trip as comfortable as possible, probably thinking that Goldie would be going with him. Not many journeyed the highway with their own iceboxes. Margie felt better about being with Elmer now that they would be traveling with the Putmans.

Margie stepped up into the truck and rummaged through the supplies. There was an assortment of canned goods as well as dried foods such as beans, rice and crackers. A large tin contained flour, another cornmeal and yet another sugar. In the icebox were milk and eggs and some of the meat left over from their sandwiches at noon. She reasoned that they should use the perishable items first.

When the tailgate of the truck was let down and hooked to leather straps attached to each side of the truck, it served as a work counter. Margie was forced to admire her father's ingenuity.

While Elmer and Alvin Putman worked beneath the hood of Alvin's truck, Margie built a small campfire and set over it a heavy wire rack she found under the bench. She made milk gravy, and into it she chipped the remainder of the meat. She would serve this on bread she toasted on a small square grill. When the meal was ready, she set it aside, climbed back up into the truck and rearranged the items beneath the shelf to make room for her suitcase and box.

The Lukers arrived while Margie and her father were eating supper. Elmer sat on a canvas camp stool, his plate on his lap. He didn't comment on the food he was served, but he ate three helpings, then set his plate on the tailgate and walked away to meet the new arrivals.

Margie heated water in a teakettle to wash the dishes, and when that was done, she crawled up into the truck, gave herself a sponge bath, then placed the washdish on an upturned box along with soap and a towel for Elmer. After combing her hair and tying it back with a ribbon, she headed for the Luker camp thinking she would get the introductions over with.

Most of the work at the Luker camp was being done by a tall, lanky boy and a young girl while a woman who didn't appear to be much older than Margie looked on.

"Hello," Margie called as she neared. The boy stopped working and returned her greeting. The young girl ignored her and continued to take things from the two-wheeled trailer behind the car.

"I'm Margie Kinnard." Margie extended her hand to the boy.

"Jody. Jody Luker."

"Glad to meet you, Jody Luker."

"I'm Mrs. Luker." The woman's clear blue eyes looked Margie over with frank female curiosity. With black curly hair, milk-white skin and lips bright red with lipstick, she was pretty and well aware of it. She preened and flashed even white teeth. Dimples appeared in each cheek. "I'm their stepmama. I guess you can tell I'm not old enough to be their real mama." She laughed and held out her hand. "Sugar. My name has been Sugar for so long I've almost forgotten my real name is Selma."

"Sugar!" the young girl snorted. "Should be Vinegar."

"Don't pay any attention to Mona. She's had her fat tail over the line all day. When her father isn't around, she says things she'd be slapped silly for if he heard them."

"And you don't?" The girl curled her lips in a sneer. "You act so nasty nice around him that it makes me want to puke."

"I apologize for the girl's behavior. The poor little thing can't help it if *she's* fat and as ugly as a mud fence." There was viciousness in Mrs. Luker's voice, and to Margie her face was no longer pretty.

"Quit pickin' on her!" Jody said sharply.

Sugar grinned at the boy and made a kissing motion with her puckered lips. He scowled and turned back to the trailer to lift out a heavy box for his sister. Mrs. Luker put her hands beneath the heavy hair at the nape of her neck, lifted it and thrust out her pointed breasts.

Margie was stunned into silence. *Oh, boy! What do we have here?* The girl, Mona, looked to be a couple of years younger than her brother and was far from ugly. She was not as slender as Sugar, but she was not fat. Margie was sure the girl was hiding hurt feelings behind her belligerent attitude.

"I must go. I'll see you again."

"There's no doubt 'bout that if you're going to be traveling with us." Sugar shrugged and raised her brows while looking Margie up and down. Her expression changed suddenly when she looked past her at the men who were approaching. A dazzling smile appeared on her face.

"I'll have something for you to eat, darlin', as soon as I get the camp set up." Sugar went to her husband and took his hand. She leaned her head against his shoulder before looking up at him.

"You mean as soon as the fat, ugly kid gets the camp set up," Mona mumbled.

Jody grunted a warning to his sister.

"This is Mr. Putman and Mr. Kinnard," Mr. Luker said to his wife, and placed his hand on her shoulder. "My wife, Sugar."

"Hello." Sugar offered her hand to each of the men, then snuggled against her husband.

Embarrassed, Alvin Putman shifted his feet uneasily. Elmer's expression was as blank as always, and it was difficult to gauge his reaction to the woman.

Mr. Luker had near-black hair brushed back from his forehead, wide shoulders, big hands and narrow hips. Except for the slightly chipped front tooth, he was a grown-up version of his son, Jody. Warm brown eyes settled on Margie. Knowing that Elmer would not introduce her, she held out her hand.

"Margie Kinnard. Elmer's daughter."

He gripped her hand and gave her a friendly smile. "Foley Luker. Pleased to meet you, ma'am."

Sugar's eyes narrowed. She gripped the front of her husband's shirt with a tight fist to bring his attention back to her.

Margie glanced back at Jody and his sister. They stood together beside the trailer they were unloading. He was talking urgently to her, his back shielding her from the others. Margie decided then and there that she would keep her distance from Sugar. She had seen her kind before. The woman was trouble.

"What are the other folks like, Ma?"

"I'm not sure yet, son." Grace stood beside her son's chair with her hand on his shoulder. "Mr. Luker's wife isn't much older than his kids. The boy is seventeen or thereabout, I'd guess. He's tall like his pa. The girl is younger by a year or two. Something's not quite right there. Mrs. Luker said to call her Sugar, as if I would. She bosses the kids around like she was queen of the May. She wasn't at all kind to the girl while I was there. I guess they'd had a set-to. The girl had been crying."

"Pa said Mr. Luker married recently. His new wife talked him into selling his ice business. She's the one who wants to go to California."

"Would you like to walk around for a while?"

"Do you mind if we wait until dark?"

"Now, son, I've told you this a hundred times." Grace knew what was in her son's mind. "Bein' blind ain't nothin' to be ashamed of. You can do some things better than some folks that can see."

"Stop kiddin' yourself, Ma. I can't even go to the outhouse unless Pa takes me."

"Not in a strange place, but you did when we were home. You will again. We'll get a place where you'll learn your way around, and you'll have a job on the radio singin' and playin' your own songs. I just know it."

Rusty chuckled. "My mother the eternal optimist."

"Optimist? What's that? Oh, never mind. That's one of them words you learned from that high-toned teacher."

"Is it dark?"

"It's dark enough. Let's walk to the road and back. Do you want your cane?"

"No." Rusty placed his hand on his mother's shoulder and walked beside her. They made a wide circle around the Luker camp. Blackie ran ahead, enjoying the scents he found along the way.

"Margie already knows that you can't see. She seems nice. I wonder why her pa didn't tell Alvin that he was bringing her along?"

"Maybe she didn't decide to come along until the last minute."

"I'm glad she did. She's someone we can visit with. I doubt Mrs. Luker will want to have much to do with us."

"Don't be pushing me on Margie." Rusty's voice was stern.

"What a thing to say! I wouldn't do such a thing!"

He laughed and squeezed the shoulder beneath his hand. "You don't fool me for a minute, Mother mine."

"I'm not trying to fool you," she protested. "I just want you to know people your age and—"

"Girls," he interrupted. "You want me to have a girl."

"What's wrong with that?"

"You know what's wrong."

"You . . . could be friends."

"Women don't want to be just *friends* with a man, Ma. They want a husband who can take care of them. How would I take care of a wife? I can't take care of myself."

"You will. When we get to California, you'll get a job

on the radio. Cousin Oletta says there's a radio station in almost every town."

"I hope that isn't the only reason you and Pa pulled up stakes to go to California."

"You know it isn't. Your pa thinks he can start an ice business in California, where it's warm all year long. Winters here in Missouri are cold, and folks don't need ice from November to March. Blackie," Grace called. "Come back here."

"He isn't bothering, Mrs. Putman," Margie called. "He just came to say hello."

"Ma?" Rusty hissed a warning.

"We're out stretching our legs. A body stiffens up sitting in that truck all day."

"Do you mind if I walk with you? I need to get the kinks out of my legs too."

"Course not. We thought we'd walk out to the road and back. It's more for my benefit than Rusty's. A friend showed him how to stand in one place and run and how to use a bar to pull himself up and down. He did it every morning back home. Glory be. It made me tired just watching him. He worked in the icehouse helpin' his pa and—"

"Ma! Margie doesn't want to hear my life story."

"Yes, I do," Margie said quickly. "Then you'll have to listen while I tell you about working in the café and about the time I paid a no-good man to take me to California and he stole my money. He left me stranded down in Oklahoma, and I had to come home with my tail between my legs."

"Nothing that exciting has happened to me." Rusty laughed again.

In spite of his blindness, he laughs easily, Margie thought before she turned her attention to what his mother was saying.

"How about the time you were playing your fiddle for a barn dance and a couple of drunks rode their horses right into the barn while you were calling a square? That was exciting."

"Oh, no!" Margie exclaimed. "What happened?"

"Blackie took after the horses, nipping at their legs," Rusty said. "One of the riders got bucked off and broke his arm."

"Served him right."

"We all thought that was the end of the dance. Know what Rusty did?" Grace said. "He yelled for the folks to grab a partner. 'Here comes "Little Brown Jug" especially for those old boys who can't hold their liquor,' he said. Ever'body laughed and began to dance again."

"Good for Blackie. I hope he got a nice bone when he got home." Margie glanced at Rusty as she spoke, and saw that his face was turned toward her. He walked alongside them as if he could see each and every step he took.

"Blackie knows that I don't see . . . well. One time he got between me and a grass fire. I knew it was there, but didn't know how close it was until Blackie tugged on my pant leg. That was the first time we realized that my dog was aware that I couldn't see."

"That's truly remarkable," Margie exclaimed. "I heard about a dog who led a man out of a burning house and about a dog who jumped into a pond and rescued a baby."

"Dogs are smarter than some people think they are.

Back home Blackie knew words like 'post office,' 'barbershop' and 'meat market.' He could lead me there."

"Will you play your fiddle for us some night?"

"Course he will." Grace didn't give Rusty a chance to answer. "He not only plays the fiddle, he plays the guitar, sings and writes his own songs. He's working on one called 'What I See.' "

"Ma!"

"He doesn't like for me to brag on him. He's goin' to give me holy heck when we get back to camp."

"When I was little," Margie said, "my granny used to brag on me. It embarrassed me then, but now I realize that she did it because she loved me. Will you sing your song for me sometime?"

"Sometime," Rusty replied.

"Were you raised by your grandma?" Grace asked.

"My mother died when I was small. Do you like writing songs, Rusty?" she asked, in order to change the subject.

"When I'm in the right mood. I'm going to miss listening to the radio while on this trip."

"His songs are good, Margie. Wait until you hear them. They'll bring tears to your eyes."

Rusty waited until they were headed back to camp before he spoke again.

"You have to take what my mother says with a grain of salt, Margie. What mother would tell her son that his songs are not worth a cup of spit?"

"Some mothers or fathers would."

They walked on in silence back to where Margie had joined them. "I'll leave you here," she said. "Maybe we can do this again sometime. It's not much fun walking by yourself."

"Sure we can," Grace said.

"Good night, Margie."

"Good night, Rusty."

Chapter 3

PALE STREAKS OF LIGHT WERE SHOWING in the east when Margie heard a noise at the end of the truck. Elmer was building a breakfast fire. The blankets he had used to make a pallet were folded and stacked on the camp chair.

"Morning," she called, and went to the basin she had left on the box overnight. After washing and running the comb through her hair, she filled the coffeepot with water from the keg and set it over the blaze. While the water was heating, she lined a skillet with bacon strips, enough for both breakfast and the noon meal, and set it over the fire.

On her way to the pantry in the truck to get eggs and coffee, she glanced at the other camps. The Putmans were eating breakfast. Jody Luker was building a fire. Foley Luker came out of a small tent that had been set up near the edge of the woods.

It was daylight by the time breakfast was over and Margie had washed and put away the utensils. Elmer came around to check the tarp that covered the truck bed and to tie down the back flap.

The Putmans left the campsite ahead of them. Grace waved. Alvin tooted the horn. As Elmer drove out to the road, Foley Luker was taking down the tent. Jody and Mona were working at the campfire.

Because they had pulled out and left them, Margie wanted to ask Elmer if the Lukers would still be part of the caravan; but he had not said a word to her, and she had said nothing to him, since the morning greeting that he had ignored. She decided to ask him anyway, and if he didn't want to answer, he wouldn't.

"Are the Lukers still part of the caravan?"

"They'll be along." He pulled his pipe from the bib of his overalls, struck a match on the steering wheel and lit it.

"Where is the next campsite?"

"Oklahoma."

"How far is that?"

"About a hundred miles."

"Is it the goal to make a hundred miles a day?"

"On the flatland. Might not in the mountains."

"I like the Putmans."

"Don't be flirtin' with that blind boy, gettin' him all hot for ya," he said sternly. "His pa won't stand for it." He spoke around the pipe stem in his mouth.

When the import of his words soaked into Margie's mind, she closed her eyes and fought a sharp battle to get her anger under control. But it blossomed.

"What do you mean by that?" she demanded.

"Just what I said. Stay away from him. He'd not understand a woman like you."

"What do you mean, a woman like me? Do you think I'm some cheap floozy who's out to get him in bed?"

"Yeah, I think that."

"What!" she exploded. "Why you nasty, dirty-minded old reprobate. I wish I'd known what you thought of me before we left Conway. I'd not have ridden a mile with you."

"Say the word. I'll pull over and let you out."

"You'd like that! And that's just the reason I'm going to stick with you all the way to California."

"Maybe you will and maybe you won't."

"You'd not dare put me out. What would your friends the Putmans think? Or the Lukers? That Sugar Luker is a floozy, if I ever saw one."

"It takes one to know one."

Angry, unguarded words spewed from Margie's mouth. "I suppose you know about floozies. The one you married left you."

"I married two," he said calmly.

"Are you saying that my mother was a floozy?"

"She was a whore."

Margie's breath left her. When she was finally able to speak, she said two words. "You're lying."

He shrugged.

"You're lying!" She shouted it this time.

He ignored her outburst and pulled into a filling station, got out and slammed the door. Margie was shaking. All her life she had heard little rumors that her mother had sown some wild oats before she married Elmer and settled down. No one had even hinted that she was anything but a pretty girl who attracted men like flies to a honey pot. Her granny had even said that her daughter was too pretty for her own good.

Unanswered questions floated around in Margie's mind. If Elmer thought her mother a whore, he might be thinking that Margie wasn't his daughter. Was that why he had been so indifferent to her all these years? Oh, Lord! Here she was at the mercy of a man who cared no more for her than he did for the old dog he'd left behind.

Margie stared out the window and waited for Elmer to finish paying for the gas and get back into the truck. She intended to take up the conversation where it had left off. Minutes after they left the gas station, the paving ended and they were once again on a gravel road. Traveling this one was like riding on a washboard. Dust flew up from the car ahead. She rolled up the window to keep from breathing it and decided to wait until they were on a smoother road and it wasn't so noisy before she questioned him further.

It was almost noon when they passed off the gravel and onto the smooth paving. It was a blessed relief. Margie cranked down the window and enjoyed the breeze hitting her face. She was debating with herself on how to open the conversation with Elmer about her mother when she realized that the truck ahead was the Putmans'.

At the top of a small rise the Putmans pulled to the side of the road. Elmer stopped a few dozen feet behind them. As if she weren't there, he got out of the truck and walked off into the woods with Alvin and Rusty. Blackie trailed along behind.

Grace came to where Margie stood beside the truck. "That washboardy road 'bout shook me to pieces." She massaged the small of her back as they walked away together.

"I've traveled this road as far as Sayre, Oklahoma," Margie said. "It's mostly paved from Tulsa on through Oklahoma. We came to spots where bridges weren't finished and we had to go around. In some places the creek was dry with a good sandy bottom, and we crossed without detouring."

"Well, looky who's here." Grace nudged Margie with her elbow when the Lukers pulled up and stopped. "They got such a late start I was sure that we'd not see them all day. But they didn't have to stop for gas. Foley told Alvin they filled up last night before they got to the campground."

All the Lukers except Sugar piled out of the car and stood beside the road. Mona walked back down the road, then toward the woods. Jody called to her, but she kept going. Grace commented on it when she and Margie took their turn in the woods.

"There seems to be bad feelings between the girl and Mrs. Luker."

"I noticed that. Jody takes up for his sister. It must be hard for both of them. I wonder how long since they lost their mother."

"Foley said two years. He married this one a few months ago."

When they were out of sight, Margie handed Grace a square of newspaper that she had softened by crushing and rubbing. She smiled at the woman's quizzical look.

"It's better than nothing. My granny taught me how to do that. She used to cut the paper in squares, crush and rub it to soften it, fold it and put it in the outhouse. It works with pages from a catalog if it's not slick paper."

Grace laughed. "Wait until I tell Alvin and Rusty—"

"Don't you dare! If you do, I'll not be able to face either one of them."

"I was funnin' you."

Later Grace clicked her tongue when she saw Mona Luker coming up the road. "I'd of give a pretty penny to have a girl, but the good Lord didn't see fit to give us one. He must have figured he gave us the best he had when he gave us Rusty, and saved the girl for someone else."

"What a sweet thing to say. Rusty is lucky the Lord gave him to you."

Grace laughed. "We'd of loved him if he'd been dumb as a pile of rocks."

Jody Luker was talking to Rusty, who leaned against the side of the Putman truck, Blackie beside him. The hood of the Luker car was up, and Alvin, Foley and Elmer were huddled around it. Alvin went to his truck, returned with a bucket of water and poured it into the radiator.

Margie climbed into Elmer's truck and made sandwiches from the bacon and eggs she had cooked that morning. She took her sandwich, along with a fruit jar of water, and went to sit on the grass beside the road, leaving Elmer's meal on the tailgate. She wasn't in a mood to talk and was glad Grace was busy making the noon meal for her family.

When Jody passed on his way back to the Luker car, Margie smiled and lifted a hand in greeting. Sugar Luker, who was sitting in the car, said something to him as he came even with it. He didn't pause or answer, but continued on to where his sister was at the back of the trailer.

Was Foley Luker so blind that he couldn't see how un-happy his wife was making his children? Or was he so fascinated with his Sugar that he didn't care?

Margie's mind was still in a turmoil over the conversation she'd had with her father. She had opened a dialogue with her questions and was determined to know why he considered her mother a whore.

When it came time to pull out again, they fell in behind the Putmans. The highway was smooth. Margie waited until after Elmer had lit his pipe before she spoke.

"I want to know why you called my mother a whore."

He was silent for a moment, then said, "You don't want to know."

"I do," she replied staunchly. "Do you think that I'm not your daughter? Is that the reason you have ignored me all these years and why you can't bring yourself to introduce me to your friends?"

"Drop it, girl. What's done is done. No sense dragging up the past."

"I can't drop something as important as this is to me. All my life I've wondered why you didn't like me. I turned myself inside out trying to please you and get you to notice me. I *wanted* a father."

"No fault of mine. I provided for you till you were grown. I gave the old woman money every month."

"Why did you say my mother was a whore?" she insisted. "Why do you have such a low opinion of me? Tell me."

"Goddammit!" he shouted. "Let it go or I'll pull over and put you out."

Margie burst into tears. She cried softly for miles. When the scalding tears abated, she wiped her eyes on the hem of her dress and rested her head against the back of the seat. One thought sustained her: She was on her way to California and Hollywood. Tonight she would get out her movie magazines. Looking through them always gave her something new to dream about. As far as Elmer was concerned, she vowed not to say another word to him until they reached California. And that word would be "good-bye."

Margie was staring out the window when they reached Miami, Oklahoma. They passed the Coleman Theater, said to be one of the most beautiful theaters in the Southwest. She had heard that Will Rogers and many other famous people had made appearances there. No wonder Miami was proud of its theater.

On leaving Miami they were again on a rough gravel road that went on for mile after mile. They crossed the Neosho River and passed through endless prairie land. About the time that Margie was sure her rear was numb, they followed the Putmans off the highway and into a cleared area where a vehicle was parked and a saddled buckskin horse, its reins trailing, grazed on the early summer grass. Two men stood beside a big black car with a carrier rack, and a little girl jumped rope nearby.

One of the men went to speak to the Putmans, then waited for Elmer to move forward.

"Howdy," the man said to Elmer, then tipped his hat to Margie. "Ma'am." He was young and dark-haired, with an obvious Indian heritage. "This is my land, but you're welcome to camp here. Be careful with your fire. A grass fire could easily spread to the hay crop I have just through that thin patch of woods."

"I'll watch the fire."

As they passed the car with the carrier rack on top, Margie glanced at the other man leaning against it, his arms folded across his chest. He was tall, big-framed and lean. All she could see of his face beneath the pulled-down, big-brimmed hat was his firm, unsmiling mouth. After they had passed him, she realized that he wore an air of authority. Was he a lawman?

Elmer stopped the truck near a circle of rocks that held the remains of previous fires, leaving a space of a couple hundred feet between their camp and the Putmans'.

Margie felt wrung out. She wanted to hurry and get supper over with. She had decided that she would ask Rusty to go for a walk with her.

Let Elmer make something of that.

She quickly set out the box with the washdish, soap and towel. Elmer came out of the woods with an armload of dead wood and built the cook fire.

When the fire was going, he left to speak to Foley Luker, who had driven into the campground. The radiator on the Luker car was steaming. Margie was climbing out of the truck with potatoes to peel when the man who had greeted them when they drove in approached with a large fish hanging from a stringer.

"Ma'am, could you use a catfish? I caught more than I can use." He had tipped his hat back, and she could see a few silver streaks in his hair.

"We sure could. There's nothing better than fried catfish."

"Rolled in cornmeal?" He smiled, creases appearing on each side of his wide mouth.

"Absolutely!" Margie returned the smile.

While he was removing the fish from the string, it began to flop. Margie let out a little squeal of alarm.

"I'll whack him on the head for you, ma'am. Your man will have to skin him for you."

"My father," Margie corrected.

"On second thought, if you have something I can lay him on, I can skin him for you in half a minute."

"Half a minute," she echoed teasingly. "Now, that, I'll have to see." She removed the washdish from the box. "Mister, will this do?"

"Name's Payne, ma'am."

He circled the head of the fish with a sharp knife, then with the pliers he took from his pocket, he pulled off the skin. It took a little longer than half a minute, but there was no wasted motion. It was as if he had done it a million times before.

"It's good of you to let us camp here."

"My pleasure. I enjoy the chance to meet folks. Most of them are good people." He quickly sliced the fish down one side and then the other. After laying aside slabs of boneless fish, he tossed the long spiny bone into the campfire.

"Thank you. I'll get water so you can wash your hands." Margie ladled water into the washdish from the water keg and set it on the tailgate. "You're welcome to stay and eat with us."

"Thanks, but my friend over there"—he jerked his head toward the big heavy car with the rack on the top—"is frying up a batch."

"Thank you, Mr. Payne, for the fish and for allowing us to camp here."

"You're welcome."

While the fish fried, Margie mixed a batch of corn bread to cook like pancakes on the griddle. She didn't know what Elmer liked to eat and she didn't care. If he didn't like the fish and corn bread, he could go eat with Sugar, she thought spitefully.

While she was bending over the cook fire, Jody Luker stopped by. "The fish smells good. Mona's cooking ours."

"Can't Sugar cook?"

"Not much." Jody didn't seem to notice the sarcasm in her voice. "I just never thought I'd meet Andy Payne. He's shook hands with the president and everythin'."

"This Mr. Payne? The one who let us camp here and gave us the fish?"

"Haven't you heard of him? Pa said he lived around here. He's the one who won the Bunion Derby. He ran from Los Angeles to New York and beat out over two hundred other runners to win."

"He *ran* from Los Angeles to New York? I can't believe it."

"He did. Back in 1928."

"I've never heard the like."

"Pa said they called the race the International Transcontinental Foot Marathon, but that's such a tongue twister it was just called the Bunion Derby. The race was thirty-four hundred miles long."

"And this Mr. Payne won it? Well, whatta ya know!"

"He's Cherokee. Pa said running is in their blood. I don't know if that had anything to do with him winning, but he did, and got money enough to buy his ranch. It's about a half mile from here. He said he came down to spend the day fishing with his friend, who is passing through."

"He certainly knows how to clean fish. I'll give him that."

Elmer had no complaints about the meal. He said nothing. Not even about the man who had so generously given them the fish—cleaned and boned. When Margie sat down to eat, he appeared and filled his plate and moved away. When he finished eating, he set his plate on the tailgate of the truck, sank down in the canvas chair and lit his pipe.

Margie wrapped the leftover fish and corn bread in waxed bread wrappers, then washed the dishes. When she finished, she filled the washdish with warm water and took it to the truck. She lit the lantern and brought down the end flap for privacy. The emotional confrontation with her father had worn her out. She would like nothing better than to go straight to bed, but she felt too dirty for that. After washing herself from head to toe, she put her clothes back on. She had worn them for two days and decided she would wear them one more day. She had three skirts and three blouses that she thought were suitable for travel. Her one dress and another skirt and blouse would be kept in reserve should she need to dress up.

She debated about staying in the truck with the lantern and thumbing through her movie magazines. That usually soothed her, but it was too hot in the truck with the end flap down. Besides, Elmer might complain about the use of the kerosene. She would reserve that pleasure for another time.

Elmer was not in sight when she rolled up the end flap and got out of the truck. The day was near an end. Only a few faint streaks showed in the western sky. A few lightning bugs flitted about.

"My ball is under your car." The voice came from a little girl who stood with her shoulders hunched up to her ears as if trying to hide.

"Hello. You lost your ball? Which end of the truck is it under?"

"I don't know."

"I'll take a look." Margie got down on her hands and knees and peered under the truck. "Is it a white ball?"

"It's red."

"Red? Ah . . . that'll make it harder to see in the dark. Hallelujah! There it is." Margie lay flat on the ground and scooted under the truck until she reached the small rubber ball. "I've got it," she called, and began to wiggle her way out.

There was no way she could keep her skirt from moving up to her thighs as she wiggled out from under the truck. When her head cleared the running board, she turned to sit up and her eyes collided with those of the man squatting down holding a lantern. She had never seen such incredible eyes: light green, like leaves in the early spring, cool and secret and surrounded with thick dark lashes.

"Oh . . . oh—" Still holding the ball, Margie grabbed to pull her skirt down to her knees. "Here's your ball," she said, and shoved it into the child's hands.

"Thank you."

Margie rolled over onto her knees to get up and felt the man's hand on her arm to help her. She was hoisted to her feet by hands strong enough to toss her across the truck. Hot with embarrassment, she swiped at her skirt to rid it of the dried grass and looked at the child standing beside the tall man. Her eyes were green like his; her dark hair was parted in the middle, and two fat braids rested on her chest.

Finally there was nothing to do but look up at the man again, her composure completely disrupted, the telltale color of embarrassment on her cheeks.

Chapter 4

She lifted her eyelids, and something about her pulled at him. There was sadness in her eyes as well as intelligence and maturity. Beneath her fragile exterior were strength and determination. He didn't know how he knew this, but he did. The large light brown eyes, flicked with amber; reminded him of the eyes of a doe who was alert and a little bit afraid.

He was not, as a rule, shy around women, but he remained quiet, hoping his nerves would settle down before he had to speak to her.

He swept the wide-brimmed hat from his head, revealing hair as black as midnight. It was thick, shiny, straight as a string, and covered the tips of his ears. He credited his reaction to her to the fact he'd not been around a pretty girl on a one-to-one basis for several months. Relieved to come to that conclusion, he continued to look at the girl who now had a bit of hostility in her expression.

Brady had learned that remaining silent gave him an edge, and for some reason unknown to him, he felt that he needed one now. Most people were uncomfortable with silence, especially women. They sought to fill it with silly chatter. Not so, this young woman. She stared at him coolly, just as silent, waiting for him to speak.

"Thanks for getting the ball." He spoke with a definite Oklahoma drawl.

Margie nodded.

"Uncle Brady told me not to throw it this way."

Her eyes left him and went to the child. "It's all right. I'm glad it wasn't lost."

He was her uncle. They looked enough alike to be father and daughter.

"You got dirty." The little girl's hair was dark, but not as dark as her uncle's, her eyes anxious.

"Don't worry about that," Margie scoffed. "This old skirt will wash."

"Brady Hoyt." The man held out his hand. Margie put hers into it. With a firm grip on her hand he introduced the little girl. "My niece, Anna Marie."

"Margie Kinnard."

"My mama and daddy went to heaven. Uncle Brady is taking me to California to live with my Aunt Opal. Uncle Brady calls me Punkie, but I don't like it much."

Brady released Margie's hand and tilted his head toward his niece. "You never told me that."

"He hasn't noticed that I don't answer when he calls me that." Big dark eyes looked up at Margie. "He wants me to cut off my braids 'cause they're too much trouble. But I'm not going to. Granny Maude, who looked after me sometimes, rolled my hair in rags and made me pretty curls like the little girl in the movies. I'll wait and see if Aunt Opal will do it."

"I bet that little girl was Shirley Temple. I've got a picture of her in one of my magazines. You'd be pretty in curls, even prettier than you already are."

"Mr. Payne gave us a fish without bones in it. Before he went home, he let me ride on his horse. He said he knew my daddy and Uncle Brady when they were just snot-nosed kids."

"Uh-oh. We'd better go before she tells you our family history."

"My daddy was Uncle Brady's twin. He looked like him 'cepts part of my daddy's eyebrow was gone. He said an Indian tried to scalp him, but he was just funnin' me. Uncle Brady said he fell on a plow when he was little."

"You're a lucky little girl to have an uncle. I never had one, but I had a grandma."

"I don't have a grandma—"

"See what I mean," Brady broke in. "You'll soon know about how Grandpa Hoyt helped Teddy Roosevelt win the war in Cuba. Come on, Punkie."

Margie was aware that Elmer was standing in front of the truck with his hands in the bib of his overalls listening to the conversation. Damn him! *He was waiting to see if she was going to flirt with Mr. Hoyt.*

She tried hard to keep a lid on her temper and debated whether or not to introduce them. She decided that not to do so would be rude.

She gestured toward the silent man. "Mr. Hoyt, this is my father, Elmer Kinnard." Whether she liked it or not, he was her father. She couldn't change that, although she was beginning to hate saying the word.

Elmer met the extended hand. "Howdy."

"And his niece, Anna Marie Hoyt." Margie was determined not to let Elmer ignore the child.

He answered Anna Marie's "Hello" with another "Howdy."

Brady debated about trying to make conversation. When he spoke to the man earlier, he received only a grunt in reply. But what the hell—

"Did the fellow get his radiator fixed?"

"Naw. One of us will have to tow him to Claremore tomorrow."

"I've had some experience with radiators. I'll be glad to take a look at it."

Elmer shrugged.

"I can tell him right off if it's fixable or if he'll have to have a new radiator. I've got a flashlight in my car."

"Anna Marie," Margie said, "would you like to stay with me while your uncle works on the car? We'll walk down and talk to Mrs. Putman." Margie sent a defiant glance in Elmer's direction. "Just this morning she was telling me how much she liked little girls."

"Can I, Uncle Brady?"

"Sure. The lady invited you. Don't throw the ball again. We might not be able to find it in the dark."

"I won't." The child's little hand burrowed into Margie's. "I like you."

"I'm glad, because I like you too."

Brady walked toward his car wondering why he was feeling so elated to discover that the sullen man was the girl's father and not her husband. He had felt the tension between the two. She never looked at him, and he never looked at her. Could it be that he was not her father and they were pretending to be father and daughter for appearance' sake?

Brady was twenty-nine years old and had never even considered the idea of marrying. When the need for sex was on him, there were a couple of women he knew who were glad to oblige him. They were not exactly whores, and he paid them in different ways. A cord of stovewood, a young, dressed-out deer, a couple of fat geese.

One of the women and her husband had been his good friends for a long time. After her husband had been killed, she had a hard time making ends meet. He knew that she would marry him at the drop of a hat, so he was careful not to let the hat drop.

The other woman . . . well, he guessed she was a good friend too. He had been surprised when she asked him to come to bed with her. She was lonely, and they had simply shared mutual pleasure.

His father had grieved himself to death over the loss of their mother. *Then Brian. O Lord! Brian.* Brady choked up when he thought of his twin. His smart, easygoing brother hadn't been able to endure the loss of his Becky to another man and had died a murderer. Knowing of his father's grief and his brother's despair, Brady swore that he would never love a woman like that. He would not allow one to get so embedded in his heart and mind that he couldn't live without her.

He clenched his teeth. There was still the problem of his spontaneous reaction to Margie Kinnard. He didn't understand the sudden urge to reach for her, hold her, cover her mouth with his, take comfort from her and give comfort in return. Sex had always been something that was important, pleasant, but not all-consuming.

Holy hell. Had grief over his twin and the added responsibility of his twin's five-year-old daughter caused him to lose his reasoning? One thing was sure: He couldn't get involved with a woman until he had Anna Marie settled. A friendly neighbor had cared for her until Brady was ready to take her. Now, two days into the journey west, Brady, unfamiliar with the needs of a little girl, was awkwardly trying to manage.

Holding hands, Margie and Anna Marie walked toward the Putman camp. A blazing campfire lit the area. Grace sat on a chair beside the truck, and nearby, sitting cross-legged on the grass, were Rusty and the Luker kids. Rusty had just finished telling them something that had made Jody and his sister laugh.

"My, my, who do we have here?" A smiling Grace held out her hand to the little girl.

"This is Anna Marie Hoyt. Her uncle is taking her to California. Anna Marie, Mrs. Putman." Margie gently urged the little girl forward.

"I'm Grace, honey. Mercy me, you're just as pretty as a buttercup."

"I'm not a flower," Anna Marie said, and timidly moved closer to the older woman.

"Course you're not. But you're pretty as one. Come sit on my knee. It's been a long time since I've held a little girl." Grace reached out and pulled the child up onto her lap.

"I don't think I look pretty. Uncle Brady isn't very good at braiding my hair."

"Humm . . ." Grace fingered the braids. "He did pretty good for a man with big old clumsy hands."

"But it's all . . . straggly—"

"A little maybe. You need some pretty ribbon to go on the ends is all. I may have a piece or two in my sewing basket." Grace set the child on her feet and got out of the chair. "Let's go see, shall we?"

Margie wandered over to where Jody was adding more wood to the campfire. His sister was sitting beside Rusty.

"Hello, Rusty."

"Margie. I thought that was you. Do you know Mona?"

"I've met her. Hello, Mona."

"Hello."

Margie got her first good look at the girl's face. Mona had dark brown hair that reached her shoulders, large, expressive eyes and a wide, unsmiling mouth. She would be quite pretty without the sour look on her face. And she was older than Margie had at first believed. She was built solidly, not fat as her stepmother had described. The blouse she wore showed well-developed girlish breasts.

"Did you get to talk to Andy Payne?" Rusty asked.

"Just briefly. I didn't know he was the famous runner until Jody came by and told me. How did you find out?"

"I knew who he was as soon as he said his name. I heard on the radio about the Bunion Derby, the race across the United States. I knew he was from near here. He put Foyil, Oklahoma, on the map."

"Heck of a nice fellow." Jody sat down beside his sister. "He said that he has known Mr. Hoyt for a long time. He'da stayed at his house, but one of Mr. Payne's kids has whooping cough, and Mr. Hoyt wasn't sure if his niece had had it."

"Mr. Hoyt is working on your car." Margie volunteered the information. "He seems to know something about radiators."

"That ought to please *Mrs. Luker*."

"Mona, don't start that!" Jody scolded.

"Well, it's true. When we drove in, she was looking him and Mr. Payne over like a starving dog looks at a meat wagon. She tried her best to get Mr. Payne to stay for supper. Daddy is so . . . dumb. She's got him twisted around her little finger so tight that he can't see anything but her."

"Sugar isn't at all nice to Mona when Daddy isn't around." Jody tried to explain his sister's dislike of their father's wife. "When he is, she's sweet as pie."

"My granny used to say that you can tell a lot about a person by the way they treat other people." Margie spoke in the silence that followed Jody's words.

Mona's head turned toward Margie. "She isn't going to like you."

Margie tossed her head. "Why would she dislike me? I've hardly spoken to her."

"She doesn't like any woman unless she is old or so ugly that a dog wouldn't take a bone from her hand."

"Thanks for the compliment . . . I think."

"Someone will have to tell me about this Jezebel." Rusty laughed lightly. "I only know what my mother told me, and I think her version of Mrs. Luker was slightly colored."

Neither Mona nor her brother said anything.

"I guess it's up to me." Margie pulled her knees up under

her full skirt and wrapped her arms around them. "She's pretty in a flashy sort of way: black hair, white skin. She has an air of helplessness, which appeals to some men. She's ill-mannered, or she'd not have spoken about Mona as she did to me, a total stranger. I think that she's a woman who demands attention, and not from other women.

"My father married a woman like her who flattered him until she got all she could from him, then she ran off and left him for greener pastures."

"That's about the same picture Ma painted for me." Rusty was smiling, and Margie was sure that he was enjoying the gossipy conversation.

"I forgot to say that she's a little older than I am," Margie said.

"A lot older than you," Mona said, and glanced at her brother. "She's thirty and claims to be twenty-five. That's not all. Daddy's her third or fourth husband."

"How do you know that?" Jody asked.

"I snooped in her things and found out."

"Holy smoke, sis! Don't do it again. As sure as God made little green apples, she'll tell Pa, and it'll give him all the more reason to think we're mean to her when he isn't around. It's what she wants."

"He thinks that anyway. She can make him think a cowpie is pudding once she gets him in that tent and—"

"Mona!" Jody said sharply.

Anna Marie came to where Margie was sitting and held up the ends of her long braids. "Look. Look at the ribbons Aunt Grace gave me."

"Pretty. The blue matches your dress."

"Aunt Grace said for me to untie them myself, 'cause Uncle Brady might lose them."

"He may not know how important ribbons are to little girls."

"Can I sit on your lap so I won't get my dress dirty? Uncle Brady said we can't get our clothes washed for a while."

"Sure. This old skirt washes easily." Margie straightened her legs and pulled the child down to sit between her knees.

"Rusty, have you forgotten you promised to play your guitar for us?" Jody asked.

"No, I'll get it." Rusty started to rise.

"Sit still, son. I'm already up," his mother said.

Grace brought the guitar, and while Rusty was strumming it, she pulled her chair closer to the group sitting on the ground. He picked out a tune, played for a while, and then Grace began to sing.

> *"Come to the church in the wildwood,*
> *Oh, come to the church in the dale . . ."*

She had a beautiful soprano voice and clearly loved to sing. When the song ended, Rusty played a few notes of "I Dream of Jeannie with the Light Brown Hair." Grace's voice was hauntingly beautiful in the stillness of the night.

When she finished, Rusty sang in a low, husky voice so full of feeling that it almost brought tears to Margie's eyes.

> *"Oh, I'm thinking tonight of my blue eyes,*
> *Who is sailing far over the seas.*
> *I'm thinking tonight of my blue eyes,*
> *And I wonder if she ever thinks of me."*

Grace and her son took turns singing. Margie couldn't remember when she'd had a more enjoyable evening. Anna Marie had long ago fallen to sleep. Margie shifted her to a more comfortable position with the child's head on her breast and absently stroked her hair as she listened to Rusty sing a sad song about a dying cowboy.

> *"Oh, bury me not on the lone prair-ie,*
> *Where the wild coy-otes will howl o'er me.*
> *In a narrow grave . . . just six by three,*
> *Oh, bury me not on the lone prair-ie."*

Margie held her breath. Rusty's voice seemed to have the power to mesmerize her. She was so lost in the song that until it was over she was unaware that someone had squatted close behind her. Instinctively she knew who it was. Brady Hoyt was close enough for her to feel his body heat and to smell his warm male scent. She felt his eyes on the back of her neck and unconsciously straightened her shoulders.

Alvin, standing behind his wife's chair, joined his son in harmony-singing "Down in the Valley." It was obvious that Rusty had inherited his musical talent from his parents. The love between Grace, Alvin and their son was so poignant it almost brought tears to Margie's eyes.

The song ended, and Rusty said, "Someone else take a turn. Tell me the tune, and I'll see if I know it." Silence. "How about you, Margie?"

"Not me. I can't carry a tune in a bucket."

"I bet that's not true," Brady murmured, his mouth close to her ear.

"But I heard," Margie added quickly, "that Mr. Hoyt sings . . . quite well."

"Really? That's good news. I don't want to hog the whole evening. What'll it be, Mr. Hoyt?"

"Name's Brady, and I don't know where Margie got that harebrained idea. I sing out only when I've mashed my finger or dropped something on my toe."

"Mona sings," Jody said.

"I do not! You just hush up, Jody." Mona stood. "I've got to go."

"Don't go, Mona," Rusty said quickly, reaching up his hand to stop her. "You don't have to sing."

"Why don't we *all* sing something? Play 'Home on the Range,' son," Grace said. "Everyone knows that."

It was Alvin who started singing the lyrics in a beautiful booming voice. "Oh, give me a home where the buffalo roam, where the deer and the antelope play . . ."

Margie was too aware of the man behind her to sing. Then, near her ear, she heard him singing softly in a surprisingly good voice. When the song ended, it was Jody who spoke.

"Mona and I had better get back, or Pa will be after us."

"Are you kiddin'?" Mona snorted. "You couldn't get him out of that tent with a team of mules if both of us were drowning in the river."

"I hope we meet up with you folks after Pa gets the radiator fixed," Jody said, ignoring his sister's comment.

"It's fixed," Alvin said. "Brady plugged up the hole with a wad of tinfoil."

Margie felt Brady get to his feet. "I don't know how long it will last," he said.

"You mean we can go with you in the morning?" Jody asked.

"That's the plan," Alvin said.

"Hot dog! I wish you were coming along with us, Mr. Hoyt." Jody was obviously pleased. "Pa knows the ice business, but he doesn't know beans about a motorcar."

"Anna Marie and I will mosey along behind you for a day or two."

"Well, now, ain't that nice to hear?" Grace exclaimed. "I'll tell ya what, Mr. Hoyt. You and that little darlin' are welcome to breakfast with us in the mornin'."

"Thank you, ma'am. I accept on behalf of myself and Anna Marie."

"It'll be a comfort having you along. And I'm a-warnin' you. I'm going to be havin' me some time with that little darlin'."

Brady squatted down in front of Margie and lifted the sleeping child up into his arms. She nestled her head contentedly on her uncle's shoulder. He stood and reached down to help Margie. She ignored his hand, rolled over onto her knees and got to her feet. She looked up to see that he was waiting for her to look at him.

"Thanks for looking after Punkie. She gets pretty tired of my company."

She nodded. "Good night, all."

Margie headed for the truck. Jody and Mona were just ahead of her talking in low tones. She was surprised when Brady appeared beside her, Anna Marie nestled on his shoulder.

"I'll walk you to your camp. It's the least I can do."

"It isn't necessary."

"I know that. I want to." After a brief silence he said,

"Mr. Luker and Mr. Putman asked me to trail along with you folks."

"You said that."

"Anna Marie needs a woman to do things for her that I can't do. I didn't realize that when we started out on this trip."

"Is that why you're going to travel with us?"

"I admit that it is. I worry about what I'd do if she got sick, or who would take care of her if something happened to me. She likes you and Mrs. Putman."

"How long have you been on the road?"

"This is our second day. I wanted to stop over here and see my friend Andy Payne."

"The Mr. Payne who gave us the fish?"

"Yeah. He'd rather fish than eat. I appreciate the attention you and Mrs. Putman gave Anna Marie tonight."

"Like tying ribbons on her braids?"

He chuckled. "She's a fussy little punkin. Wants to look pretty. Did you want to look pretty when you were a little girl?"

"It's been so long since I was a little girl, I've forgotten. Anna Marie is smart and sweet. It's a shame she lost her mother."

"Yeah? It's more of a shame she lost her father."

They neared the truck, and he turned toward his camp. "Good night, Margie."

"Goodnight, Mr. Hoyt."

Margie climbed into the truck, unrolled her pallet, undressed and lay down, but it was a long time before she went to sleep.

Chapter 5

Alvin came to the camp as Margie was pouring water on the breakfast fire. He had what appeared to be a map in his hand.

"Mornin'. It looks like it'll be a fine day."

"Yes, it does."

He then went to the side of the truck where Elmer was putting away his tools.

"I figure that if we get on down through Tulsa to Sapulpa, it'll be a long enough day. What do you think?"

"Fine with me, but what about Foley?"

"If his radiator lasts until Tulsa, he can get it fixed there."

"How long would we have to wait for him?"

"As long as it takes. The agreement we made when we started was that we'd stay together. He'd have to wait for one of us if something went wrong. There are four of us now. I'm glad we ran into Hoyt. It would take a brave or a foolish bunch to mess with us now."

"I don't know. Something about that fellow rubs me the wrong way," Elmer said.

On the other side of the truck, Margie became alert at the mention of Brady Hoyt's name. She had been looking off toward the Putman camp watching Rusty shave and wondering how in the world he could use a straight-edge razor without being able to see.

"What do you mean?" Alvin asked.

"He came out of nowhere. We don't know him."

"I'd met you only a few times when we decided to hook up and make this trip together."

"That's different. I knew about you for several years. Being in the ice business, you'd probably heard about me."

"Why didn't you say you were leery of Hoyt last night? The three of us discussed it and agreed to ask him to join us."

"Don't you think it's strange that a man would travel with a female kid that ain't his? It don't appear to me to be somethin' a feller on the up-and-up would do. He could be a-kidnapping that kid."

"Tarnation, Elmer. Andy Payne said he'd known Hoyt for years. Knew his family."

"Another thing. How do we know that fellow was Andy Payne? 'Cause he said so?"

"Why would he lie?" Alvin stepped back and looked at Elmer like he'd not seen him before. "He didn't come right out and say he was Andy Payne, the man who won the Bunion Derby. Rusty recognized the name and asked him if he was the racer. He and Rusty talked about stuff that only the real Andy Payne would know."

Elmer ignored Alvin's logic. His stubbornness began to irritate Alvin.

"Times are hard all over, Alvin. I don't need to tell you

that. Boxcars are full of hoboes riding the rails looking for work. There's fellers out there that'd cut your throat for a dollar."

"I know that, Elmer. I'm glad to have another man with us," Alvin insisted. "I hope Hoyt stays with us all the way to California."

"If the kid gets sick, it'll slow us down."

"If that happens, we'll handle it when the time comes A bank here in Oklahoma is robbed almost every day," Alvin argued. "Bootleggers are running up and down the highway day and night, hijacking cars and trucks. Alone in a campground, we would be sitting ducks. Our trucks, with their heavy springs for hauling ice, would be perfect for hauling booze."

"You don't think the three of us and the Luker boy could hold off a bunch of cowardly bootleggers?"

"I wouldn't call them cowardly. I'd call them dangerous crooks. We've got to keep together for the sake of our families."

"How many more are you going to want to take in?"

"Christ, Elmer! Don't put this on me. You could have had your say last night." Alvin folded the map and put it in his pocket. "We should stop and noon before we get to Tulsa. Do you want to take the lead?"

"No. You're doing fine. I'll look for you along the way."

"If something happens that we get separated, the next campground is west of Sapulpa after we cross the Rock Creek. The bridge has a brick deck. Turn off at the next road on your left. There's a place where we can camp, or so the man who drew me the map said. He didn't swear to it." Plainly irritated with Elmer, Alvin went on to speak to the Lukers.

Margie filled her fruit jar with water and got into the truck. Not a word had passed between her and her father since the afternoon before when he called her mother a whore. This morning he appeared when breakfast was ready, picked up his coffee mug, his plate of raw-fried potatoes and the last of the white bread she had toasted on the grill, and went to sit in his usual place on the running board of the truck.

Margie had been frying the potatoes when she saw Brady and Anna Marie going to the Putman camp. A few minutes later Grace and Anna Marie had gone to the woods. How much easier it would have been for Brady, Margie thought, if Anna Marie had been a little boy. It must be difficult for a five-year-old girl just to tell her uncle she needed to go to the outhouse or the woods.

Later Margie had heard talk and laughter coming from the Putmans' camp, and she envied the family's closeness. To go to California had been her dream; but the first attempt had ended in disaster, and now this second attempt to get there was total misery—not the hardship of the trip, but being with a father who hated her and hated having her along.

Now, as they followed the Putmans out of the campground, Brady was tossing a ball to Anna Marie. They were waiting to follow the Lukers, who were packing up to leave. They're always lagging behind, Margie thought, and wondered how long it would take Brady Hoyt to get tired of waiting for them.

By midmorning, after weaving slowly through the construction workers on the highway, they drove into

Claremore, the home of the famed cowboy actor Will
Rogers. Margie was well aware that he didn't live here
but in California, where he made movies. She would like
to see the big house where he was born and spent his
childhood, she thought wistfully, but she doubted that
she'd get the chance.

Elmer stopped at a gas station. After filling the gas
tank, the attendant brought out a rubber hose and filled
the water keg in the back of the truck. After he had paid
the attendant, Elmer drove to a grocery store. He didn't
say a word to Margie when he left to go inside. He returned with a paper sack, put it in the back of the truck
and continued down the street to an ice dock.

Margie had debated about letting him know that they
were out of ice, but she decided not to break her silence
until he did. He took a pair of ice tongs from the long box
attached to the side of the truck where he kept his tools
and disappeared inside the icehouse. Margie got out of
the truck, let down the tailgate and put down the box they
used for a step. She got back into the truck telling herself
she had done that to keep him from setting the block of
ice on the ground and getting it dirty.

On the way out of town they passed two motor inns
and a souvenir shop with a sign proclaiming it an Indian
trading post. Margie remembered that when she passed
through Claremore the year before with Ernie Harding, a
man at a gas station told her that Claremore had been a
busy Indian trading center back in the olden days and had
been named for an Osage chief. He said that Will
Rogers's home was between Claremore and Oologah, but
that Will claimed Claremore as his home because nobody
but an Indian could pronounce "Oologah."

She smiled thinking about it and remembered that Will Rogers had said that he had never met a man he didn't like. He must be a terribly nice man because she had met plenty of men she didn't like. Ernie Harding, the man who had stolen her money, for one. And, in spite of the guilty feeling about it, her father was another.

A few miles out of Claremore they stopped behind the Putmans, who had pulled off the highway and onto a space on the inside of a curve. It was flat and grassy with timber to one side. Elmer took off immediately for the patch of brush and scrub oak.

Margie had laid out the cold fish and corn bread on the tailgate when the Lukers arrived, and behind them Brady's black sedan.

"Margie! Margie!" Anna Marie called as she ran toward her. Then when she reached her: "Go to the woods with me . . . please. I gotta go . . . bad."

"Sure, honey." Margie flipped a cloth over the food on the tailgate to protect it from flies and took the child's hand. The two of them ran for the small patch of woods. They didn't speak until Anna Marie had hiked up her dress and Margie had unbuttoned the back flap of her drawers.

The child looked up at Margie with tear-filled eyes. "I had to go so bad—"

"Your uncle would have stopped."

"I didn't want to tell him. I miss Granny Maude."

"I bet she misses you too."

"Daddy took me to Granny Maude when . . . he had to work." Anna Marie choked back a sob. "I . . . don't have any . . . paper."

"I have some right here in my pocket. Do you want me to help you?"

"Yes, ma'am." More sobs. "I'm . . . nasty . . ."

Margie knelt down. "You're just a little nasty, honey. When we get back to the truck, we'll get inside and I'll wash you with a wet cloth." She wiped the tears from Anna Marie's face with the edge of her skirt.

Brady was waiting by the truck. "I was worried when you took off like that, Punkie." His eyes flicked to Margie, then back to his niece. He knelt down, studied her face, and saw evidence of tears. "Are you all right?"

"Uh-huh."

He stood and took her hand. "Mrs. Putman has a treat for you."

"I can't go . . . yet." The child looked pleadingly at Margie.

"I've something to show her in the truck. I'll bring her over in a few minutes." Margie held Brady's eyes with hers before taking Anna Marie's hand. "Come on, honey." She climbed into the truck and turned to help Anna Marie get in. Brady was there and lifted the child up. Their eyes caught again and held, then he nodded and walked away.

Anna Marie was in a much better mood when she and Margie walked over to where the Putmans were parked. Grace came to meet them with a big smile of welcome.

"There's my pretty girl." She grabbed Anna Marie and gave her a hug, then said, "Hello, Margie. How are you standing the trip so far?"

"So far, all right."

"I'm enjoying every bit of it. I always did like to see

new things. I chatter about everything to Rusty. We're about to drive Alvin wild. When he gets tired of us, he sings and drowns us out," she said with a giggle.

Lucky you, Margie thought, then said, "See you tonight, Grace."

Margie was aware that Brady was squatted on the ground beside Rusty, and Blackie lay sprawled on his belly close by. Margie could feel Brady's eyes on her. She had taken less than a dozen steps back toward the truck when he appeared beside her.

"Margie, wait a minute. What was that all about?"

"She had to go to the outhouse," Margie said without looking at him.

"Good Lord. I thought she was hurting someplace."

"She was."

"Why didn't she tell me? I would have found a place to stop."

"She was embarrassed. She . . . had a little accident."

"Good Lord. Poor kid. I don't know much about taking care of kids—never been around 'em, especially little girls."

"You'd better learn fast. It's a long way to California."

Elmer appeared from around the back of the truck and stood quietly watching them.

"Thanks, Margie." Brady tipped his hat and turned back toward the Putmans.

When they pulled onto the road again, Anna Marie was sitting between Alvin and Grace, and Rusty was riding with Brady.

*   *   *

"Did you see that?" Sugar Luker, waiting in the car for Jody and Foley to tie the tarp down over their two-wheel trailer, spoke over her shoulder to Mona when the Putmans passed. "The little girl is riding with the Putmans. Well, well. It looks like the blind dolt is going to ride with Brady."

"Don't call him that!" Mona said sharply.

"I'll call him whatever I want, Miss Ugly Muffin, and you'd better not talk to me in that tone of voice if you know what's good for you."

"Yeah, I suppose you'll tattle to Daddy."

"Now what's goin' on?" Foley slid in under the wheel, and Sugar moved to the middle of the seat to sit close to him.

"Nothin' important, darlin'. I was just remarking that the little girl is riding with the Putmans and their son is riding with Mr. Hoyt. Mona is having one of her grouchy spells. If you say one little thing to her, she blows up."

"She called Rusty a dolt. I told her not to call him that just because he's blind."

"I said colt." Sugar moved her hand up on the inside of her husband's thigh.

"You did not! You said dolt. You know you did. You're just trying to make me out a liar." Mona shook off her brother's warning hand.

"That's enough, Mona," Foley said sharply. He started the car and pulled out onto the highway. "I'm glad Brady knew about plugging holes in radiators. I hope it holds. I don't want to have to put in a new one."

"Did he say what he's going to do when he gets to California?" Sugar asked.

"Turn around and come back as far as Colorado. He's got some ranchland out there."

"Then what's he doing here?"

"He came to take his brother's little girl to her aunt somewhere in California."

"Couldn't he afford to take the train?"

"I didn't ask him. We're going to have to break camp earlier in the morning from now on. And pack up faster." Foley looked in the mirror on the side of the car to see what was behind him. "If Hoyt is going to follow us, he isn't going to want to wait for us every morning."

"Tell that to Jody and Mona. Before we started I told you that I'd never camped out in my life and didn't know the first thing about cooking over a campfire. I wanted to go on the train. Remember?" she said with a pout in her voice.

"I know that. The train costs more. We've got to have enough money to start a business in California. This is the cheapest way for us to get there."

"You're right. You always are, darlin'." She squeezed his thigh. "I'll do the best I can."

"That's all I ask, honey."

"We should offer to let Brady's niece ride with us part of the time. Jody could ride with Brady."

"She'd ride with him if given half a chance," Mona mouthed to her brother.

"Mona would give her eyeteeth to ride with him," Sugar said to Foley in a low, confidential tone. "But, darling, we must be careful with our young lady. I think he's a little too old and too experienced for her. A footloose man will take advantage of a *green* girl if he gets a chance."

"I think you're jumping the gun, but if it will make you any happier, I'll keep an eye on her."

In the backseat Mona clenched her hands into fists. Her face was set in hard, angry lines. She rolled angry eyes toward her brother. He shook his head, silently asking her not to let Sugar goad her into another set-to that would just upset their father.

When Foley pulled over and stopped to check the radiator, Brady pulled in behind them. Foley had already lifted the hood by the time Brady got out. The stop also gave Blackie a chance to get out and sniff around.

"Lost any water?" Brady asked.

"Not a drop," Foley said, grinning.

"Then it looks like it'll hold. Save your tinfoil, though, just in case."

With the hood up so that the men couldn't see inside the car, Sugar turned and thumbed her nose at Mona.

"You're a bitch!" Mona said softly.

"Yes, I am," Sugar agreed with a wide, pleased smile. "And it's a hell of a lot of fun!"

Brady was enjoying Rusty's company. The miles flew by while they discussed everything from music to politics. Rusty was well informed.

"I'm not sure Roosevelt's New Deal is going to get the country back on its feet. I think what will do it will be the jobs created by making war supplies for England and France. That Hitler fellow has got absolute power in Germany now. He says he's going to purify Germany both ethnically and politically. What that means, I think, is that he wants to get rid of everyone who isn't a German. I'd bet my bottom dollar that he's gettin' ready to start a shootin' war."

"I've been kind of out of touch with what's going on for several months now," Brady admitted.

"I listened to all the news broadcasts when we were home. I'm missing it on this trip."

"Have you thought of getting a battery-powered radio?"

"They're big, bulky and expensive. I told Pa not to bother. I'll catch up when we get to where we're going."

"And where is that?"

"A town just south of Bakersfield. Pa, Mr. Kinnard and Foley Luker plan to start up an ice business. Out there ice sells year-round. In Missouri there's a lull during the winter months. Folks don't use much ice when it freezes every night."

"How long has Alvin known Mr. Kinnard?"

"He doesn't really know him. They met because they were in the same business and hitched up this plan with Foley Luker. Foley wasn't married then."

"He's hooked now." Brady followed his remark with a snorting sound.

"Ma gave me her version of his new wife." Rusty chuckled. "My mother can be a bit catty at times. She's got definite opinions on some things. I don't think she was far off the mark about Mrs. Luker. I asked Margie, and she said almost the same, only in a softer way."

"Luker seems to be a pretty levelheaded guy except where she's concerned. A woman who'd flirt with another man behind her husband's back isn't worth shootin', to my way of thinkin'."

"She flirt with you, did she?"

Brady nodded, then realized Rusty couldn't see him. "Yeah," he said. "And with Andy Payne too. Andy said that she reminded him of a black widow spider. She scared the crap out of him. He couldn't get away from her fast enough."

"She's sure to give Mr. Luker trouble." Rusty reached back to scratch Blackie, who was lying on a crate behind the front seat. "He doesn't know it now, or maybe he doesn't care, but he'll lose his kids over her if he doesn't change his ways soon. Neither one of them will put up with her much longer."

"Mona is a pretty girl."

"Is she?"

Brady glanced over and saw the interest on Rusty's face. "Yeah. Pretty brown hair that hangs a little down on her shoulders. Big brown eyes. Curves in all the right places. Sixteen or seventeen, I'd guess. If I was ten years younger, I'd set my cap for her." He continued to glance at Rusty and caught his smile.

"How old are you, Brady? Do you mind my asking?"

"Naw, I don't mind. I'm twenty-nine."

"I'm twenty-two. I've been blind for twelve years."

"You've not let it stop you."

"It's stopped me on this trip. At home I knew my way around. I could go to town, to the barbershop, the post office and the grocery store. When we settle, it'll take me a while to learn my way around again, but I can do it."

"Alvin told me that you write songs. I'd like to hear some of them sometime. I listen to *Grand Ole Opry* from Nashville every chance I get, but I've never met a song-writer."

"You just haven't been in the right places. Before we

get to California you'll be wanting to slam my guitar against a tree trunk." Rusty chuckled. "My folks think I can get a job singing on the radio. You know the old saying, a mother's love is blind? Well, in this case it's also deaf."

Brady laughed. He was surprised at how easy it was to visit with a blind person. He found himself describing things he had barely noticed before.

"We're crossing the Arkansas. I'm surprised they don't have a toll on this bridge. The river is wide at this point, but there's not much water down there."

Later he said, "Almost every other building is empty in these little towns we've been going through. There's a dirt road a little way over from the highway. I'm seeing several wagons. We just passed one piled high with household furniture and with a cow tied on behind. The folks must be moving on. I wonder how they got across the river. Maybe they came down from the north.

"I was damn lucky." Brady maneuvered the car around a stripped-down Model T that was barely moving. "I worked over near Rainwater and Ponca City when the oil first came in. They were paying good wages, and I saved enough to get a little start or I'd be riding the rails looking for a job."

"Pa said you're a rancher."

"Yeah. Me and another fellow have a little ranch in Colorado. My partner is Cherokee. There isn't anything about a horse, wild or tame, that he doesn't know about. He graduated from the Cherokee Seminary down at Tahlequah and is smart enough to do anything he sets his mind to. But all he wants to do is raise horses, which is fine with me. I met him through his sister and her husband while I was in Rainwater. Radna and Randolph Bluefeather are an unforgettable pair. Sometime I'll tell you about them—that is, if you're not already tired of hearing my voice. I don't know when I've talked this much."

"I appreciate every word. You paint a good picture. I've been able to see in my mind what you've been telling me."

"It looks like this is where we'll stop for the night." Brady followed the Lukers off the highway. "I bought a hunk of meat back there at the store. Do you reckon your mother would make us a stew?"

Chapter 6

THE SUN WAS DROPPING BEHIND the western horizon when Elmer followed Alvin into the camping area west of Sapulpa. A rattletrap car, the two front doors missing, was already there, and three men were sitting or squatting on the grass nearby. Alvin drove to the far side of the area before stopping, leaving room for Elmer, Foley and Brady to pull in behind him.

Elmer stopped a good fifty feet behind Alvin, got out and stood watching Alvin motion for him to move closer. When he made no move to get back into the truck, Alvin came to speak to him.

"I think we should be closer tonight, Elmer. There's three men over there, and it looks to me like they're boozin' it up."

"They're not camping. They'll move on out pretty soon."

On hearing Elmer's curt words, Alvin opened his mouth, closed it, glanced at the three men on the other side of the campground, then spoke with exaggerated calm.

"Well, I just thought I'd mention it."

Margie got out of the truck. Elmer Kinnard was stubborn as a mule! Frustration rolled through her. During the hours she had been cooped up in the truck with him he had not said one word. She had made up her mind during the afternoon that she would endure whatever she had to endure because every day brought her closer to California.

But how long would Alvin put up with Elmer being so obstinate? Her fear was that the others would cut them loose and leave her alone with him. Oh, Lord! What would she do?

She would sacrifice her pride and beg Brady Hoyt to take her with him and Anna Marie, if it came to that.

Margie had tried to look at one of her movie magazines during the afternoon, but the jolting in the truck gave her a headache, and she had to lay it aside and sit silently watching the landscape go by. It had been a long, cheerless afternoon, and she was glad it was time to stop for the night.

Desperately needing a little conversation, and caring not a whit if Elmer liked it or not, Margie headed for the Putman truck to speak to Grace and Anna Marie.

"Margie, guess what?" Anna Marie, clinging tightly to Grace's hand, called as she approached.

"What? Tell me quick." Margie hadn't spoken a word since noon, and her voice seemed rough to her when she answered the child.

"Aunt Grace is teaching me the ABC song."

"Forevermore! I'll have to hear it," Margie exclaimed. "Your uncle will be surprised."

"We were just talking about that, wasn't we, Annie?"

Grace cupped the child's head and held it to her side. "When I told her that our son's name was Russell Allen, but we call him Rusty, she decided that she'd like to be called Annie."

"Oh, but Anna Marie is such a pretty name."

"You can still call me Anna Marie, Margie."

"I think I will, if you don't mind."

"I don't mind. I like to ride with Aunt Grace. Can I ride with you sometime?"

Margie didn't know what to say. She was afraid of what Elmer's reaction would be if she invited the child to ride with them. Anna Marie wouldn't understand his refusal to talk to her.

The Lukers came in and parked close behind Elmer's truck, and Brady's car moved around to close the space between Elmer's truck and the Putmans'. Brady was taking a bundle off the top carrier on his Model A Ford when Anna Marie broke loose and ran to him.

"Uncle Brady! Want to hear me sing the ABC song?"

"Sure! Punkie, let her rip."

"A B C D E F G, H I J—that's all I know. Aunt Grace said I learned fast. Mr. Putman sang with me."

"He did, huh?"

"He knows lots of songs. He knows one about old MacDonald. And he knows how to go hee-haw, hee-haw. Maybe he'll show you."

"I've always wanted to know how to go hee-haw." Brady smiled down at the child. At times she reminded him so much of his lighthearted brother that his heart would stumble and almost stop.

"I'm goin' to play with Blackie."

"Stay close, Punkie."

"I will." Anna Marie ran toward the Putman camp, and Brady wondered how he had ever thought he could make the trip alone with a five-year-old girl. He thanked God for the kindness of Mrs. Putman and for Margie. He wanted to talk to her and waited until he saw Elmer walk off toward the woods.

Brady went to the back of Elmer's truck. Margie was inside kneeling beside the cupboard. "Margie—" It startled her when he spoke her name. She rose to step from the truck. Brady reached in and grasped her around the waist. Before she could protest, he had lifted her down as easily as if she were no heavier than Anna Marie.

"Oh, my! I'm too big for that!"

"Big? I doubt you weigh much over a hundred pounds dripping wet."

"I do. About ten or fifteen pounds over."

"That still isn't very big." He stood there looking down at her with his remarkable green eyes squinted. "I'm leery of that group parked over there." He jerked his head toward the parked car and the men lounging on the grass beside it.

"Is that why you're wearing a gun?"

"It's best to be prepared," he said by way of an answer.

"Mr. Putman said as much."

"If they're going to pull something, they'll wait until dark."

"What could we do if they did? There's three of them."

"There are five of us counting Jody."

"Six counting me."

He grinned. "Does Elmer have a gun?"

"I don't know, but I do. It's just a little one, but I know how to shoot it."

"But would you?"

"Doggone right," she said staunchly. "A friend gave it to me before I left home. He took me out into the woods and showed me how to use it." She smiled into his eyes. "I confess that I can't shoot the eye out of a running jackrabbit, but I did hit a barn door a few feet away."

The twinkle in his eyes caused a blush to redden her face. "Will it fit in your pocket?"

"In my apron pocket." She glanced toward the Lukers' trailer, which Jody and Mona were unloading. "Do you think there'll be trouble?"

"I don't know. But it's best to look for it and be pleasantly surprised when you don't find it."

"Are you and Anna Marie eating with the Putmans?"

"We've struck a deal. I'll help furnish the grub, and Mrs. Putman will cook it." Brady looked past Margie to see Elmer at the front of the truck watching them. He spoke to him. "I was just telling your daughter that we'd better keep an eye on that bunch over there by the other car. Do you have a gun?"

"My squirrel rifle."

"Sometimes just a show of strength will cause a bunch bent on robbery to back off."

"What makes ya think they're goin' to rob us? They don't look dangerous to me."

"They may be just good old boys out boozin' it up. But I don't plan to be caught with my pants down if they've got something else in mind." Brady turned, then said, "See you, Margie."

Unable to understand Elmer's reasoning, Margie

climbed back into the truck again and began to lay out the supplies for supper.

While Foley was putting up the pup tent, Jody built a cook fire. Sugar complained to Foley that the tent was too close to the trailer and car where Jody and Mona slept.

"They'll hear everything we say and . . . do," she whispered seductively. "They're with us all day. I want you all to myself at night."

"Just for tonight. Those fellows over there may spend the night here, and we shouldn't be too far away from the others."

"Whose idea is that? Alvin Putman's? He's an old fuddy-duddy, and his wife doesn't give me the time of day." Sugar knew how to use her voice. She had let it drop into a sorrowful tone.

"You might like her if you got to know her," Foley said. "Don't you think it's worth trying?"

"No, I don't. I only want you." Sugar hugged his arm and pressed her taut breasts against him.

"We have a long trip ahead of us. It will be more pleasant for all of us if we could be sociable."

"She don't like me."

"You don't know that."

"I wasn't going to tell you, darlin', but Mr. Hoyt keeps looking at me. He was stealing glances all the time he was fixing the radiator."

"I can't blame him for that, Sugar. I like to look at you too."

"But, darlin', he looks at me like . . . like he wants to see me without my clothes on."

"If he bothers you, I'll put a stop to it."

"But . . . but he scares me."

"Don't worry. I'll watch him."

"I'm glad, so glad, I've got you to take care of me." Sugar knew when to back off after she had planted her little seed of distrust, and changed the subject. "I'm trying so hard to make Mona into a young woman you'll be proud of, but every time I open my mouth she cuts me off." Sugar pouted and snuggled against Foley.

"She'll come around. By the end of this trip the two of you will be the best of friends. I'm counting on it."

"I hope so, darlin'. I really do. Jody takes her side. He spoils her. I like Jody. I really do. He's such a sweet boy."

Mona stirred the burning embers of the campfire before she placed the kettle of beans her brother had cooked the night before on the grate. She glanced with resentment at the tent where she could hear the low voice of her father and the giggles of her stepmother.

Embarrassed that her father would be such a fool over a woman so shallow and conniving, Mona sought to busy herself to keep from thinking about what was going on in the tent. She had begun to ladle the corn bread batter into the skillet when she looked up to see two men approaching. She glanced quickly over her shoulder. Jody wasn't in sight.

"Somethin' smells mighty good." The man who spoke had a pleasant, clean-shaven face. He was younger than his companion and wore a billed cap.

Mona stood with the pancake turner in her hand. Jody came from around the trailer and placed the bowls he carried on a box near the fire.

"What do you want?" he demanded.

"We were wonderin' if ya could spare a meal? We ain't et all day, and what you got there looks and smells larrupin.' " The man eyed Mona in such a way that his words had a double meaning.

Jody's eyes went from one man to the other and didn't like what he saw. Somehow the smile on the younger man's face struck him as being as false as a three-dollar bill.

"Pa," he called. When there was no answer, he called again, urgently. "Pa, come out here."

A full minute went by before his father came out of the tent, followed closely by Sugar. On seeing the men she tossed her hair back over her shoulders, pulled her shirt tightly down over her breasts and tucked it into the waistband of her skirt.

"Howdy, folks." The young man spoke to both, but his bold eyes were on Sugar.

"Where did you come from?" she asked, as if she hadn't already spotted the three men in the car at the end of the campground.

"We're from over there." The man gestured toward the car.

Sugar flounced over and took the turner from Mona's hand. "Haven't you ever seen a man before?" she whispered irritably. "You're burning the corn bread!"

Jody gave Sugar an angry glance, then spoke to his father. "They want a meal, Pa."

"Give it to them. Mona, dish them up a plate of beans. We have plenty."

"That's mighty good of ya, mister."

"Doesn't your friend want to eat?" Sugar asked, nodding her head toward the car where the other man sat on the running board.

"No, ma'am. He's kind of under the weather."

Mona ladled beans into two bowls and stuck in spoons. It was Jody who handed them to the men. The young one hadn't taken his eyes off Sugar, and she was well aware of it.

"Here's a nice, hot corn bread pancake." Sugar scooped up the bread and took it to the younger man, who had squatted on his heels to eat. When she leaned over to put it on his bowl, he looked down at her cleavage and boldly winked at her.

"Where you folks goin'?" The older man's eyes moved constantly.

"California," Sugar answered while giving him the corn bread. "We're in the ice business. We're going to build an icehouse in California."

"That right? I've not known anyone in the ice business."

Sugar laughed. "You should have come up to Joplin. We had a big icehouse up there."

"I suppose you sold it."

"Of course. How do you think we got the money to build another one."

"Sugar—," Foley admonished, and shook his head.

Jody's anxious eyes went to his father. *The stupid woman would get them killed.*

"Where's the corn bread batter, Mona?" Sugar was enjoying the stranger's attention. "And get a bowl for your father."

Mona ladled the batter into the skillet, then retreated. Jody had filled a bowl with beans for his father. He tried

and failed to catch his eye when he took it to him. He was
sure the bulge beneath the shirt of the older of the two
men was a gun.

"Where are you fellows headed?" Foley asked.

"Here and there. Lookin' for work."

"You'll not find work sitting out here in a campground," Jody said, and nudged his sister back toward the
trailer.

"Jody," Sugar scolded, "that wasn't very nice."

The younger man stood and placed his empty bowl on
the box, then went back and sat down.

"That was a mighty good supper, ma'am. A good cup
of coffee would top it off."

"We're short of coffee," Jody said.

"Since when?" Sugar asked. "Fill the coffeepot, Jody.
I'd like a cup myself."

"If Pa don't catch on to her now, he never will," Mona
whispered to Jody when they went to the back of the
trailer where they stored the foodstuffs.

"The old one has a gun. Slip around to the other side
and go tell Brady."

Jody rummaged in the trailer for a while to give Mona
time to get past the Kinnards. He filled the pot with water
from their water barrel and set it on the rack over the fire.
He poked more sticks into the blaze and decided that he
could use one for a weapon if it came to that.

"Where's Mona?" Sugar demanded. "This is her job."

"She went to the woods." Jody filled a bowl for himself and backed away from the fire so that he could watch
both men.

"What do you know of the highway ahead?" Foley
asked.

"Sixty-six is paved to Chandler." The younger man leaned back on his elbow, leered at Sugar and spoke to Foley. "Is she your wife?"

"She is."

"Thought maybe she was your daughter. She's pretty and kind of . . . young, ain't she? I'd give a pretty penny to get me a woman like that."

"Watch your manners," Foley snarled, and got to his feet.

"Can't blame a feller for lookin' and . . . hopin'."

Jody lifted the lid on the coffeepot and poured in a scoop of coffee. When he stepped back from the fire, he was relieved to see Brady Hoyt approaching.

"Ma'am." Brady tipped his hat toward Sugar. "Howdy, Foley."

"Howdy, Brady. Coffee'll be ready in a minute."

"Thanks." Brady stood with his thumbs hooked in his belt, his hand just inches away from the butt of his gun. "Where are you fellows headed?"

"That's what ever'body wants to know these days." The older man stood and backed up a couple of steps.

"Yeah." The younger man was still leaning on his elbow, stretched out on his side on the ground. "What would ya say if we told ya we ain't goin' nowhere? We're waitin' here to rob a train. Haw, haw, haw."

Brady's cold eyes settled on the man's face. "You're going to get mighty hungry before one comes along. Move on. You'll have better luck catching a train down by the railroad tracks."

"Are ya tellin' us to leave?"

"You heard me."

The older man's eyes flicked to Sugar, who was hanging on to Foley's arm. "The pretty woman give us beans and corn bread and invited us to stay for coffee."

"Is this a social visit, Mr. Hoyt?" Sugar asked frostily.

"I guess you could say that, Mrs. Luker."

"Then I suggest that you tend to your own business. We don't have to get your permission to invite folks to have supper with us. I don't appreciate you coming into our camp and telling our guests to move on."

"I'm sorry if I offended you."

"I asked Mr. Hoyt to come down," Mona said. "This is just as much my camp as yours. I've a right to invite him to come for coffee."

Sugar, forgetting herself and the role she played, retorted angrily. "You think so? You're just a snot-nosed kid. You weren't getting any attention, so you switched your fat butt up there to get him."

The young stranger chuckled. He was enjoying the situation. His eyes darted to Foley, who had gripped his wife's arm and was frowning down at her. The older man continued to move back, one small step at a time. Jody scooped up an armload of sticks and dropped them on the fire. It blazed up, lighting the area and allowing them to see Alvin coming toward them, his shotgun in the back of the third man.

The older man made a move to grasp his own gun through his shirt.

"Don't," Brady said sharply, and drew his gun from the holster. "I've seen that trick before. Drop your hands. Get up and get over there beside him," Brady said to the younger man. "I can shoot both of you before you can reach the gun strapped to your leg."

Sugar shrieked and clung to Foley, making it impossible to depend on him for help.

"Put your hands on the top of your heads. Both of you." There was a ring of authority in Brady's voice. "Jody, get the gun under the shirt first. The bastard thought to turn sideways and shoot me through his shirt. The laughing jackass was going to lie on the ground, lift his leg and shoot. Nice dinner guests you have, Mrs. Luker."

Alvin urged the third man forward. "This one was creeping up on Kinnard's camp."

Sugar was wailing and hanging on to Foley. Brady gave her a look of disgust. When Jody handed him the gun he took from under the older man's shirt, Brady checked to see if it was loaded, then holstered his own gun.

"Come here, Jody. Take his gun and shoot 'em if they make a move. I'll get the gun off the braying jackass."

Brady walked over and swiftly kicked the man's feet out from under him. The would-be robber hit the ground. A stream of foul words came from his mouth.

"Watch your mouth. There's ladies present."

"Ladies? That hot tamale ain't no lady." He jerked his head toward Sugar. "She's a whore if I ever saw one. Give me five minutes with her, and she'd be on her back spreadin' and beggin'."

"Hush your filthy mouth!" Foley snarled.

Brady palmed the small gun he took from the holster strapped to the man's leg. "Turn over on your belly, put your hands behind you and keep them there."

"What'll we do with them?" Alvin, ignoring Foley, spoke to Brady.

"Tie 'em up. Got any rope, Jody?"

"Not much."

"I have some. Keep them covered, Alvin. I'll get it."

"Don't worry. This old scattergun would take all three of them down with just one little twitch of my finger."

As Brady passed Elmer's truck on his way to his car, Margie stepped out and confronted him. She had been standing behind the truck watching what was going on in the Luker camp.

"You were right," she said.

"They're a dumb bunch."

"What are you going to do?"

"Tie them up for the night. Before we leave in the morning we'll turn them loose or send the sheriff out for them."

"What'd they do?" Elmer's voice startled Margie. She hadn't known he was near.

"They had robbery on their minds. Alvin caught one of them sneaking up on you with a gun in his hand."

"Fiddlesticks! I've been keepin' my eyes open. I didn't see anything. They're just down-and-outers wantin' a meal."

The man was an idiot.

Brady shook his head in dismay and moved so that his body blocked Elmer from seeing him pat the pocket on Margie's apron to assure himself the pistol was there.

"I'll talk to you later. Okay?" he whispered, then squeezed her arm and moved on.

Chapter 7

W HAT WOULD THEY HAVE DONE after they robbed us?"
Jody asked.

The would-be robbers had been bound hand and foot
and each tied to a wheel of their old car.

"My guess would be that they'd have disabled the
other cars, taken mine and left with one of the women as
a hostage, most likely Mona," Brady replied.

"Why Mona?" Jody asked, glancing at his sister, who
stood beside Rusty and Blackie. "Why not Sugar? She
was the one playing up to them. She told them that Pa had
sold his icehouse, letting them know he had money to
start another business."

"Your pa better put a muzzle on her, or he'll never
make it to California." Alvin spoke firmly, and all eyes
went to him. He moved to stand behind his wife, who had
a sleeping Anna Marie cuddled in her lap. He put his
hand on her shoulder, then said, "With shenanigans like
that, she could get us all killed."

"The young one flirted with Sugar," Jody said, "but he was watchin' Mona."

Mona gasped and began to sputter. "Well . . . why, that gutter trash! I . . . I wouldn't look at him if he had gold and silver hanging all over him!"

A nervous little laugh came from Jody. "Sugar would be mad as hops if she knew there was a man alive that preferred Mona over her."

Elmer had let the campfire die down and had taken his blankets to the edge of the woods and bedded down. Margie was embarrassed that he hadn't offered to take part in securing the would-be robbers. Not that he had been needed. Brady had been very efficient in handling the situation, giving Margie cause to believe that he had done something like this before.

"I'll keep an eye out tonight," Brady was saying. "Not that I think those fellows are going anywhere."

"I'll spell you in taking a watch." Alvin's statement was echoed by Jody.

"Blackie and I can take a turn," Rusty offered. "Nothing moves that he doesn't know about."

"That's makes four of us," Brady said, accepting Rusty's help. "Assign us two-hour shifts, Alvin."

"Thanks for what you did," Grace said. "I thank my lucky stars we ran into you, Brady Hoyt."

"It's a two-way street, ma'am." Brady went to where Grace sat with Anna Marie. He lifted the child in his arms. "Thanks for looking after her. I'll bed her down in the car."

One of Anna Marie's shoes slipped off. Margie picked it up, followed Brady to his car and opened the door. The space between the two seats had been filled with their belongings, and on them was what appeared to be a mattress from a crib. Brady placed the child on the bed and removed her other shoe and her stockings. After flipping a sheet over her he softly closed the door.

"I throw a bedroll down here beside the car in case she wakes up in the night. The first night, she woke up crying for her daddy. It about busted my heart." He reached for Margie's arm when she turned to leave. "Stay with me for a while. It isn't late."

"I could take a watch—"

"No. I don't want you sitting here in the dark by yourself with everyone else asleep."

"We can build up the fire."

"Those fellows are puredee trash. They have filthy mouths. There's enough men to keep watch."

"Brady," Foley Luker called as he approached. "I didn't get a chance to thank you and tell you that Sugar is sorry for the way she spoke to you. She felt sorry for the men."

"It's quite all right, Foley. We've got them trussed up. Each had a gun, and I found a shotgun in their car. I think they were waiting here for someone to rob. Four of us were a little more than they wanted to take on all at once, so they thought to rob you and get a hostage."

"I'da helped, but Sugar was upset—"

"Jody and Mona kept their heads and were a big help."

"Hey, cowboy," the voice of one of their prisoners came out of the darkness. Brady didn't answer, and the man called again. "Cowboy, I gotta piss."

Brady ignored him and spoke to Foley. "Maybe you should speak to Mrs. Luker and tell her that she should be more careful with the men she meets on the highway.

Some of them are good, hardworking men down on their luck, but some are outlaws: bootleggers, thieves and hijackers."

"I've already told her that and cautioned her about mentioning we were going to California to start a business. She'll be careful from now on."

Margie closed her eyes and gritted her teeth. *Dear God, never, please never let me fall so desperately in love that I make a complete fool of myself like this man is doing.*

Brady's thoughts echoed Margie's. *You poor besotted fool.*

"I've got to shit too, cowboy." The voice was followed by laughter. "Can that pretty little gal take me to the woods?"

"Jody is taking one of the watches tonight," Brady said to Foley.

"Is that necessary?"

"I think it is."

"You've got them tied up, haven't you?"

"We want to make sure they stay that way."

"It's goin' to be a long night, cowboy. Where's that pretty little brown-haired gal? How about lettin' me fuck her to pass away the time? Trussed up like I am, she can give me a good ride."

Brady's patience came to an explosive end. "That came from one of your wife's supper guests, and he's talking about your daughter, Mr. Luker," he said with heavy sarcasm, and placed his hand on Margie's arm. "Stay while I take care of this. I don't want Punkie to wake up and find herself alone."

"Chester says he'll fuck the blonde with the titties if

she'll help him get it up." Raunchy laughter came out of the darkness.

Brady went swiftly to the Putman camp and pulled a long stick out of the blazing fire. Holding it like a torch, he carried it ahead of him to where the three men were tied.

"All right, smart-mouth," he snarled. "Repeat what you just said. Come on, say it again if you've got the guts. Say it so I can shove this torch down your throat." He swung the blazing stick so close to the man's face it singed his eyebrows.

"Hey, cut it out! I was just . . . jokin'. Hey!" he yelled again. "Yo're burnin' me."

"Not so brave now, are you, horseshit? Listen up. I'm saying this one time. If any more filth comes from your mouth, I'll shove this fire stick up your ass. Understand?" The man silently cringed away from the blaze. Brady swung it back and forth in front of his face. "Understand?" he said again.

"Yeah! Yeah! Are ya crazy? Ya burned me!"

"I meant to. What's your name? Give it to me straight, or I'll burn every hair off that bump on your shoulders."

"Persy. Homer Persy."

"Homer Pussy. Suits you. You're messin' with a real hard-ass when you mess with me, Pussy. You think you're tough. Where I come from you wouldn't last five minutes."

"Name's Persy. You . . . burnt me—"

"That little singe is just a start. I don't mess around with piles of shit like you. I could sit here and whistle 'Yankee Doodle' while you burn to a crisp and warm myself at the fire." Brady stood and looked down at the other two men. "That goes for all of you. If you want to see daylight, keep your mouths shut."

"We've not said nothin'," one of the men muttered.

"A word of warning. If this shithead gets me riled up enough, he'll be greeting the devil before morning. And naturally I'll not leave any witnesses. It'll be to your advantage to keep him quiet."

Brady gave each man a long, hard stare, then walked away before he allowed himself to grin. He returned the stick to the campfire.

"They'll be quiet."

"I don't like what he was saying," Jody said.

"Don't let it bother you. It's what you'd expect from their kind."

"Rusty is going to take the first watch," Alvin explained. "Mona said she'd like to stay awhile. When Rusty's time is up, Jody will take a turn. He'll wake me, and I'll wake you near morning."

"I'm sorry Pa isn't . . . able to help." Jody stumbled over the words. "He's not been the same since he met . . . her."

"Don't worry about it, son." Alvin put a hand on the boy's shoulder. "Maybe it's best that he stay and keep an eye on her. She might get to feeling sorry for them and cut them loose."

Brady went back to his car. Margie had opened the front door and was sitting sideways on the seat, her feet on the running board. She slid out of the car as he approached and stood beside it.

"Don't go." It seemed to Brady that he was always saying that to her. "Rusty and Mona are taking the first watch. Then Jody. Alvin is next, and he'll wake me for the early morning watch."

"Then you'd better get some sleep."

"I'd rather talk to you. Let's sit in the car for a while."

"I'm sorry about Elmer. I could take his place," Margie said after she had gotten back into the car and moved over on the seat to make room for him.

"I thought we'd covered that."

"We're part of this caravan. We should do our part."

"I'll do your part. You're helping me with Punkie." He turned sideways to look at her. His arm went over her head to rest on the back of the seat behind her. "Tell me to mind my own business if I'm speaking out of turn. But you and Elmer don't seem like a father and daughter to me."

"He is my father! Do you and the others think that there's something fishy about me being with him? You can ask anyone back in Conway, Missouri, and they will tell you that Elmer Kinnard is my father."

"Hold on. I didn't mean to get you riled up. It's just . . . well, forget it."

"No, I won't forget it. My mother was Elmer's second wife. She died when I was little. He sent me to live with my grandmother and had nothing more to do with me. We lived in the same town, but I might as well have lived at the North Pole as far as he was concerned."

Once she started talking, the words poured out. She told him about her dream to go to California and about the disastrous trip the year before.

"Elmer's third wife left him a month or so ago. He came to the café where I worked and said he'd sold his ice business and was going to California and I could go with him. Here I am. I didn't know how much he disliked me until we were on the way. I want to see Hollywood. I'm determined to put up with him until I get there."

While she was talking Brady's hand had slipped off the seat behind her and gripped her shoulder. Neither one of them seemed to be aware of it.

"Then what will you do?"

"Get a job."

"It may not be easy finding a job that will support you."

"I'll find one."

"If Elmer dislikes you, why did he ask you to come with him?"

"I've wondered about that. It may be because he wasn't sure if he would stick with Mr. Putman and Mr. Luker, and he'd rather have me with him than to go on alone. I just found out that he dislikes me because of my mother."

"That seems unfair."

"Not to Elmer. I don't know what has made him so cantankerous, so cynical. I'm afraid that the others will get so disgusted with him that they'll cut us out of the caravan."

"If that should happen, we'll find a place for you."

"I have some money—" She turned to find his face close to hers and pulled back. "I've been running off at the mouth, haven't I? You've hardly said a word."

"It must be a long day riding in a car without someone to talk to. I have Punkie. I'm getting used to carrying on a conversation with a five-year-old."

"It's not so bad. I have plenty of time to daydream."

"What do you dream about?" His hand now was stroking her shoulder and arm.

"Oh, this and that. Mostly about Hollywood. I just want to see it and . . . the movie stars." Her heart was beating too fast. It was making her breathless. "Enough about me. What will you do when you get to California?"

"I'll take Punkie to her Aunt Opal and hope that Becky's sister wants her."

"Oh, she will. How could she not want her sister's little girl?"

"I sent her a wire. She said to bring her, but they may not take to each other. Opal may be like Punkie's mother."

"Oh."

"Yes, oh. You're too polite to ask, so I'll tell you that Punkie's mother was . . . not very motherly. My brother was both mama and daddy to her."

"That's too bad. She loves you. Can't you take her to your home and keep her if you're not sure that Opal will be a good mother to her?"

"I can't keep her on a horse ranch ten miles from a town without a woman to take care of her. And she needs to be where she can go to school. I have the money from my brother's house, and this car belonged to him. I'll sell it when we get to California and leave the money with Opal. Then I'll send a little now and then, to help out."

"My grandmother said that children need love or they'll grow up like weeds and not flowers."

"What are you? A rose? A daisy? I know, you're a Missouri bluebonnet." When he chuckled, she felt the vibration against her arm.

"I didn't mean that I'm a flower. I'm more like a weed. A pesky one that pops up among the petunias!"

"I don't believe that for a minute." He sniffed. "You smell like a honeysuckle vine." His arm tightened.

Margie's heart fluttered like a hummingbird loose in her chest. Her shoulder was tucked under his arm. She was pressed to his warm, hard body from hip to knee.

He reached for the hand in her lap. "If I kiss you, will you slap me or yell? I prefer the slap. You'll wake Punkie if you yell."

Surprised, she turned to look at him. His lips swooped down on hers. His kiss was hard and quick. A groan came from him when he lifted his head.

He pressed his forehead to hers. "Ah . . . sweet girl! It didn't do the trick." He spoke in an agonized whisper.

Unable to utter a sound, she waited for him to explain.

"I've wanted to do that since I first saw you. I thought that once I'd kissed you, I'd get you out of my system." He lifted her hand and pressed it palm-down over his heart. "Feel that? When I'm near you, it takes off like a wild mustang." *And sweetheart, that's not all that comes to attention, but I can't tell you about that now.*

"Maybe if I kissed you again, slowly, the ache would go away." His whispered words were seductive, his breath warm on her wet lips.

"You could try . . . it."

He turned her so that her breasts flattened against his chest, and he skipped his fingers up and down her spine. He ran his tongue over her lips, then kissed her soundly, deeply, passionately. His lips left her mouth, moved to her cheek, her closed eyes, her brow. Then, as if he couldn't stay away, he kissed her parted lips again, knowing in some far corner of his mind that this wasn't going to banish his thoughts of her.

He suddenly feared that he would never grow tired of kissing her. Liking to kiss her was one thing, he told himself. Being wildly in love with her was another. Loving a woman would be more dangerous to his peace of mind than falling into a bed of rattlesnakes. He'd not make the same mistake his brother made. Nosiree! He had learned firsthand what comes from a man giving a woman his heart and soul.

He lifted his head and laughed a little, afraid for her to know just how near he had come to falling in love with her. It was foolish to even think that they would hitch together even if he did decide that she was the one to share his life, but not his heart. All he had was half of a ragtag horse ranch, and she had dreams of Hollywood—of all places! He loosened his arms to allow her to lean back away from him.

"Well, now. We've got that out of the way."

His words were like a dash of icy water. She felt them all the way to the tips of her toes. She took a deep breath before she could speak.

"Yeah, we did. Now I've got to get back."

Brady got out of the car and took her hand to help her out. "Thanks for staying with Punkie."

"You're welcome. Good night." Margie hurried away, tears of disappointment blinding her.

Now that she and Rusty were alone, Mona could think of nothing to say. Her tongue clung to the roof of her mouth. She hugged her sweater around her, for the evening breeze was still cool, and looked her fill of him, knowing that he wouldn't know—or at least she didn't think he would. He sat quietly with the shotgun beside him and Blackie's head beneath his hand. Jody had built up the campfire before he left, and in the flickering light she could see Rusty's eyes turn in her direction.

"Mona? Tell me what you see." His voice was little more than a whisper. "You were looking at me."

"How did you know?"

"I'd be looking at you . . . if I could see."

"Your hair is dark red and . . . your hands are . . . nice."

He held his hand out toward her. "Come closer. I don't want our staked-out friends to hear what we say."

She moved across the blanket to sit close, but not touching him. His hand came in contact with her upper arm. He moved it after he had touched her.

"Tell me what you look like. I already know that you're pretty."

"Who told you that?"

"Brady. He said if he was younger, he'd set his cap for you."

"You're kiddin'! He didn't say that."

"He did. He said you have brown hair. Do you mind if I touch it?"

"Ah . . . no."

He took a strand of her hair and rubbed it between his thumb and forefinger. Then with the palm of his hand he stroked her hair from the crown of her head to the ends.

"It's soft," he said as if to himself. "And thick."

"I usually wash it in rainwater." Her heart was beating so fast she feared it would jump out of her chest.

"It feels like silk. May I touch your face?" he asked

after he had threaded his forked fingers through her hair at the nape of her neck.

He touched her cheek and paused, waiting for permission to continue. She turned on her knees facing him and lifted his other hand to her face. Her breath caught as he ran his fingers over her chin, along her jaw, and stopped at her lips.

"Full on the bottom, thin on the top," he whispered. "And unsmiling." Then, "Ah . . . that's how I imagined you. Lips tilting at the corners. Open your mouth . . . please." He moved the knuckle of his forefinger along the edge of her teeth. "Nice and even," he murmured.

His fingertips moved up the hollows of her cheeks and rested on the cheekbones. He trailed his fingers over her eyes and up to her brows, thick and straight.

"Big brown eyes," he murmured.

"How do you know?"

"Brady said they were brown. I can feel that they are big." With fingers from both hands at her temples he combed through her hair. "Thank you for letting me see you." His hands moved over her shoulders and down her arms. "You're not very tall."

"How do you know?" She released a giddy laugh. *How many times had she said that?*

"I just know. Your head will fit under my chin."

"I'm taller than that."

"Stand up and we'll see. And don't stand on your toes. That would be cheating." After they had stood he grasped her upper arms and pulled her against him. Her chin touched his chest; his chin rested on the top of her head. She closed her eyes for one delicious moment. "See there," he said. "I was right."

Mona stepped back. "Brady told you."

"No. Your shoulder touched mine about halfway between the top of my shoulder and my elbow that first night. I knew then about how tall you were." He grasped her hand, and they sank back down onto the blanket.

"That's remarkable! I don't know how you know these things."

"It's not remarkable. When you can't see, your other senses, such as touch and smell, kick in. I can tell by the smell of vanilla when Ma is stirring up a cake and from the yeast when she sets bread to rise. I can tell by holding your hand that in the past you've worked hard, but not recently, because the roughness on your palm is softening. I know the things your stepmother says to you hurt you and are lowering your self-esteem. Don't let her do that to you."

"I don't know how to stop her," she confessed. "Pa is so smitten with her."

"He's bound to come to his senses soon. Don't let her get your goat. If you do, she's won."

Mona said nothing. She knew that what he said was true. They sat quietly while minutes passed, their clasped hands resting on the blanket between them. She wished that she had something interesting to say, but could not think of a thing. When she realized that she was holding on to his hand as if it were a lifeline keeping her from being swept away by a flood, she was embarrassed and relaxed her grip a little.

"How old are you, Mona?" His voice was soft and even. No wonder he sang so beautifully.

"Seventeen. I'll be eighteen by the time we get to California. Jody is twenty."

"Brady thought you were about sixteen."

"I look young for my age because I don't wear a lot of rouge and lipstick."

"Paint? I've never seen a painted woman. If I have, I've forgotten about it."

"How long have you . . ."

"Go ahead and say it. How long have I been blind? Since I was ten. I'm twenty-two now."

"Then you remember what a lot of things look like."

He smiled. "Yes, and it gives me an advantage. When something is described to me, I see it in color. My mother and father will never grow old. In my mind I see them as they were twelve years ago."

"What do you miss the most?"

He thought for a minute before he answered. "I'd like to drive a car. I know I never will. I'm resigned to it. I'd like to *see* a picture show. I've *heard* a few. I went to 'hear' *King Kong*. A friend and I sat up in the balcony, and he described it to me. It was exciting. Especially the last part when the ape was on the Empire State Building and the airplane was flying around. I'd sure like to know how the filmmaker did that."

"I've not been to many picture shows."

"I listen to the radio a lot. It puts me in contact with the whole world." He pulled a heavy pocket watch from the bib of his overalls and held it to his ear. "I heard it chime the half hour a while ago. The time has gone fast. Our two hours are almost up."

"I didn't know there was such a thing as a chiming pocket watch."

"I saved the money I earned playing my fiddle and singing for dances, weddings and even funerals. We ordered it from a company that imports from Germany. I doubt we'll get much more from there, except maybe trouble now that fellow Hitler has taken over."

"You know about a lot of things."

"I've been showing off for you." He laughed, his eyes on her face as if he were seeing her. "Do you think we can do this again?"

"What?" she said, pretending not to know. "Sit up and guard bad men?"

"You're smiling."

"You know everything!"

He tilted his head. "I know someone is coming toward us. I bet it's Jody." He held tightly to her hand and whispered as they stood. "Will you talk with me again?"

"Uh-huh."

"It's time I took over," Jody said. "I set my alarm. I'll walk you back to the car, sis."

"Thanks for staying with me, Mona."

"You're welcome," she murmured. Then nervousness struck her. She felt almost giddy. "Does Sugar know I stayed with him?" she asked her brother as they walked away.

"What do you care if she knows?"

"She'll have something nasty to say about it."

"Ignore her."

"That's easy for you to say. She's not on you like she is on me."

"Give her enough rope and she might hang herself. Pa will get his fill of her and come to his senses. If he doesn't, I'll get a job when we get to California, and we'll strike out on our own."

"He expects you to work in his ice business."

"I'll not work for him with her there."

"Oh, Jody, what can we do?"

"Nothing right now. But a lot can happen between here and California."

Chapter 8

THE EARLY MORNING SUN was sending long fingers of light through the tops of the trees and shedding a pattern of lacy shadows on the campground when the three-car caravan pulled out. Anna Marie was with the Putmans again. Brady and Rusty stayed behind to wait for the sheriff. Grace's worried eyes stayed on her son for as long as she could see him.

"Stop worrying," Alvin urged.

"I can't help it."

"You're the one who insisted that we not coddle him. He's a man now, Gracie, not a boy. You've got to start treating him like one."

"But we don't know Brady very well. He's never been around a person who's blind. He told me so."

"We've got to trust him to look after Rusty just like he's trusting us to take care of Anna Marie."

Grace looked down at the sleeping child in her lap, and the thought came to her that if Brady wanted to be rid of the little girl, this was his chance. He knew that she and

Alvin would take her as their own. Oh, Lord! What if he drove off and left Rusty in that campground?

"He's crazy about that kid," Alvin was saying, as if he knew what was in her mind. "She's the daughter of his twin. Did you know that?"

"She told me." Grace stroked the hair back from the child's face. "She said he looks just like her daddy and talks like him."

"Poor little tyke."

"She said sometimes she forgets he's her uncle and not her daddy."

"I wonder what happened to her parents. Brady hasn't said."

Grace placed her hand on her husband's thigh. "I can't help worrying about Rusty."

"Well, stop it." Alvin's hand left the wheel and patted hers to soften his command.

"We both know that he'll never be able to be completely on his own."

"I've heard of other blind people who are, and he's smart as any of them," Alvin said defensively. "He should marry and have a family like any normal man."

"He likes the Luker girl."

"That's a good sign. He likes Margie too."

"Not like he likes Mona."

"How do you know that, Miss Know-It-All?" Alvin teased.

"I just do. That's all. I don't want him to fall for her and have her break his heart."

"Don't borrow trouble. People don't die of a broken heart. My hope is that he finds a nice girl, marries and has kids who will love him and look after him when we're gone."

"I wish he liked Margie. She's a steady, sensible girl."

"Don't push the girl onto him, Grace."

"I won't, but I can wish, can't I?"

"He'll make that decision for himself. Brady accepted him in spite of his limitations, just as others have done. The right woman will see beyond his blindness and love him in spite of it."

They rode without speaking for a while. Then Alvin's chuckle broke the silence. He asked with a touch of pride in his voice, "Did you see how he handled the shotgun I put in his hands? The crooks didn't know he was blind."

"Why couldn't Brady have left the crooks tied up out there? The sheriff would get them. It's his job."

"Because he was afraid that if people came along and turned them loose, the crooks might kill them for their money and car," Alvin said patiently. "When we get to Sapulpa, I'll go straight to the sheriff's office. I told Brady we'd stop alongside the highway in Davenport. He'll meet us there."

"Mr. Kinnard is strange," Grace remarked after Alvin had turned to go into town and she looked back to see that Elmer had pulled to the side of the highway to wait. "I wonder why he's so unfriendly. His daughter is nothin' like him."

"Unfriendly? He's been downright ornery the last few days. He wasn't that way when we first talked of taking this trip."

"I've never heard him say a word to Margie. He acts like she isn't even there."

"That's their business, Gracie, and has nothing to do

with us. Here we are at Sapulpa. Now, where is the sheriff's office?"

"Why do we have to wait here?" Sugar complained when Foley pulled over to the side of the highway and stopped. "Why do we always have to follow along behind the Putmans?"

"We agreed when we planned this trip that Alvin would lead the way. He knows where the campsites are."

"We could find them if he gave us the maps. Where's he going?"

"He's going into Sapulpa to tell the sheriff what happened and that Brady is waiting for him at the campground with the men who woulda robbed us."

"They looked so pitiful. I just thought they were hungry. I still don't think that they were going to rob us." Sugar let her lower lip tremble. "I guess everybody hates me."

"Nobody hates you." Foley wrapped his arm around the steering wheel and stared out the windshield.

"Yes, they do. I hate her guts!" Mona, in the backseat, mouthed silently to her brother.

"I explained to Brady and Alvin that you felt sorry for those guys and wanted to give them a meal." Foley turned to look long and hard at his wife.

Mona made a gagging gesture with her finger in her mouth. Jody shook his head at her, but he was grinning.

"I wish we could go on by ourselves. Just our little family." Sugar snuggled her face against Foley's neck.

"We can't do that. If we had been alone last night, the robbers would have taken everything we have. They might have killed us. I'll not take that risk with my family."

"But, darlin' . . . I'm tired of traveling."

"Already? We've been gone only ten days."

"I want a bath. And I want to sleep in a real bed. With you," she added in a whisper.

"I explained that it would be a rough trip."

Sugar sniffed. "It's worse than I thought it would be."

"When we get to Oklahoma City, I'll see about getting a motor cabin for the night. How's that?"

"Would you? Oh, darlin', you are the sweetest thing." Sugar threw her arms around his neck and covered his face with kisses.

Mona looked at her brother and crossed her eyes. He burst out laughing.

Foley looked over his shoulder. "What tickled your funny bone?"

"Mona yawned and a fly flew into her mouth." Jody tried to keep a straight face while telling the lie to his father.

When Foley turned back to Sugar, who was snuggled against him, Jody winked at his sister. She put her hand over her mouth to control her giggles.

While waiting for the Putmans to come back to the highway, Margie passed the time looking at her movie magazines. When Elmer got out of the truck and leaned against the fender to watch the traffic go by, her hands stilled on the magazine and she looked at him through the truck's dusty windshield. He stood with his arms folded across his chest, his old felt hat pulled down, shielding a face that, no doubt, showed not a trace of expression.

How could he be her father? Could her mother have

had a secret lover? No, she told herself. If her granny had had the slightest suspicion that Elmer was not her father, she would have told her, because she had no use for the man at all. Oh, but she wished he were not so uncompromising and obstinate.

She had been embarrassed last night when he hadn't offered any assistance. And again this morning when he never thanked Alvin or Brady for removing the threat to all of them. She had no doubt that if she mentioned it to him, he would dump her out along the highway like so much garbage.

What would he say if he knew that Brady had kissed her? She answered her own question. Plenty. It would prove to him that she was the slut he believed her to be.

She had relived those kisses a hundred times. Brady's mouth had been warm and firm and had moved over hers with familiar ease. There had been nothing tentative or hesitant about the kiss. When he raised his head, his eyes had searched hers before he kissed her again. She had been stunned by his brazen action.

It hurt her that he considered kissing her as something to "get out of the way." She had walked away feeling as if her heart had been stomped on. But during the long sleepless night she had come to realize that she had only herself to blame. He was a man, after all, a very virile man. To be loved by a man like Brady Hoyt would be any girl's dream.

She could have protested. She could have slapped him as he suggested. Instead she had sat there and let him have his way with her.

It was going to be hard facing him in the light of day, but face him she must. The best way to handle the situation would be to act as if it had meant nothing at all to her. It had happened. There was nothing she could do about it now. But she could make sure that it didn't happen again and that he never know how his kisses had thrilled her to her curled-up toes.

Margie saw the Putman truck coming back to the highway and behind it a sheriff's car. Alvin stuck out his arm to signal a left turn. The Sapulpa sheriff turned right to go toward the campground. Elmer got back into the truck, and they were on their way again.

They passed through the towns of Kellyville, Bristow and Depew. The highway between Depew and Stroud was under construction, and Elmer had to dodge around the graders working to prepare it for paving. Stroud was a sleepy little town, but it had once been a tough, prosperous place. The Great Depression and Dust Bowl conditions were leaving deep scars on the towns and emotional wounds on the folks who lived in them.

A dozen years before, cattle drovers had shipped their animals from Stroud, but the bars that had made money selling illegal whiskey were gone, as were most of the businesses on the main street. The worst drought in recent history had reduced the price of wheat to thirty-three cents a bushel. The banks had foreclosed, and the families were moving on.

Davenport was merely a wide spot in the road. Alvin pulled over beneath a row of oak trees and stopped. To Margie's surprise, Elmer went on around him and pulled into a gas station. A big yellow dog got up, stared at them, then walked a few feet and flopped down again. After the man in grease-covered overalls put gas in the truck,

Elmer followed him inside the small brick building, digging into his pocket for money to pay for the gas.

Margie looked back down the highway. Anna Marie and Grace were standing beside the truck. The Lukers were behind the Putmans. There was no sign of Brady's black sedan.

It was hot inside the cab of the truck even with the windows down and the windshield tilted to let in a breeze. A big blowfly came in the window, and Margie fanned it away with a movie magazine. Soon it got tired and flew out again. Minutes passed. She craned her neck to see inside the station. Elmer was sitting down, his legs stretched out in front of him, his hands clasped across his midsection, as if he planned to stay there awhile.

Margie needed to use the outhouse. She waited for what seemed to her a quarter of an hour before she got out of the truck and went to the door of the station.

"Mister," she said, and waited until the man acknowledged her. "May I use your outhouse?"

"Yes, ma'am. Ya just go right ahead and help yoreself."

"Thank you."

Margie was in the two-hole outhouse before it occurred to her that Elmer might go off and leave her, as Ernie Harding had done when she went to the outhouse at Andy's campground down near Sayre. She hurriedly finished what she had come to do and went back to the truck. She climbed into the back and filled a fruit jar with water from the keg. It was warm but wet, and soothed her scratchy throat. When she returned to the cab of the truck, she brought a handful of crackers and a hunk of cheese.

She ate slowly, and when she finished, Elmer still

lounged in the chair inside the station. Margie suspected that he planned to spend the noon stop there so as to avoid talking to the others in the caravan. She went to the back of the truck again and wet a cloth to wipe her face, after which she spread on a layer of Pond's cream, enjoying the soothing effect on her windburned skin.

Later she fanned her face with the movie magazine, trying to brace up her sagging eyelids. But she fell asleep with her head resting against the back of the seat. When Elmer got into the truck and slammed the door, she woke with a start. He was eating a hot dog he must have bought at the small café across the street. Alvin's truck passed, and Elmer pulled out onto the highway and fell in line behind it. Margie looked back and was relieved to see Brady's sedan following the Lukers.

The afternoon passed slowly. After Chandler they went through several small towns. Near Arcadia, Margie spied the old round barn she had seen when she passed this way before and wondered what advantage it had over the rectangular barns with the big haylofts.

On the outer edge of Oklahoma City, they turned off the highway and followed Alvin into a field already occupied by four other campers. Elmer swung out and away from the others and parked with the back of the truck facing the campground. Margie got out and stretched. Brady passed and waved. She lifted a casual hand and began gathering firewood left by another camper.

Jody Luker came by while Margie was slicing potatoes into a skillet.

"Hi, Margie. I don't think we'll have any trouble tonight." He gestured toward the other campers. "They've all got kids."

"Have you heard what the sheriff had to say this morning when Brady turned over the men who might have robbed us?"

"No, but I'm on my way to find out."

She was opening a can of corn to serve over the fried potatoes when Jody came back by.

"Brady said the sheriff couldn't hold them because they hadn't actually committed the robbery, but he said he'd keep them there until we got on down the highway. Brady took some parts off their old car. He said it'd not be running anytime soon."

"I'm glad of that."

"Pa's unhooking the trailer. He promised Sugar they'd stay in a motor cabin tonight."

"You and Mona will stay here?"

"Yeah. I'll put up the tent for Mona. I just hope Sugar don't run Pa out of money before we get to California."

Margie watched Jody walk away and thought that he was a son a man should be proud of. Mona was lucky to have a brother like him to look out for her. Foley Luker was ten times a fool, but, then, most of the men she had come in contact with were, including Ernie Harding and her own father. She could even add Brady Hoyt to the list. *He had kissed her as if it were a chore to get out of the way!*

On the other side of the list were Mr. Putman and Rusty. They seemed nice and trustworthy. On further thought she added Yates and the funny little man called Deke at Andy's Garage in Sayre . . . and Harry back at the café in Conway. He had thought enough of her to give her the pistol and show her how to use it.

"I can't be cynical like Elmer," she murmured to herself. "I got into this mess because I wanted to go to California. I'll stick it out if it kills me."

Homer Persy watched Brady and then the sheriff drive away from the campground. He went behind the car, dropped his drawers, removed his underwear and attempted to clean himself.

He swore using every foul word he'd ever heard.

"I'll get that son of a bitch if it takes the rest of my life." He burned with the desire for revenge.

The hick sheriff had *laughed* and held his nose when he discovered that Homer had messed on himself. The cowboy had sneered at him. "If I'd known he wasn't housebroke, I'd of put a diaper on him."

He'd get even. Nobody treated Homer Persy like that and got away with it.

Homer threw his soiled underwear in the bushes and put on his britches. He had caught a grin on the face of Ross, the man his Uncle Chester had brought along. It hadn't sat well.

"If not for yore bungling, we'da had a hostage and been long gone. You let that hick get the drop on you."

"I told you I wasn't for takin' a hostage. Kidnappin' ain't somethin' folks sneeze at," Ross shot back.

"Well, you can just get yoreself on down the road. Ya ain't ridin' back in this car." Homer was itching for a fight.

"Neither are you," Ross growled. "Unless you know how to put it back together."

"I suppose you do."

"Yeah, I do. I've already picked up the parts that cowboy threw in the bushes."

"Well, get at it. That cowboy and them women are headed for California. There ain't but one way to get there—down old Highway 66."

"I'll fix your car, but I ain't havin' no part in hurtin' no women."

"I ain't heared nobody askin' ya to be part. Did you, Uncle Chester? Did you ask him to come with us?"

Chester Ford grinned and shook his head at his nephew. "Yo're more like yore grandpa ever'day." Chester took pride in his infamous relative, Bob Ford, who had killed Jesse James.

"And just as sneaky as the back-shootin' bastard," Ross muttered under his breath, and lifted the hood on the old car.

Chapter 9

Brady FOLLOWED THE LUKERS into the campground near Oklahoma City. He was irritated with the sheriff back in Sapulpa.

"I've got a jailhouse full of bootleggers and bank robbers. I've not got time to mess with petty crooks."

"Well, dammit, they wouldn't have been 'petty crooks' if we hadn't got the jump on them."

"I know. Aggravatin' as hell, ain't it? Happens every day. I get my hands on a piece of shit that hasn't done quite enough to be sent up for; but you know he's goin' to, and you got to wait for it."

Homer Persy had been so angry he was practically frothing at the mouth and, before the sheriff got there, had threatened to get even. Brady and Rusty had sat in the car, laughing and holding their noses to further irritate him. Homer had calmed down, however, by the time the sheriff arrived, and vigorously denied the robbery attempt.

"I'll sign a complaint if you want," Brady had said.

"Wouldn't stick. This one"—the sheriff indicated

Homer—"smells like a privy. I don't want him stinkin'
up my jailhouse."

"Then we'll be on our way."

Both Brady and Rusty had taken delight in the fact that
neither the crooks nor the sheriff was aware that Rusty
couldn't see.

Now with his hand on Rusty's back Brady guided him
to where Alvin had stopped the truck. Blackie followed.
Brady had had only a glimpse of Margie when he drove
in. She had answered his wave halfheartedly and disappeared in the back of the truck.

"Uncle Brady!" Anna Marie ran to meet him. "Guess
what?"

"You learned another song." He grabbed her up in his
arms. She planted a kiss on his cheek.

"How did you know?"

"A little bird told me."

"Did it, Rusty? Did a bird tell him?"

"I might remember if I got a hug."

Brady moved so that Anna Marie's arms could circle
Rusty's neck. Rusty held the child while she kissed him
on the cheek. With Brady's hand against his back they
walked on.

"I've not ever been kissed by such a pretty girl."

"How do you know?" Anna Marie asked with the
frankness of a child. "You can't see me."

"No, but as sweet as you are, you've just got to be pretty."
He put his nose against her face. "And you *smell* pretty."

"I like you, Rusty. Almost as much as Uncle Brady.
Will you sing songs tonight?"

"How could I refuse? And I like you too." A tug on his
shirt told Rusty they had reached the camp. He stopped

and set the child on her feet. She ran to the car to get her jump rope.

Jody joined them, and while Grace prepared the evening meal, Rusty and Brady took turns telling what happened after the sheriff had arrived.

"Do you think they will follow?" Alvin asked.

"I didn't see any sign in their car that they're prepared for a long trip. It'll take them a while to fix it unless one of them is a crackerjack mechanic."

"Speaking of mechanics," Alvin said to Jody, "how's your pa's radiator?"

"It's still holding. He's takin' his Sugar to a motor cabin tonight."

"You and Mona are staying here?"

"We'll be all right. Pa can't afford two cabins."

"Then, come eat with us tonight." Grace came to stand beside her husband. "I cooked a pot of stew last night."

"We . . . couldn't impose. Pa's leaving the trailer. We'll find something."

"Won't do. You'll eat with us." Grace glanced at her son. He was combing the burs out of Blackie's fur, but he was listening intensely. "Scoot now. Go fetch your sister."

"Well, if you're sure."

"I'm sure. Mona can help me clear up afterward. I think we should have a singing tonight, Alvin. Maybe some of the other campers will join us. Why don't you invite 'em? They look like decent folks."

While eating, Brady sat where he could see the Kinnard camp. Margie fixed herself a plate of food, then moved around to the other side of the truck, where he couldn't see her. Elmer sat on the canvas chair beside the cab of the truck.

If he was smart, Brady told himself, he wouldn't get to within ten feet of Margie Kinnard lest she become too important to him. He could like her, be interested in her welfare, without falling in love with her. He didn't want to love her or any woman right now. The time wasn't right for him.

Besides, he'd seen what love could do to a man. Love with the wrong woman was having your heart and soul twisted, tied and knotted and then . . . stomped on. Even as he thought this, he was planning on how he could get Margie to come over to the Putman camp for the get-together.

It had seemed reasonable to him, at the time, that once he'd kissed her, she would become just another pretty girl. He was dead wrong. He'd thought of her sweet mouth and soft body all day. Thank the good Lord she was a girl whose dreams didn't include a piss-poor cowboy, a girl who had set her sights on Hollywood; otherwise he'd be in deep trouble.

While Mona and Grace were washing the supper dishes, Alvin, holding Anna Marie's hand, walked over to visit with the other campers. Soon he was squatted down talking to a man in a battered straw hat and Anna Marie was running and playing with the children.

Brady made a quick decision. He went to his car to check the water and the oil. When he finished, he headed for the Kinnard camp.

"Evenin'," he said to Elmer, who sat back in his canvas chair, his arms folded across his chest, eyeing Brady as if he had just crawled out from under a rock. Margie was washing dishes on the tailgate of the truck.

"If all goes well, we'll be in Amarillo in a couple of

days." Brady squatted on his heels and poked a stick into the campfire.

Elmer grunted.

"Truck runnin' all right?"

Silence. Brady sat back to wait him out.

Finally Elmer said, "I ain't goin' to hold you up, if that's what's worryin' you."

"I'm not losing any sleep over it. Foley's radiator is sure to blow soon. I'm hopin' it happens before we get to where the towns are a hundred miles apart."

Elmer grunted an incoherent reply.

"Alvin keeps his truck in good shape; checks oil and water regularly."

"You think I don't?"

"Didn't give it a thought." It was a challenge for Brady to force Elmer to carry on this conversation. He wasn't going to let him freeze him out. The bastard. He'd like nothing better than to put his fist through the man's face. "Been in the ice business long?"

"You plannin' on sellin' ice?"

"No. I raise horses."

"Then whater ya wantin' to know for?"

"Well . . ." Brady scratched his head and spoke casually. "I guess I was wondering if it was the ice business that turned you into such an ornery son of a bitch."

Elmer didn't turn a hair.

"And the more I talk to you, the less I give a damn," Brady added.

"I ain't no fool. You didn't come to talk to me. You're sniffin' after the female."

"Something wrong with that? She's a nice girl and she's pretty."

"Nice? She's a thief is what she is!"

Brady stood. He had never wanted to hit a man so badly in all his life. "That's a hell of a thing to say about your daughter." His voice was low and angry.

A sound like a snort came from Elmer, and he got to his feet. Standing with his hands tucked into the bib of his overalls, he looked Brady in the eye.

"Ya ain't knowin' what she is. She run off with a feller last year and stole his money. Name was Ernie Harding from Conway. He dumped her. She come a-crawlin' back to town with her tail 'tween her legs."

"You took his word that she stole his money?"

"Damn right. It's in her blood. She's set her sights on seein' Hollywood, bein' a *movie star*. Don't that beat all? She's got about as much chance a bein' a movie star as I have pissin' from here to California."

"I don't understand how a girl like Margie would be related to *you*."

"I ain't a hundred percent sure she is. Take my advice. Stay away from her, or she'll sucker ya in and take everythin' ya got."

"I've not got much."

"Then ya ain't got nothin' to worry 'bout except maybe catchin' the clap." Elmer walked away.

Brady watched him leave. There were no words to describe the contempt he felt for the man. If Margie was what her father said she was, she was sure to land a job in Hollywood, because she was a damn fine actress.

*   *   *

Margie had heard every word that passed between Brady and Elmer.

Damn, damn, damn him! she thought. *I wish to God I was anywhere but here.*

Ernie Harding had gone back to Conway and spread the story that she had taken his money in order to excuse his going off and leaving her stranded in Oklahoma. Elmer had believed him.

Margie pressed her palms to her hot cheeks and scooted around to the other side of the truck. She leaned against it and hid her face against her bent arm. Too humiliated to even cry, she stood there, stiffening the legs that wanted to sag from the weight of her heavy heart.

She hoped and prayed that Brady would leave. To have him look at her with contempt would be more than she could endure.

Her prayers were not answered. She felt a gentle hand on her shoulder. It was the final straw. A tremor shook her. She swallowed repeatedly to hold back the agonizing sobs that refused to be controlled. Silently they bubbled up. She cried as she had never cried before, tears wetting her arm.

"Hey, don't cry."

It seemed to take all her natural strength to say, "Go away . . . please."

"I don't believe what he said. I'm smarter than that."

"He . . . said that I'm a—he said I took Ernie's money. He believes—he'll tell everybody."

"They won't believe it either." Brady tried to turn her into his arms. She resisted.

"Go away. Please. I wish . . . I wish I'd never come on this blasted . . . trip."

"What kind of man is he to say these things about his daughter—"

"Unless they're true? Is that what you think?"

"No, it isn't what I think. I think he's an embittered, sick man who doesn't even like himself."

"He . . . hates me because of my mother."

"He must have loved her once."

"No. There's no love in him."

"Hold your head up, Margie girl. Don't give him anything to gloat over."

"Please go. I've got to finish the dishes."

"The Putmans are inviting all the campers to a singing. Will you come over?"

"No!" she answered quickly. "I'm going to bed."

"If you don't come, I'll come after you." He looped her hair over her ear and massaged the nape of her neck.

"Don't come back. It'll just make things worse."

"Are you afraid of him?"

"No. He'll not . . . hurt me that way. He has other ways."

"Finish the dishes. Then come over."

"Please go before he comes back."

"All right. But if you don't come over, I'll be back; and if he says anything, I just might knock his block off." He patted her on the back and walked away.

She waited until she was sure that he was gone before she lifted her head from her arm. Oh, Lord. How could she ever face him or the others? Elmer had branded her a thief, made fun of her for wanting to see Hollywood. He had insinuated that she was a loose woman. He had probably said the same to Alvin and Grace and the Lukers. He must really hate her. She wiped her face on the hem of her skirt and went back to the dishpan.

Margie had planned all day to tell Alvin about the campsite at Andy's Garage just this side of Sayre, where Ernie had taken her money and deserted her. It was probably called Deke's Garage by now. In the one letter she received from Leona after she had married, she said that Andy had sold the garage to Deke, the man who sometimes helped him, and that he and the girls were moving with her and Yates to a ranch in Texas.

If Alvin would agree to camp there for the night, Deke would tell them that she hadn't stolen money from Ernie, that it was the other way around. The only way she was going to be able to speak to Alvin before they pulled out in the morning would be to go over there tonight.

Once she came to a decision, she hurriedly finished the evening chores, then climbed into the truck with a pan of water. The first thing she did was hold a damp cloth to her puffy eyes, hoping to erase the results of her tears. After washing she put on her blue-checked gingham skirt and blouse. It was her second-best dress. Soon she would have to find a place to wash her underwear and the two skirts and blouses she had worn all week.

Her heart felt like a rock in her chest as she brushed her hair and added a touch of color to her lips. She wanted to leave the truck before Elmer returned. She jumped down and hurried over to Brady's car before she lost her courage. Pausing there, she was assailed by sickening doubts. What if she was ignored? What if Grace no longer wanted to associate with her? What if Brady had second thoughts about what Elmer had said?

Her eyes searched for him. Rusty was playing a rousing tune on his fiddle while Alvin piled wood on the bonfire, and Grace, holding on to Anna Marie, greeted the people coming from the other camps. They came with stools and chairs and quilts for the little ones to sit on.

Brady and Jody appeared out of the darkness carrying a heavy log. When they dropped it on the fire, sparks flew in all directions. Brady paused, kicked at the log with his booted foot, then turned and came toward her.

"How did you know I was here?"

"I've been watching for you." He held out his hand. Mindlessly she reached for it, but held back when he tried to pull her toward the gathering.

"No. I'll wait here. I'm only going to stay long enough to talk to Mr. Putman."

"You're coming with me."

"No. Please—"

"You're coming. Must I remind you that I'm bigger than you are?"

Brady reached into the car for a blanket, then, holding her hand tightly, pulled her along with him. He skirted the crowd to a place out of the direct light of the campfire and spread the blanket. Margie sat down quickly, hoping not to attract any attention. Brady sat close, but not touching her.

Tilting his head so that he could see her profile, he studied the lines of her face. Brady felt that he was a fairly good judge of character, and he couldn't, for the life of him, associate her with the description her father had given him. It just wasn't possible.

He saw the trembling of her lips just before she turned to glare at him. "Stop looking at me!"

"I like looking at you. You're pretty."

"Yeah. Sure. You think I'll be an easy tumble after

what Elmer said. Well, because I let you kiss me doesn't mean it'll go any further."

"We kissed each other. Remember?"

"I remember, and that's the end of it."

"I'm not asking for more."

"Thank you." She turned her face away, but not before he saw the moisture in her eyes.

"You can ride the rest of the way with me and Punkie if you want. I'd appreciate the help."

"You don't need my help. Grace will help with Anna Marie."

"Even so. You've got a place with me if you want it."

"And you'd expect payment. How? On my back?" She bit the words out angrily.

He didn't reply. A strained minute passed before she looked at him. He had turned away from her, but she could see the muscle flex in his cheek as he clenched his teeth.

"Brady? I'm sorry," she said in an agonized whisper, and placed her hand on his arm. "Please—I'm sorry."

He looked at her then. His eyes were shadowed by the thick, stubby lashes, but the set of his mouth told her that he was not pleased.

"You'd best be careful, Margie, that some of Elmer's cynicism doesn't rub off on you."

"Oh, Lord! You're right. I can't let that happen. But it's so hard when he says . . . those things." Her eyes were torn away from his face when Anna Marie ran to her and threw herself in her arms.

"Margie! I haven't seen you all day. Can I give you a hug?"

"There's nothing in the world I want more than a hug from you right now." She wrapped her arms around the child, closed her eyes and breathed in the sweet, innocent smell. "I've missed you."

"I 'bout know the rest of my ABCs."

"Forevermore! When did all of this happen?"

"While I was riding with Aunt Grace. She likes me."

"I'm not a bit surprised at that."

"Do you like me?" Anna Marie's arms were tight around her neck.

"More than you know." Margie glanced at Brady and found him gazing at her. She hugged the child and closed her eyes as her mind went back to when she had asked her granny why her daddy didn't like her.

He likes you, honey, He just doesn't know how to show it. That had satisfied her for a while, but later she had known differently.

Margie opened her eyes to see Brady still watching her. One long leg was stretched out, the other bent at the knee, his arms resting on it. She pulled her eyes away from his quiet face and tickled Anna Marie's nose with the end of her braid. The child giggled happily and hid her face against Margie's shoulder.

"Can I ride with you tomorrow? I'll sing my ABCs."

"Ah . . . I don't know, honey. We'll have to talk that over with your uncle."

"Can I, Uncle Brady? Please. I'll be nice."

"I'm feeling left out, Punkie. It's my turn to have you ride with me. I want to hear the songs you've learned and hear you sing the ABCs."

"Maybe Margie can ride with us. Can you, Margie?"

"I don't know about that either, Punkie," she said, using Brady's pet name for his niece. "Look now, Rusty has the guitar, and Mr. Putman is going to play the fiddle."

"All right, folks." Alvin's booming voice reached out over the campground. "Let's sing a few hymns. We'll start out with 'The Old Rugged Cross.' I think everyone knows that one. If anyone has a favorite, holler it out."

Alvin waved the bow of the fiddle like a baton. He and Grace started the singing, and as soon as the crowd gathered around the campfire joined in, he played the tune on the fiddle. Rusty picked chords on the guitar.

When the song ended, they sang "Shall We Gather at the River" and "In the Sweet Bye and Bye." Then someone suggested "Red River Valley." Alvin passed the fiddle to Rusty, then pulled Grace up beside him, and they sang the ballad in harmony.

When they finished, Jody called out, "Sing a cowboy song, Rusty."

"Which one?" he asked, and he and his father changed instruments again.

"How about 'Strawberry Roan'?"

Rusty sat down and casually let his hand drop to Mona's shoulder to make sure she was still beside him. The touch was noticed only by his mother. When he began to strum the strings of the guitar with slender, knowing fingers, all conversation ceased. He lifted his head and flashed a sudden bright smile around the circle and began to sing.

"Oh, that strawberry roan, oh, that strawberry roan,
He goes up in the east, comes down in the west,
To stay in his middle, I'm doin' my best,
Stay on that strawberry roan, stay on.
Stay on that strawberry roan!"

Rusty was a natural entertainer. His voice had a husky throb that drifted gently on the night breeze. The crowd was enthralled. When he finished the song, they clapped and shouted, "More, more!"

"All right." Rusty was smiling. There was no doubt that he was enjoying himself immensely. "How about 'The Cowboy's Lament'? It's got a lot of verses, if you can put up with them." Laughter followed his words, and he began the sad song.

> "As I walked down the streets of Laredo,
> As I walked out in Laredo one day,
> I spied a poor cowboy wrapped up in white linen,
> Wrapped up in white linen as cold as the clay."

Even the excited children were quiet as Rusty sang verse after verse of the sad song about a cowboy who had done wrong. When he finished, they were silent for a few seconds, then clapped their appreciation.

Chapter 10

Rusty has an amazing memory," Margie said. "Imagine being able to play the violin and the guitar without being able to see them."

Brady grinned. "I think he has a crush on Mona."

"Goodness. I hope that she'll be kind to him if she can't return his affection."

"She seems to be taken with him."

"I hate to think of what Sugar would say to that." Margie snuggled the sleeping child close to her.

"Because he's blind?" There was resentment in the softly spoken words.

"She calls him a dummy."

"Dummy? He's got more brains in his little finger than she's got in that head of hers."

"Maybe, but it's a pretty head. You have to admit to that."

"Mrs. Luker is a different breed of cat."

"What do you mean?"

"She's like an alley cat. She'll never be satisfied with one man. My guess is that she's using Foley to get to California and will dump him as soon as they get there."

"He seems to be completely in love with her."

"She's got him bamboozled, all right. He'll wake up and find himself alone, broke and depending on his kids in his old age." Brady moved to take Anna Marie from Margie's lap. "Punkie's asleep. I'll lay her down here on the blanket."

"No. Let me hold her." Margie pulled Anna Marie's dress down over her thin little legs and cuddled the warm, trusting little body. "I hope her aunt will love her and give her a good home."

"I'll not leave her until I'm sure she'll be all right." He turned his face away, but not before Margie saw that his eyes were bleak and bitter.

"Is the aunt married?"

"She was. I don't know if they're still together. Brian said something about her husband being a fly-by-night."

"A child needs a mother and a father."

"My brother doted on her, but she never had much of a mother. Becky was the most selfish, self-centered person I've ever known." His eyes had turned hard. There was not a flicker of kindness in their depths.

"Elmer never had any use for me. I was lucky to have my grandmother."

"Have you noticed how Punkie's always asking people if they like her? I suspect that Becky told her many times that she didn't even like her."

"How could she have been so cruel?"

"When Punkie was just a little tot, Becky got mad at her for some little thing and told her that she hated her. Brian slapped Becky then. And he loved that woman with every breath in his body." He bit out the words, low, husky, angrily.

Margie turned questioning eyes to him, but he was looking toward the campfire. At the memory of Anna Marie's mother, he had bristled like an enraged porcupine. He turned to Margie, and their eyes clung for a breathless moment. Strange sensations went zigzagging along her nerves.

"Poor little thing," she said almost to herself.

The campfire was dying down and the gathering breaking up. Folks were picking up their sleeping children and calling to those who had been too excited to sit still.

"Don't look so worried. I'll bring Alvin over," Brady said as he saw the expression of anxiety move over her face when she lost sight of the man she had come to talk to. His voice was sincere and had almost the same tone he used when talking to Anna Marie. He got to his feet and walked away.

Margie hadn't realized how comforting Brady's presence was until he left her sitting alone on the blanket holding the child. Grace was saying good-bye and wishing the other travelers good luck, her voice friendly as she called out that she hoped to see them again on down the line. Mona helped Rusty put the instruments in the cases, and Jody folded Grace's canvas chair and took it to the truck.

"I'll take Punkie." Brady was back beside her. "Alvin will come over to my car."

He lifted the child from her arms, stood and reached to help her up. She was grateful for the strong hand. Her legs were trembly from sitting so long. After regaining her balance, she released his hand and followed him to his car.

"She should have her little face and hands washed before she's put to bed." Margie watched as Brady removed the child's shoes and stockings.

"I've been washing her in the morning. I'm going to have to find a place soon to wash her clothes."

"Margie?" Alvin's voice came from behind her. "You wanted to see me?"

As Margie turned, Brady closed the car door and moved away. She called to him, "Brady, you don't have to go. What I have to say isn't confidential."

"If you're sure." He moved close. His hand found hers behind her back, and he interlaced her fingers with his.

"I'm sure. Mr. Putman, I traveled this road as far as Sayre, Oklahoma, last summer. Just this side of Sayre, at Andy's Garage, is where the man I had hired to take me to California stole my money and ran off and left me. The people there took me in and helped me get part of my money back—enough to get home. Andy had a nice campground, and when I was there, he even lent washtubs to people who needed to do their washing." Margie explained about Andy selling the garage and that it was probably called Deke's Garage now. "Deke is a funny little man, but oh so nice."

"Our map suggests we go on to Texola."

"Oh, well . . ." Disappointment slumped her shoulders. "Will you at least pull in there so I can say hello?"

"Elmer wouldn't stop if you asked him?"

"Heavens no. If he thought it was what I wanted, he wouldn't stop if he was out of gas."

"Ride with me tomorrow," Brady said. "We'll stop so you can see your friends."

"I can't!" she exclaimed fearfully. "If I do, he might not let me back in the truck, even to get my things."

"Dammit to hell," Brady swore, then spoke to Alvin. "Would it not be worth a short day to have a place to wash?"

Alvin removed his hat and scratched his head. "Grace is anxious to wash and tidy up the truck. All right," he said after a few moments of silence. "If there's room for the four of us, we'll stop at the garage. It might be that Foley can get some work done on his radiator. It'll have to be done before we cross the desert."

"Oh, thank you." In her excitement Margie squeezed Brady's hand tightly.

"Do you know what has caused the change in Elmer? When I first met him, he wasn't this disagreeable." Alvin slapped his old felt hat back on his head.

"To tell you the truth, I don't know him very well. He's always been . . . ah . . . distant with me. But he had friends back in Conway and was congenial with his customers at the icehouse."

"Maybe it's the strain of the trip, and he'll get into the swing of things in a day or so."

"Don't count on it, Mr. Putman," Margie said sadly.

"Well, good night. I doubt that we'll get an early start. We'll have to wait for Foley and his 'bride' to get back." Alvin walked off into the darkness, leaving Margie alone with Brady.

"I'm so glad we'll stop at Deke's. Thank you for speaking up. Deke will tell you that I didn't take Ernie's money."

"You don't have to prove that to me."

"Yes, I do. I can't bear for someone to think I'm a thief and a . . . loose woman. There's nothing I can do about the last, but I can at least prove that I'm not a thief."

He turned her toward him and tipped up her chin with his thumb. She lowered her lids and refused to look at him.

"Look at me. You've hardly glanced at me all evening. If I didn't know better, I'd think you were ashamed of something."

"I'm not!" She lifted a rebellious face to glare at him.

"Then hold up your head and act like it. You'll be stepped on if you're lying down but not if you're standing up looking folks in the eye."

"You think I'm silly for wanting to see Hollywood."

"I've not said that."

"Elmer does. He sneers every time I look at a movie magazine."

"I'm not Elmer."

His eyes searched her face. His thumbs beneath her chin refused to allow her to lower it. Suddenly he smiled. A pulse began to flutter lightly in her throat. His expression grew tender, and he reached to brush a lock of hair from her face. His hand cupped her cheek, then moved down her arm to grasp her hand and pull her around to the other side of the car.

"What are you doing?"

"I want to kiss you again."

"Why?"

"Because you're pretty and sweet and . . . I want to."

"And because you think—"

"Don't even think it!" he said quickly. The sweet softness he felt when he held her against him sent a powerful longing coursing through him.

She was drained of thought and will and just managed to whisper shakily, "Please."

Moon and sky were blotted out by his dark face. His mouth was gentle even though he kissed her deeply, again and again, as if he had long been thirsty and was drinking at a cool well. The feel of his lips was strange and caressing. A feverish pounding in her temples spread to her stomach and lower. His hand slipped down to her buttocks, holding her there, his hard muscular thighs forcing intimate pressure upon her. Euphoria spread throughout her taut body, relaxing her painfully tensed muscles. Tomorrow she would probably hate herself and him, but that was tomorrow. Right now she felt a wondrous warmth suffusing her.

His mouth was persistent, ardent, relentless, snatching away her breath as well as her poise. There was a rightness to the sensation of his hands on her buttocks pressing her closer. Then the feeling of something rockhard pressing against her lower stomach jerked her to awareness that this was going too far too fast. With a sob in her throat she began to struggle.

He raised his head. He was trembling. She could feel the tremor in the body pressed to hers and suddenly remembered Ernie Harding pressing her up against a tree in a dark campground—

"Stop! Please stop!"

The scared way she looked at him caused a hot flash of anger to wash over him.

Hell, it was only a kiss. He wasn't raping her!

"What's the matter?" he growled. "What's the harm in a few casual kisses? You've done it before."

Casual kisses. His words sent a cold chill throughout her body. She strove to pull back, but his grip was too strong. The thought that she had been used to provide him with a cheap thrill was so humiliating she wanted to sink into the ground. She swallowed dryly, feeling the frantic clamor of her throbbing pulses even as some devil prodded her to bait him.

"No harm at all. I've been wondering how good a kisser you were. I got only a little sample the other night. Not bad . . . for a cowboy."

"Think so?" A new wave of anger made his skin hot. He lowered his face until it was only a breath away from hers. "That wasn't even my top-of-the-line kiss." One of his hands gripped the nape of her neck; the other was flat against the small of her back. Before she could retort he clamped his lips to hers.

His mouth savaged hers relentlessly, prying her lips apart, grinding his teeth against her inner lips. She tried to drag her head back; but his hand held her in position, and she couldn't wrench it from his grasp. His teeth were biting into her lips, his fingers wound into her hair; she moaned in pain and struggled. He was taking her breath. When she thought her lungs would burst, he moved his mouth to the side of her face, and she took in great gulps of air through her open mouth.

She tried to speak, to protest, when she realized his hand was on her breast, but her voice seemed to have dried up. Her heart was racing, and she felt a sudden revulsion in the pit of her stomach.

He looked down into her face, his breath quick and

warm on her wet mouth. Trembling, she shook her head in silent disappointment.

"Is that how you wanted it? Hard? Rough? Is that how Ernie kissed you before you accused him of stealing your money?" he asked in a strangely thickened voice, anger making him say things he'd later regret.

Helpless tears gathered in her eyes. The moonlight shone on her face, making them look like stars.

"So you *did* believe him." *I hate you*, she silently shrieked. Her disillusion was so complete she went cold and stiff. Through swollen lips she whispered on a ragged breath, "Get away from me."

"Gladly." He withdrew his hands from her body, held them up palms-out and stepped back. Anger at her rejection dissolved the hunger that tormented him.

He forcibly kept himself from saying anything more as he watched her move around the car and disappear in the darkness. A mix of anger and regret pervaded him. He scowled to himself and wondered what devil in him had caused him to manhandle her like that. But once he had started, he couldn't seem to stop.

Damn her!

He didn't want to feel anything for her. Pacing alongside the car restlessly, he hated the strange, twisted feeling that churned about inside of him. For a minute he had felt the twinge of desire to know love, but seconds later he discarded the idea. That wasn't what he wanted. He couldn't afford to be tied down.

Well, what the hell to do now? He'd sure made a mess of things.

* * *

Margie was weary but calm now. She had managed to stumble through the darkness to the truck, climb into her bunk and survive a horrible night. *A few casual kisses.* They had meant no more to him than that. She had been stupid to think they might have meant more. In spite of all he had said, *he did believe Elmer's characterization of her as a thief, a shallow, silly woman with her head in the stars.*

Heartbroken, she had cried herself to sleep.

This morning, with her back to the Putman camp, where Brady and Anna Marie were having breakfast, she had fried mush and boiled coffee without breaking down.

The shock of having Elmer shred her character to Brady, followed by Brady's treatment of her, had sapped her strength and controlled her thoughts. Overnight it had worn away to some extent, and she had regained some of the use of her mind. Now, after pouring water on the campfire, she leaned against the side of the truck, ready to leave the campground when Elmer started the engine.

Elmer had appeared, eaten his breakfast and prepared for the departure without as much as acknowledging that she was there. Now he sat in the truck, waiting for Alvin to take the lead and pull out of the campground.

Foley and Sugar returned at sunup. Sugar was not happy to see Mona and Jody with the Putmans, Mona helping Grace put away the breakfast things and Jody coming out of the woods with Rusty.

"I wanted coffee," she said in a loud, angry voice. "They've not even started a fire."

"You've had coffee, Sugar." Foley had backed the car up to the trailer and was working on the hitch.

"I wanted some to take with me." Her voice was like that of a spoiled child.

"I'll stop and get you some as we go through Oklahoma City," Foley said patiently.

"I thought we were going to have a good time last night." Sugar paced back and forth alongside the car. "The dance floor in that run-down joint you took me to was no bigger than the top of this car."

"It was the nearest one without going into town."

"The booths were full, and there was no place to sit. How did you expect me to have a good time in a ratty place like that?"

Foley straightened and looked at her. "Other folks were having a good time. You danced—"

"Only with you!" She stopped, put her fists on her hips and glared at him.

Her words brought him to his feet. He stared at her for a moment.

"Well, damn!" He turned his back and continued working on the car hitch.

"Oh, honey . . . darlin', I'm sorry." Sugar ran to him, wrapped her arms around him from behind and pressed her face to his back. "It's just that this trip isn't what I thought it would be."

Foley turned, and instead of putting his arms around her, he gripped her shoulders, held her away from him and looked down into her face.

"I told you before we started that it would be a hard

trip and that we had to be saving with the money or we'd not have enough to get a start in California."

"But we're never alone, and we have to kowtow to that stiff-shirt about where we stop and how long we stay."

"Alvin organized this trip. He's doing a damn good job. Didn't you learn anything from the other night? It's safer to travel in the caravan."

"Let them go on. We could stay here for another day or two."

"And do what?"

"We'd think of something," she said coyly, and tried to snuggle close to him. "Let the kids go on with Brady. We'll catch up."

"Are you out of your mind? My kids stay with me."

She jerked away from him. "You love them more than me," she accused, and managed to put a sob in her voice.

"Of course I love them. They're my flesh and blood." Foley pulled her into his arms when she began to cry. "You'll understand when you have children. You said you wanted some."

"I . . . don't now."

"Course you do. You're just tired. In a couple days we'll be in Amarillo. Think of that. We'll go out dancing again. Now, dry up. The kids are coming."

"The kids are comin'," she echoed, then pulled away from him and got into the car.

"I did not!" Mona was laughing and protesting something her brother had said as they passed the car. They went on to where their father was attaching the trailer to the rear.

" 'Lo, Daddy. Have a good time last night?"

"Sure did, honey. How about you? Didn't you make a fire?"

"The Putmans asked me and Jody to eat with them."

"That was good of them."

"They had a singing last night, Daddy," Mona said. "Everyone in the campground came."

"Mr. Kinnard didn't come," Jody interjected.

"No one was surprised at that. Both Mr. Putman and Rusty played the violin and the guitar." Mona was in such a happy mood she didn't even think about her voice carrying to Sugar in the car.

"Mr. and Mrs. Putman sing harmony like you and Mama used to do," Jody said.

"Rusty sings and writes songs," Mona added. "He's writing one about the highway. Only one verse so far, but he'll finish it before we get to California."

Jody picked up the tools Foley had been using. "I bet there was forty people around the campfire last night. I wish you had been there, Pop. You like to sing."

"Sounds like you had a good time." Foley took a rag out of his hip pocket and wiped his hands as Alvin pulled up alongside.

"Ready to go? We'll stop just this side of Sayre at a place called Deke's Garage if there's room for the four of us. It's a small campground. If we take a short noon, we should get there before it fills up. We may be able to do some washing there."

"I reckon the womenfolks will like that."

"How's the radiator?"

"Sproutin' another leak."

"Let's hope it holds out until we get to the garage. Maybe you can get it fixed there."

"Maybe so."

"Bye, Grace. Bye, Rusty," Mona called. "See you tonight."

Alvin waved and drove on.

"Looks like Mrs. Luker was poutin' again," Grace said. "I reckon she didn't have a good time at the honky-tonk last night."

Chapter 11

THERE WAS NOTHING ABOUT THE DAY that was different from the day before except that the wind was stronger, flinging up fine particles of sand and grit. But not even a beautiful, quiet day could have erased Brady's black mood.

Nothing eats at a man more than realizing he has made a complete ass of himself.

It started during breakfast when Grace made a teasing remark about him and Margie sitting together during the singing and then walking off into the dark together. Brady didn't know what to say, so he said nothing.

Margie had not even glanced at him as he passed on his way to speak to Foley and had managed to be on the other side of the truck when he returned to his car. He sat in it and waited for the Lukers to pull out, then followed the car and trailer down the ribbon of highway.

As soon as Anna Marie awakened, she had gone to a makeshift outhouse with Mona, then came back to the car. Now she slept curled up beside him in the front seat, her head on the pillow he had dragged up from her bed in the back.

On the outer edge of Oklahoma City the two trucks and the cars stopped for gas at different stations. Alvin waited along the shoulder of the road until they were lined up again, then pulled out onto the highway.

The land west of the city was flat and green from spring rains. They passed through the small town of Bethany, then crossed the Canadian River. After Yukon, the next town was El Reno.

Brady regretted that there would not be time to visit Fort Reno, where the Remount units of the United States Cavalry, essentially cowboys, broke and trained horses and mules. Some of the stock was shipped to such far-away places as the South Pacific, Burma and China, where Americans were stationed.

The Kinnard truck was a hundred feet or so ahead of Foley Luker. Brady could see it up ahead and envisioned Margie silently looking at the same landscape he was seeing.

He had decided last night, while he tossed and turned on the bedroll he had thrown out beside the car, that he didn't have good sense when he was around that woman. It was why, he reasoned, he couldn't keep his hands off her.

Why in the hell hadn't he just let her go instead of dragging her behind the car to kiss her?

If he had half the brains he was born with, he'd sell the car when they reached Amarillo, the next large town, and take Anna Marie to California on the train. After she was settled with Opal, he'd hitch a ride back to Colorado and work like hell to build up his ranch.

While Brady was deep in thought, Foley slowed suddenly. Brady's hand shot down to keep Anna Marie from rolling off the seat when he was forced to slam on the brakes to keep from smashing into the back of the trailer hitched to Foley's car.

"Damn! What's goin' on up there?"

"That's enough," Foley shouted, and looked over his shoulder to glare at his daughter. "I'm sick and tired of this bickering between you two. It's going to stop! Hear?"

"I've had about all of her I can take!" Mona's shout was as loud as her father's. "I can never do anything to suit her."

"Mona . . . this isn't the time," Jody said.

"It'll never be the right time with her," Mona retorted, and shook her arm out of her brother's grasp. "Know what, Daddy? I had a good time at the singing last night, and I just . . . I just wanted to tell *you* about it. She had to chime in and ruin it." Angry, reckless words poured from the girl. "And she has no right to call Rusty a dummy."

"She didn't mean it the way you took it." Foley sent another glance over his shoulder.

"Yes, she did. She thinks everyone is a dummy but her! Even you, Daddy, if you want to know the truth."

"I'm warnin' you, Mona!"

"Rusty's smarter than she'll be if she lives to be a hundred. Can she play the violin? The guitar? Does she know anything about President Roosevelt's New Deal or that German overseas who's stirring things up? Rusty can talk about a lot of things. All she knows is how to make life miserable for me and Jody and how to butter you up."

Frustrations of the last few months bubbled up and came spewing out of Mona's mouth like a fountain.

"This constant bickering between you two is driving me crazy!" Foley slammed on the brakes and slowed the car to a mere crawl.

"I'm sorry, darlin'. I'm sorry." Sugar ran her hand up and down the inside of Foley's thigh. "I worry that Mona is becoming too attached to a hopeless cripple. The man will have to be taken care of for the rest of his life. Do we want our girl tied to a man like that?"

"*Our* girl?" Mona yelled. "I'm not your girl just because my daddy married you. I had a mother who never said unkind things. She never called me a warthog or told me I was ugly and would never get a man. And Rusty is not a helpless cripple!"

"See there, darlin'? They've already got her hooked into feeling sorry for him. How else will they get a woman to take care of a blind—"

"Just . . . shut up!" Mona yelled, and burst into tears.

"She'll never let me be a mother to her," Sugar whispered to Foley with a broken sob. "The Putmans have turned her against me."

"Mona, you will have respect for my wife—"

"How about her having respect for . . . me?" Mona's voice broke as she sobbed.

"I never called her fat and ugly," Sugar whispered, desperate to get Foley's attention.

"Yes, she did, Pop." Jody leaned forward. "She's been on Mona's back since the week after you married her. More so since we started on this trip."

"It was for her own good, darlin'. I wanted her to take pride in herself and be *pretty*."

"Shut up!" Foley shouted. "All of you, just shut up!" He slammed his foot down on the gas pedal, and the car shot ahead.

Behind Brady, in a Model A Ford coupe with a rumble seat, the driver swore.

"What the hell they slow down for?"

"Hell, I dunno. Stay back a ways. I ain't wantin' that asshole cowboy knowin' we're behind him." Homer Persy sat with his booted foot up on the dashboard.

Homer's Uncle Chester had borrowed the car, or rather taken the car, from his mother's barn, where it had been sitting since his father's death a year ago.

"I ain't knowin' why yo're all put out 'bout taking Granny's car." Homer let his arm dangle out the window. "She can't drive it nohow."

"It was Pa's. She's got a fondness for it, and she's still grievin'."

"How long's she goin' to grieve, fer God's sake?"

"Ma'll be back from Sister's in a week. I got to have the car back 'fore then."

"Don't worry, Uncle Chester."

"I'm worried and I'm tired. We drove like hell to catch up with these yahoos. Where we goin' to get gas money to get back home?"

"The one with the slutty woman has money. She said he sold his ice business. He'da not put it in the bank the way they're goin' bust."

"How you figure to get it?"

"The time will come."

"It better come soon."

"I got it all figured out, Uncle."

"Stop callin' me that. Makes me feel like I got one foot in the grave already. I ain't but eight years older than you."

"Lordy. You must be damn near thirty. That's older than dirt. Are ya too old to get it up, *Uncle*? Is your pleasurin' days over, *Uncle*?" Homer pushed his hat back on his head and let his foot drop to the floor of the car.

Chester ignored the jabs. "Whatta ya mean you got somethin' figured out?"

"I ain't got but ten dollars in my pocket. How much you got?"

"Not that much. Ya said ya had money."

"I didn't say I had it. I said I know where to get it. And I do."

"You'll not be gettin' any more from your pa. That's certain."

"I'll never ask that tight-ass for another dime. There's folks along this highway just sitting there askin' for their money to be took."

"And there's police along this road just waiting for them that take it. We was lucky back at that campground. I still ain't figured why that sheriff let us go."

"We didn't rob anybody, that's why. He couldn't arrest us 'cause someone *thought* we was goin' to rob them. 'Sides, he took our guns. The asshole will sell 'em and make a little extra money. All them lawmen are crooked as a snake's back. But I'm well-heeled. I got me a shotgun in the rumble seat and a forty-five right here in my coat pocket."

"Well, I don't want to tangle with that cowboy. He don't look like he's got no quit a-tall. He's all yours."

"I ain't no fool. I won't go against him head-on. When his tires get slashed, he ain't goin' to know who done it. When he gets bashed in the head some dark night, he ain't goin' to know who done it. When I screw the eyeballs out of that blonde, he ain't goin' to know who done it."

"You better hope he don't. You can get yoreself killed screwin' a woman who don't want to be screwed."

"Ah, shit! I've screwed plenty a women that didn't want it. I put the fear in 'em, and they never let out a peep 'bout it after I got done with 'em."

"He might not care if ya screw her eyeballs out."

"He'll care. He stopped and patted her up the night he went to get the rope to tie us up. He'd care even if he didn't like her. Big, upstanding man like him has got to be a hero."

"Do as you want, but I ain't rapin' no women."

"Ain't ya got the balls for it no more, *Uncle* Chester?"

"I ain't wantin' my neck stretched."

"I'm goin' to do whatever'll piss off that cowboy the most before I bash his head in. He ain't gettin' away with what he done to me. I aim to see that he pays." Homer's young face turned hard.

He didn't shit in your pants. You did.

Chester had always known his sister's oldest boy was wild. Now he wondered if he wasn't a little crazy. Robbing a store was one thing; wanting to kill someone was another. This was the first he'd heard him talk about raping and killing. It made him nervous. He took a drink out of a quart fruit jar that sat on the seat beside him. His face twisted.

"Where did you get this rotgut anyway?"

"Ain't nothing wrong with this rotgut. It kicks like a mule. It's supposed to."

*   *   *

"We're passing Fort Reno, Rusty," Grace said. "This is where they break and train wild horses for the army. My, my. There must be a hundred horses in that field. All kinds: pintos, roans, buckskins, blacks, browns, all colors but pink. All look to me like range horses. Course, I ain't never seen a range horse but once. That poor thing was wilder than a turpentined cat. They got good fence around the fields so the stock can't get out. There's men on horseback bringin' in another batch."

Grace continued to talk, painting pictures with words for Rusty. "Lots of buildings here, big barns and quarters for the men. Pretty place, trees and bushes a-growing along the walks. Oh, my, there's two cowboys right there by the fence holdin' on to a mule that's buckin' like crazy.

"What do you reckon they're doin', Alvin?"

"I ain't knowin', sugar foot. But I bet they be knowin'."

"Did you see that, Alvin? That cowboy was a-holdin' on to that mule's ear with his teeth!"

"Doggone if he wasn't."

"Phew! Bet a dirty old ear wouldn't taste good!"

"Sure is flat country out here in west Oklahoma," Alvin commented after they passed the fort. "Not at all like our hills back home."

"Out here is where they're having the dust storms," Rusty said. "I can kind of smell dust in the air."

"I hope we don't have one while we're passin' through. There's a cloud bank in the southwest. Could be bad weather is comin' this way."

Alvin took his eyes off the road long enough to glance at his wife and son. He was a lucky man. They were his life. He'd do whatever he had to do to give them a better future in California. He felt sorry for Foley, the poor bastard. He would never know love and contentment with that baggage he married.

"You've been quiet, son. Have you got something on your mind?"

"No, Ma. Well, yes. I'm thinking about a song I'm writing. The lines 'They are blind that will not see, none so blind as a man like me,' keep going over and over in my mind. I'm trying to put them in a song."

"Oh, son," Grace exclaimed. "That's not like you. It's so sad."

"Folks like sad songs now'days, Ma. The chorus will go something like this:

> *"Come back, love, to my eager arms.*
> *Come back, love, with your magic charms.*
> *Give me hope or I'll change to stone,*
> *Give me love or I'll die alone."*

When he finished singing, Grace grabbed his arm. "That was beautiful. Wasn't it, Alvin? It just made me want to cry."

Rusty laughed. "A good song should make you laugh, cry, or put you in a romantic mood. I'm working on another song. The words will be something like this:

> *"Though my heart is sometimes heavy,*
> *My blind eyes filled with tears,*
> *I only have to know you're near,*
> *And my heartache disappears."*

"That's pretty too. Have you picked out a tune to go with it?" Grace asked.

"Not yet."

"What are you going to call it?" Alvin asked.

"I've not decided, but I may call the first one 'What I See.' I've not decided a title for the second one."

"Call it 'Mona,' " Alvin teased.

"Alvin!"

"It's all right, Ma. That's not a bad idea. I'll tell her you said so, Pa."

"She's pretty. Not a painted-up hussy like her pa married." Grace sent a sideways glance at her son. "Pretty brown hair and eyes and a sweet girl—"

"You don't have to sell me, Ma. Brady already told me."

"Now, when did he do that?"

"While I was riding with him. We had some good talks. Brady knows a lot about a lot of things."

"I thought he was gettin' sweet on Margie. But when I mentioned her this morning, he turned colder than a North Pole well driller. Didn't say another word."

"He was all right with her last night," Alvin said.

"Poor girl. I pity her having to ride all day beside that grouchy father of hers." Grace shook her head and clicked her tongue. "Never did see a pair like 'em. You'd think he'd be proud as punch to have a pretty girl like her for a daughter."

"Well, he ain't. Margie told me last night that she didn't even know him very well."

"What will she do when she gets to California?" There was concern in Rusty's voice. "She surely won't stay with him."

*   *   *

In the truck behind them Margie was worrying about the same thing. What would she do when they reached Bakersfield? She still had to get down to Los Angeles if she was going to see the Hollywood she had dreamed about for so long. She had looked it up on the map. It was a little more than a hundred miles from Bakersfield. If she couldn't get a ride, she'd have to take the bus, which would take a big bite out of the money she had saved to live on.

Would she be able to get a job that paid enough to support her? She had only enough money for a couple of weeks if prices weren't high. Surely she could find a job in that length of time. One thing was sure: She'd lie down on the highway and let the cars drive over her before she'd ask Elmer for help.

All morning he had ignored her as if she weren't there, just as he had done for the past week. When he stopped for gas, he came out of the filling station drinking a bottle of orange soda pop. When the bottle was empty, he put it on the floor and pushed it under the seat.

Brady had been a dark blot on her mind all day. The humiliation of hearing her father tell him she was a whore paled in comparison to having Brady treat her like one. Seeing the cowboys on the horses as they passed Fort Reno brought to mind the fact that Brady wouldn't stay long in California. He would dump Anna Marie on her Aunt Opal and be gone despite his pretending to care for the child.

He had seemed to like and respect her at first. And she had liked him . . . a little too much. It was going to take all the courage she could rake up to endure the rest of the trip knowing that he and Elmer believed her to be a thief and a woman of loose morals.

Well, what did she care? She was going to Hollywood. *But she did care. She cared a lot.*

Brady had said for her to hold up her head and if anyone gave her any sass to spit in their eye.

Oh, Lord, she hoped that she would be able to do that when they camped at Deke's. She would never spit at anyone, but she prayed that she would be able to hold up her head.

Deke Bales was a little man who wore cowboy boots and a big hat. He had been in love with Leona, the woman who lived in the house beside the garage and took care of Andy Connors's girls. While Andy was in the hospital, a big Texan took over the garage and he and Leona fell in love. When Andy got out of the hospital, Yates took him, Leona and the girls to his ranch in Texas.

Margie hoped that they were happy.

The day passed slowly. They paused only briefly at noon because they wanted to get to Deke's before other campers occupied the campground. They passed Weatherford, Clinton and a little place called Foss. When they reached Elk City, Margie knew that they were close.

After leaving Elk City they began to see the signs: CAR TROUBLE? NEED GAS? DEKE'S GARAGE AHEAD. A big yellow sign with black letters read SEE THE WORLD'S LARGEST RATTLESNAKE. DEKE'S GARAGE AHEAD. Another read SEE TRAINED BUFFALO AND THREE-LEGGED CHICKEN. CAMPGROUND FOR A FEW GOOD FOLKS.

When they came up over the hill and Margie glimpsed the nest of small buildings beside the highway, she became misty-eyed. Beside the garage was the house with porches on front and back, a small barn and shed behind it and a privy to the side. As they neared, she could see the campground.

Thank the Lord. It was empty.

Chapter 12

ALVIN PULLED HIS TRUCK off the highway and stopped in front of the garage. Elmer followed. Deke came out wiping his hands on a greasy rag.

"Howdy."

Margie fought nervousness and tried to settle her breathing. Alvin's big body obscured her view of Deke. Seconds turned into minutes. Was Deke not going to let them stay? If Alvin got back into the truck to drive on, she vowed to jump out before Elmer drove away. She was determined to say hello to the man who had helped her when Ernie took her money even if Elmer drove off and left her here. She was sure that Alvin or Brady would come back for her. Then Alvin was coming toward the truck.

"We can camp here," he said to Elmer. "He asks that we leave the campground as we find it. I assured him that we would and said that some of us would buy gas before we left. Is that all right with you?"

"Guess it's got to be."

Relief made Margie giddy. She flung the door open

and got out of the truck. Deke was standing in the open doors of the garage. He was just as she remembered him: bowed legs, buckteeth, a small pug nose, hair like a straw stack and practically no chin. He was near Margie's age and several inches shorter. After she had become acquainted with him, and after he had jumped to her defense heedless of the odds against him, she no longer considered him ugly.

She hurried across the hard-packed drive to the garage.

"Deke! Remember me? Margie."

The little man cocked his head, then opened his arms.

"Margie! Darlin'. Course I remember you." He hugged her, then held her away from him with his hands at her waist. "I wondered 'bout ya, darlin'."

"I wondered 'bout you too, Deke. I'm so glad to see you." The warm welcome brought tears to her eyes.

"I'm glad to see you too, darlin'. Come sit here in the shade and tell me how ya been. I'll get ya a bottle of soda pop. Orange all right?"

Margie sat on the bench. She was aware that Elmer's truck was following Alvin to the far end of the campground, then turned toward the woods in order to make room for the Lukers and Brady. Brady's car passed slowly. Margie didn't look up even though Anna Marie called to her. To Brady and Elmer, Deke's display of affection would just be further proof of her loose morals.

She didn't care.

"Here ya are, darlin'." Deke wiped the water off the bottle of pop with his hand before handing it over to Margie.

"Thank you." Margie tipped the bottle to her lips and took a long swallow. "Oh, this is so good. I was thirsty. Tell me the news, Deke. What do you hear from Leona?

Whatever happened to her brother's boys after Virgil was killed?"

"Leona's doin' fine. The girls love livin' on the ranch. Virgil's boys proved to be pretty good kids. One of 'em is working in the oil field. Another helps me out here once in a while. They're keepin' the family together. But how about you, darlin'? Whoer ya with?" Deke asked bluntly. "Is he treatin' ya right?"

"I'm riding with my father."

"Well, now, that's good to hear."

"Deke, would you believe that Ernie Harding went back home and told everybody that I had stolen his money? My father believes it."

"Why, the sneakin', lyin' polecat! Don't worry, darlin'. I'll set your pa straight on that. I'll take him in to see the records at the courthouse if I have to."

"No. Don't talk to him, Deke. He won't believe you. He wants to think the worst of me. But I would appreciate it if you would tell Mr. Putman how it was. He's very nice. So are his wife and son. I don't want them to think I'm a thief."

"I'll do that. I'll make a point of it. What's goin' on 'tween ya and your pa, darlin'? Yo're not happy, are ya?"

"No. This trip has been a nightmare."

They stood, and Deke slipped the empty pop bottle into a rack. "Come to the house. I want ya to meet my mama."

"Deke, I wanted to stop here so bad I told Mr. Putman that you might let us do some washing. Will it be all right if we heat water in your iron washpot?"

Margie was aware that Brady had come up behind her. She refused to turn and acknowledge him. Her heart jumped out of rhythm, but there was no stress on the face she presented to Deke.

"Course it's all right. For you, darlin', I'd do their washin' myself." He looked beyond Margie. "Howdy, mister."

"Howdy. I was just going to ask if I could draw water from your well."

"Sure ya can. Name's Deke Bales." Deke stuck out his hand.

"Brady Hoyt. Glad to meet you."

After Deke had shaken Brady's hand he said, "It's kind of late in the day to be startin' a washin', but yo're welcome to do it. Them clouds in the southwest looks to me like they may be kickin' up a storm."

Brady tilted his hat and surveyed the clouds. "You may be right. Clouds with a tinge of green sometimes mean hail. I'll speak to Mrs. Putman."

"Margie!" Anna Marie ran to Margie and grabbed her hand. "Guess what? Aunt Grace took me to the privy. It's clean like the one back home."

"Well, that's nice."

"Come on, Punkie. Let's go see Grace."

"I want to stay with Margie. Mister, can I see the chicken with three legs? And the snake?" Anna Marie gave Deke a pleading smile. "Uncle Brady read the signs."

"The snake is in that tank at the side of the garage, little sweetheart. Your daddy will have to hold you up."

"Daddy's in heaven. This is my Uncle Brady, but he looks just like my daddy. How did you catch him?"

"Darlin', I'm the best snake catcher in Oklahoma. I just grabbed hold of that snake, pulled him up out of a hole, threw him over my shoulder and put him in the tank."

Anna Marie looked at him with round, puzzled eyes. "Did he bite you?"

"If he had, I'd justa bit him back."

Margie smiled. "Honey, Mr. Bales likes to tease little girls."

"You're a little honey, that's sure. You go on and look at Mr. Hoover. I call him that 'cause he was the snake in the grass that got us into the Depression. Later I'll take you out to see Mr. Roosevelt, my buffalo, and Mrs. Roosevelt, my chicken. I'm takin' Margie in to see my mama. She's waitin' there on the porch."

Brady took Anna Marie's hand. "We'll see the snake later. We need to go talk to Aunt Grace."

Margie went up the path to the house with Deke. They were met on the porch by a short, heavyset woman with white hair coiled and pinned to the top of her head. She wore a granny dress that fell from her shoulders to her ankles. It was easy to picture her as Deke's mother.

"Mama, this is Margie. Remember me telling you about the girl that was dumped here by that slimy little piece of horse dung who took her money?"

"That was last summer, wasn't it? Hello, Margie. Deke was ready to tear that man up."

"Hello, Mrs. Bales. *That man* left me in the best possible place."

"Come in, dear. I'll make you a glass of tea."

"Uh-oh. I've got a customer. Make yourself at home, Margie." Deke took off down the path to the garage.

"I can't stay long." Margie followed Deke's mother

into the house. "I'll have to get back to the truck and fix supper."

"I was going to ask you to eat with us, dear. You and Deke can visit."

"I'd love to, but I'll have to prepare something for my father."

"He's welcome to come too."

"He wouldn't come, Mrs. Bales. He's kind of . . . difficult."

"All right. After supper you and Deke can visit. Have a seat and tell me about the trip so far."

Margie told Mrs. Bales about meeting Andy Payne, the man who ran from Los Angeles to New York.

"We camped on his land. He came down and gave each of us a big fish."

"I get hungry for fish, but Deke has no time to go fishing these days."

"Mr. Putman mapped out our trip. They had a singing at the camp last night in Oklahoma City. There must have been thirty or forty people there. Both Mr. Putman and his son play the violin and the guitar.

"The night before that, three men intended to rob us but were caught and turned over to the sheriff."

"Oh me, oh my. There's a lot of bad men along the highway now'days. Bootleggers come through here all the time. The bank in Sayre was robbed a few months ago. I worry about Deke. I say, 'Son, if they want your money, give it to them.' But knowing Deke, he'd not do that. He'd fight 'em."

"I'm afraid you're right."

"I tell him that if somethin' happens to him, I'd be all

alone. I want to make him think before doin' somethin' foolish."

Margie spent a pleasant half hour with Deke's mother, then declined a second glass of tea.

"I must go and fix a meal for my father. It was one of the things I agreed to do if he would let me come with him."

"There is a tank out back, dear. Deke filled it this morning so the sun would take the chill off. You're welcome to use it."

"Oh, thank you. I remember bathing in it when I was here before. There's nothing I've been wanting more."

"When you're ready, tell Deke. He'll see to it that no one comes near."

"Will it be all right if I bathe a little girl?"

"Of course. Anyone you want. Deke will empty it and fill it again in the morning."

As Margie passed the garage, she saw that the Luker car had been pulled inside and the front end jacked up. Deke was standing on a box so he could lean in under the hood. She walked on, dreading to pass Brady's car, and was relieved when she didn't see him.

Jody was building a fire beside the Luker trailer. Sugar's tent was up. She wasn't in sight, so Margie assumed that she was in it. Mona was tossing the ball to Anna Marie.

"Mona, Mrs. Bales said that we can bathe in the tank out back. I used it when I was here before."

"You've been here before?"

"This is the place where the man stole my money and ran off and left me. I'll forever be grateful to Mr. Bales for helping to get part of my money back so I could go home."

"He's strange-looking."

"That may be," Margie snapped. "But he's a lot nicer than some *big, so-called handsome men* I've known."

Mona noticed the dull red that covered Margie's cheeks and wondered what she had said to cause it.

"I wasn't saying anything against him, just that he's strange-looking."

"Not after you get to know him."

"Can I go with you and Mona?" Anna Marie swung on Margie's hand.

"We're going to take a bath in a tank. You can go if it's all right with your uncle."

"I'll ask him," Mona said. "Mr. Bales is going to put a new radiator in Daddy's car. That means that we'll stay here all day tomorrow. We'll have time to do the wash and for it to dry. I'll wash my clothes and Jody's, but I'm not washing Sugar's."

"We'll go to the tank right after supper."

Margie made egg toast. She beat eggs, dipped in slices of bread and fried them in the big iron skillet. After she'd stacked a half dozen slices on a plate, Elmer miraculously appeared with his knife and fork in hand.

"Gettin' kind of hard up, ain't ya?" he said as he picked up the plate.

Margie was stunned. He hadn't spoken to her in days. It took a few seconds for his words to sink in.

"What do you mean?" She knew what he meant, but she wanted to hear him say it.

"I saw ya lovin' up to that ugly little freak."

"Don't you dare call Deke a freak. He's more of a man than you'll ever be."

Elmer's mouth made a thin line. He glared at her with

cold eyes but didn't retort. Margie was suddenly awash with anger. Loud, reckless words poured from her mouth.

"He's got more decency in his little toe than you've got in your whole damn body. He's a kind, decent human being. Something that you're not!"

"Watch your mouth—"

"Then watch yours. I heard you shredding my reputation. You want people to think I'm a loose woman, a strumpet. You know it isn't true."

"Bullfoot. All I know points to it." Elmer went to the other side of the truck. She followed.

"Since we started on this trip you've treated me like I was something that had just crawled out from under a rock. I'm tired of riding all day with a mean, grouchy, self-centered old penny-pincher who doesn't have enough manners to fill a thimble."

"Then get your stuff and get out."

"Oh, no! You're taking me to California like you promised. I've lived up to my part of the agreement, you'll live up to yours."

Margie climbed into the truck, despising the tears that flooded her eyes and desperately wishing she were anywhere but here. Not wanting anyone to see her give way to tears, she pulled the rope that dropped the tarp at the end of the truck bed. Everyone in camp must have heard her shouting. It would only confirm what Elmer had said about her. It would give them all something to talk about.

She sat down on the bunk and let the tears flow. After a few minutes she straightened her shoulders, pushed her hair back and wiped her eyes. She would gain nothing by sitting here feeling sorry for herself. She would go take a bath, hold up her head, and if anyone gave her any sass, she would spit in his eye! That went for Mr. Brady Hoyt too.

Margie cleared up the supper dishes, then climbed into the truck to get a clean towel and soap. When she got out, Brady was waiting with Anna Marie.

"Ready to go, honey." Margie ignored Brady and smiled at the child.

"I got soap."

"So do I. Let's go get Mona." She held her hand.

"Margie—"

"Yes." Her voice was as cold as she could possibly make it.

"Will you wash her hair?"

"Of course. Come on, honey."

Margie thought she heard him mutter something as they walked away. But she didn't care to hear what it was. Her attention centered on the four Lukers standing beside the camping trailer.

"Why didn't you tell me that there was a bath facility here?" Sugar demanded. She stood apart, accusing all of them.

"I didn't know," Mona said. "Margie told me." With a towel over her arm Mona turned as Margie approached. "Didn't you?"

"Yes, I did. Are you ready to go?"

Sugar whirled around and headed for the garage. "Well, I guess I'll just have to go ask that pig-ugly little monster myself."

Margie stepped in front of her. "I'm in no mood to put up with your hateful attitude, Mrs. Luker. Don't insult my friend again unless you want a handful of that dyed hair pulled out of your mean, stupid head!"

"Well, who do you think you are?" Sugar sputtered.

"I know who I am. Hasn't anyone ever told you who you are? You're a self-centered bitch. And you've got the manners of a guttersnipe. Come on, girls."

"Ha, ha, ha." Mona chortled softly as they walked toward the garage. "You sure told her, and I'm glad you did it in front of Daddy."

"I get tired of always trying to do the right and polite thing and letting bitches like Sugar walk over me. I guess you heard me yelling at Elmer. He'll probably leave me here."

"You could ride with Brady."

"I would not ride with Brady. He—" Margie would have said more, but she looked down to see Anna Marie tilt her head to look up at her. The child was drinking in every word that was said and no doubt would repeat them to her uncle.

Deke was squatted beside the radiator he had taken from the Luker car.

"Will you be able to fix it?" Margie asked.

" 'Fraid not, darlin'. I'll have to get another one from Elk City. I know a fellow over there who does salvage work. He'll have one or know where I can get one." He stood wiping his hands. "Ready to jump in the tank? I put a tarp around it since you was here. I'll go let it down."

"This is Mona Luker, Deke. Mrs. Bales said she and Anna Marie could bathe with me."

"Howdy, ma'am."

They followed Deke to the tank beside the barn where he pulled on a tarp he had strung on a wire.

"Ain't nobody out back to see ya, darlin', but Mr. Roosevelt and a couple of horses."

"Who's Mr. Roosevelt?" Mona asked.

"My buffalo. I'm not sure he knows he's a buffalo. He's been making eyes at Mama's milk cow." Deke pulled a small platform up beside the tank. "Something for you to step out on to keep your feet from getting dirty. I had to build this for Mama so she could get in the tank."

"Thanks, Deke. It's going to be a treat to take a bath."

"Take your time. Nobody will bother you."

The next thirty minutes were pure pleasure. When Margie sat down, the water covered her breasts. After she had scrubbed herself and washed her hair, she held Anna Marie on her lap while Mona washed the girl's hair, then held her over the water while she rinsed it. Margie loved the feel of the little arms around her neck and the sound of her childish laughter.

After they had all bathed, Margie climbed out, put on her dress and lifted Anna Marie out onto the platform. While Mona was dressing she asked a startling question.

"What are you wearing tonight when Brady takes us to town?"

Margie didn't answer until after she had pulled Anna Marie's dress over her head.

"I'm not going to town."

"Huh? Brady said that—"

"Brady doesn't speak for me." Her tone was sharp.

"Don't you like Uncle Brady anymore?" Anna Marie asked while Margie was tying her shoe.

"I never said anything about not liking your uncle, honey. I'm just not going with them to town."

"Will you stay with me and Aunt Grace?"

"We'll see."

"I know what that means. It means no. Uncle Brady says it sometimes."

When they stepped from behind the tarp and headed back to the campground, Rusty and Jody were sitting on the bench behind the garage.

"You girls took your time," Jody called. "Deke said Rusty and I could be next."

"If I'da known that, I'da picked up a cowpie and put it in the tank," Mona retorted. Her cheeks had turned rosy. Her eyes were on Rusty's smiling face as, with his hand resting lightly on Jody's shoulder, they came toward her.

"See what I have to put up with, Rusty? Let me have that bar of good-smellin' soap, sis. Me and Rusty might want to catch us a girl tonight."

"I left it in the tank."

"No, you didn't. I know you better than that."

"Oh, all right. But it'll take all of it to clean you two up."

"Count me out," Rusty said. "I brought my own."

"Bet it isn't lilac like mine."

"No, it's a plain old bar of P&G."

"Save some for the washpot tomorrow."

As they passed by the garage, Brady was there with Deke.

"Hey there, darlin'," Deke called. "Ever'thin' all right?"

"Fine. The bath was wonderful."

"Get yourself all pretty, we'll go to town tonight."

"Oh, Deke, I don't think so. Not tonight."

"I want to show off my best girl, darlin'." Deke put his arm around her. "When I come waltzin' into the PowWow with you on my arm, old Booger's eyes is goin' to pop right out."

Margie refused to look at Brady when he came out to pick Anna Marie up in his arms. He didn't move away, so she knew that he had to be listening.

"There's a drawing tonight at the picture show if you'd rather go there," Deke said.

"I'll be ready. You decide where we'll go."

"It'll be a while, darlin'."

"Thanks for bathing Punkie." Brady walked away with the child in his arms.

"Are you going with . . . *him*?" Mona asked as they neared the campground.

"Him? You mean Deke? Yes, I'm going with *him*."

Chapter 13

CHESTER STOPPED THE FORD COUPE on the top of the hill when the lead car of the caravan pulled into the space in front of the garage.

"*She-et!*" Homer snorted when the two trucks and the cars followed. "Hell. Looks like they're goin' to camp there. I thought they'd at least pull off the highway onto a back road."

"Whater ya goin' to do now?"

"Shit! Shit! Shit! Drive on. We can't be but a mile or two from a little burg called Sayre."

"How do you know that?"

"Dammit to hell! I can read. The sign way back there said five miles."

"Ya don't have to be so shitty 'bout it," Chester grumbled.

"Things ain't goin' right. I wanted to get at that cowboy tonight."

"Maybe we can go on past and come back through the woods when it's dark."

"I want the car close by."

"Sometimes ya don't get ever'thin' ya want. We're 'bout outta gas."

"We'll get some in Sayre, then go back to Elk City. I saw somethin' back there that looked good."

"I'm hungry too. We ain't et since mornin'."

"If what looks good turns out to be good, ya can have ya a big old fat steak—later on."

"We goin' to hold up somebody?"

"Ain't sayin' till I size the place up."

She needed a haircut. Margie bent over. With her hair hanging from the top of her head, she brushed it vigorously. Then while it was still slightly damp, she parted it on the side, brushed it over and held it back with a shiny clasp.

A dark blue jersey skirt gathered on a wide band and the white blouse that went with it were the only things she owned that didn't need ironing. She dressed, pulled on her stockings and slipped her feet into black pumps. She hated wearing black in the spring, but her white shoes were so run-down at the heels she was ashamed of them.

After touching up her eyelashes with Maybelline mascara she tinted her cheeks with a little rouge and put on her lipstick. Margie studied her face in the small, round hand mirror and wished that she could see the overall effect. Then, again, maybe she was better off not seeing the overall effect, she told herself, and put away the mirror.

The last things she did before leaving the truck were to

dab a little Evening in Paris perfume behind her ears and to make sure the three twenty-dollar bills, all the money she had in the world, were secured with a big brass safety pin to her brassiere.

Elmer was sitting in his canvas chair when she climbed down. Ignoring him, she walked across the campgound and up the path to the house. It was almost dark. A bird wheeled overhead, searching for one last meal before seeking its nest for the night. The chubby figure of Mrs. Bales occupied the porch swing.

"Come on up, my dear, and have a seat. My, don't you look pretty."

"Thank you. It's hard to look presentable when everything you have to wear is crammed in a suitcase."

"Deke will be out in a minute. I'm glad he's gettin' away from here for a while. He sticks close because he doesn't want to leave me alone."

"I've no idea where we'll be going."

"That nice Mr. Putman put Deke's mind at ease. He said he'd keep an eye on things while he's gone."

"And he will. He's very reliable."

"Deke jumped into the tank. That tank's had a workout since suppertime. After the two young fellows, that tall one with the little girl got in, then Deke. Deke will pull the plug and let the water out tonight. It'll be good on the garden."

"I thought we were in for a little rain tonight. I'm afraid of storms especially while camping."

"We've got a good storm cellar. A few weeks ago Deke thought sure a cyclone was comin'. He took me and two camper families to the cellar. It blowed real good, but we only got a dab of rain out of it."

As Mrs. Bales talked, Margie saw the headlights of Brady's car flash on. The car backed up even with the garage and stopped. Deke came out of the house, the screen door slamming behind him.

"I thought I heard you out here, darlin'." He was wearing a white shirt with a string tie. His coarse, straw-colored hair had been slicked down. "Mama, Mr. Putman is goin' to keep an eye out. Switch the porch light on and off several times if you think there's somethin' he needs to know."

"I'll be just fine. Go on with Margie and have a good time."

"Ready, darlin'?"

After saying good night to Mrs. Bales, Margie took Deke's arm and they walked down the path to the garage. When they appeared to be headed for Brady's car, Margie pulled back on Deke's arm.

"Deke? We're not going with them, are we?"

"Darlin', you wouldn't want to ride to town on my cycle. Brady's takin' the kids to town and invited us to go along."

"I want time to visit . . . just with you."

"That makes me feel ten feet tall, darlin'. Come on now, I want to show you off."

Brady sat silently behind the wheel. Mona sat in the backseat between Rusty and Jody.

"Get in, darlin'. Not too close to that old boy. You're my girl tonight."

Margie moved across the seat to make room for Deke. It was impossible not to come up against Brady's long, hard body. She heard him draw in a harsh breath as if being close to her were as unpleasant to him as it was to her. Deke crowded in beside her and slammed the car door.

"All set?" Brady asked.

"All set," Deke agreed, and put his arm across the back of the seat. Margie moved close to him to allow as little contact with Brady as possible. "There's a picture show and a roller-skating rink in Elk City along with a few honky-tonks. In Sayre we have the PowWow right in town and the Starlight farther on down the highway."

"Don't let me keep you from going to the picture show," Rusty said. "I'll enjoy hearing it, and Mona can whisper in my ear and tell me what's going on."

Deke looked over his shoulder as they pulled out onto the highway. "You can't see?" he asked bluntly.

"With my eyes I see a few shadows and a flickering light now and then. But I can hear a cloud passing overhead, so be careful what you say."

"Well, I'll be hornswoggled. I talked to you when you and the young fellow got out of the tank, but I didn't know you were . . . that you were blind."

"Thank you," Rusty said cheerfully. "I've had a lot of practice foolin' folks into thinking I can see."

"Let's stop in down here at the PowWow, Brady, and see what's goin' on. That all right with you, darlin'?" Deke's arm tightened around Margie. "When you get to Main Street, turn left. It's on the next corner. They've got a dance floor and one of them new jukeboxes you put a nickel in. Bootlegger money paid for it, but that ain't none of my business."

Lord, help me get through this evening. Margie was so miserable by the time they parked in front of the Pow-

Wow that she wanted to cry. Brady had said a total of two words. In the backseat Mona giggled, Jody teased and Rusty seemed to be enjoying himself.

The outside of the honky-tonk was decorated with wagon wheels and steer horns. Margie vaguely wondered what they had to do with a place named the PowWow. There was, however, a painted wooden Indian beside the door.

Several cars and two motorcycles were parked in front. Three horses were tied to a rail on the side of the building.

"Some of the boys from the ranch where I used to work are here. Their eyes will bug out when they see ya, darlin'." Deke led the way, with Margie anchored firmly to his side. She was uncomfortably conscious of Brady behind them.

Rusty's arm was tucked inside Mona's, their fingers entwined. "One step up," she whispered when they reached the door.

The large room had booths down two sides of the dance floor and a bar across the far end. On the jukebox Gene Autry was singing "That Silver-Haired Daddy of Mine." Half of the booths were occupied and nearly all of the barstools.

"Hey, Deke. Who opened the gate and let you out?"

"Same damn fool that let you out, cowboy."

"Howdy, Deke. Introduce me to your lady."

"Not on your life, Bulldog. She's not for the likes of you."

Deke was greeted boisterously by friends as he led the way to a booth in the back. It was evident that he was well liked and that he was enjoying the spectacle he was creating.

As she slid into the booth, Margie looked up to see Brady heading toward the bar.

"I'll get us somethin' to drink." Deke said. "What'll ya have, darlin'?"

"Cola, if they have it."

"How about you, Mona?" Rusty asked.

"Cola for me too."

"Lead the way, Jody." Rusty placed his hand on Jody's shoulder. "I'm buying for my girl tonight. You too, if you behave yourself."

They followed Deke back up the line of booths to the bar. Deke stopped along the way to talk to several men wearing big, Texas-style hats.

Mona's eyes were shining. "Isn't Rusty something? I never thought I'd ever meet anyone like him. He called me his girl because that's what Deke called you."

"Don't be too sure. He likes you . . . a lot."

"Do you think so? Sugar is being mean about me and Jody spending time with the Putmans."

"What does your father say?"

"Nothing."

"Then what do you care what she thinks?"

"I'm afraid of what she'll say in front of Rusty. She has no sense at all when she's on one of her tears. She'll have it in for *you* now. Watch out for her."

"There isn't anything she can do to me that hasn't already been done."

"What happened between you and Brady?" Mona asked with the frankness of youth.

"Nothing. There's nothing between me and Brady."

"I thought you liked each other . . . a little."

"No more than I like you and Jody and Rusty."

The music changed on the jukebox. Someone was singing, "I don't know why I love you like I do." Two couples were dancing on the small floor.

"Here they come. Just look at him." Mona's eyes were on Rusty. "You'd never know that he's blind. He's cheerful all the time and so . . . smart."

"Uh-oh. I think you're falling for him."

"I can't help it, Margie."

Deke set a bottle of cola and a glass on the table and then slid in beside Margie with a bottle of beer. Rusty moved over close to Mona to make room for her brother.

"You should've seen Rusty, darlin'. Booger didn't know he couldn't see. Rusty pulled a handful of change from his pocket and counted out the coins just pretty as ya please."

"How do you do that?" Margie asked.

"Easy." Rusty reached into his pocket and put a handful of coins on the table. "The dime is the smallest and usually the thinnest. The penny is next, then the nickel and the quarter."

"Well, doggone if ya ain't right."

Rusty slid the coins off the table into the palm of his hand and put them back into his pocket as a darkwhiskered man stopped at the booth.

"Ya goin' to let me dance with yore woman, Deke?" His watery eyes honed in on Margie and he winked.

"Hell no! You're drunk, Hooter."

"I ain't that drunk."

"Yeah, ya are. 'Sides, I'm goin' to dance with her. Ain't that right, darlin'?"

"Right." Margie gave him her hand. He helped her slide out of the booth. "This is one of my favorite songs."

"Mine too." Deke put his arm around her and pulled her close. She was surprised how smoothly he moved. She hardly noticed that he was a couple inches shorter than she was. He sang softly with his cheek pressed to hers. "On a day like today, we pass the time away, writing love letters in the sand."

"I didn't know you sang, Deke. You should get together with Rusty before we move on."

"The blind boy?"

"He plays the violin and the guitar."

"It'll be a day or two before I can get that radiator fixed. We'll have us a singin' before you go."

When they finished the dance and went back to the booth, Jody jumped up before Margie could sit down.

"May I dance with your girl, Deke?"

"If it's all right with her and if ya promise not to get fresh."

"I swear it. Margie?"

Again Margie was surprised. "Where did you learn to dance, Jody?"

"We danced at home. The folks took us with them when they went to dances, mostly in the homes of their friends. And we had a Victrola. Mama danced with me, and Pop danced with Mona."

"How nice."

"Yeah. I look back and wonder how things can change in such a hurry."

"Maybe they won't be so bad when you get to California and are settled again."

"Sugar had a fit when we left tonight. She wanted to come, but with you and Deke there wasn't room in Brady's car. She accused Pa of letting Deke take the radiator out of their car so he wouldn't have to take her out someplace tonight. I keep wondering how long he'll put up with it."

"I take it she's different from your mother."

"As different as night and day. Mona and I still don't understand how Sugar got her hooks in Pop, but he may be starting to see that she isn't all she pretends."

"He was probably lonely when he met her."

"He had me and Mona."

"That isn't the same. My goodness. Look, Jody. Rusty and Mona are going to dance."

"She probably talked him into it. She likes him a lot."

"I can see that she would. He's a really nice person."

"I can't imagine what it would be like to be blind."

"Especially after being able to see."

"Mona will keep them from plowing into anyone. I'll move up over a little closer so if they bump into someone, it'll be us."

"Jody, if I had a brother, I'd want him to be just like you."

"Thank you, Miss Kinnard," he said, and whirled her around to come beside Rusty and Mona. "Hello, kids. Your mama let you out tonight?"

"We're doin' the town. Can't you tell? Has he gotten fresh yet, Margie?" Rusty asked.

"No, and I don't expect him to, doggone it."

"I could put a bug in his ear."

"I don't need your help, Romeo." Jody flashed him a grin. "And don't get fresh with my sister."

"Jody!" Mona hit her brother on the arm. "Tend to your own business."

Margie's eyes locked with Brady's as they passed near to the bar. He stood with his back to it, his arms folded over his chest. The scowl on his face goaded her into a slow smile.

The cowboy was not having a good time!

They were in the middle of the dance floor when the music ended.

"My turn."

Before Margie's mind could jerk awake to what was happening, Brady had her hand and was pulling her out onto the dance floor and into his arms. She was too surprised to speak and totally unaware the song coming from the jukebox was one of her favorites, "You Made Me Love You."

They swayed to the music for a short while before they began to dance. He turned so that his big body shielded her from those in the booth, held her firmly, lowered his head and pressed his cheek to hers.

"Stop playing up to Deke. He's crazy about you." The words were growled in her ear. She pulled back so that she could see his face.

"He is not. That's just the way he is with everyone. But if he wants his friends to think I'm his girl, it's all right with me," she snapped.

"What will he tell them after you leave to chase your rainbow in Hollywood?"

"*My* rainbow? What about *your* rainbow, cowboy?" She tried to move away from him, but he was holding her so tightly against him that she could only tilt her head back and glare at him.

"What about it?"

"You want to palm a sweet little girl off on someone she doesn't even know so you can go on your merry way free of responsibility."

"You know nothing about it."

"Don't tell me I don't know what it's like to be dumped. It's the story of my life."

"What's put your back up?"

"You don't know? You're the most insensitive clod I've ever met."

"There's a limit to how far you can push me, little tease."

"Your threats just scare me to death."

"I mean it when I say stop playing up to Deke. He'll begin to think you mean it. I doubt he's had many women as good-looking as you pay attention to him."

"Maybe I do mean it. What's it to you? Deke and I understand each other. I don't need you telling me what to do."

"You need someone, you little twit, or you'd not be in the mess you're in." The hand holding hers came to her chin and lifted it. Light green eyes as cold as ice glared down at her.

"Whatever mess I'm in has nothing to do with you, Mr. Know-It-All Hoyt."

"I'm warning you, Margie. Climb down off your high horse or—"

"Or what? Now, let go of me before I kick you. I don't want to dance with you. I don't want anything to do with you."

"Too bad, Miss Mule-Headed Kinnard. We're finishing this dance. And if you kick me, I'll swat your butt right here on the dance floor."

"I'm surprised that the upright Mr. Hoyt would dance in public with a thief and a strumpet."

"Hush up!"

"I won't—"

"You'd better hush or I'll whirl you right out the door and lay my hand down hard on your rear end."

Margie missed a step and stumbled. "And I'd scream 'rape' so loud every man in this place would be on you like a duck on a June bug."

He said nothing, but she knew he was angry. The arms encircling her pulled her so close her breasts were crushed against his chest. She had to admit that she and Brady fit perfectly against each other. She could feel the warmth of his body through her dress, and the wild beating of her heart against his. Was his breath coming faster than usual, or was it just wishful thinking on her part that she had disturbed him just a little?

If I could be with you one hour tonight. If I was free to do the things I might . . .

Margie floated along in a haze, only vaguely aware of the crooning voice coming from the jukebox or that the arms holding her had loosened and now held her gently. Brady pressed his cheek to hers. Her steps matched his as if they had been dancing together forever. She closed her eyes and wished just for an instant that the song would never end. But it did.

Brady took her arm and led her back to the table and shoved her at Deke when he stood.

"Here's your girl. Thanks for the loan."

With a feeling of anger and frustration Brady strode back along the booths toward the bar. As he approached it, he was suddenly knocked off his feet by a meaty fist that slammed into his face.

Chapter 14

WHILE BRADY WAS DANCING WITH MARGIE, two men had come into the PowWow and moved down the bar to stand behind a big, rough man in a billed cap.

"That was a shitty thin' to do," one of the men said to the other. "Slashin' a man's truck tires is low as ya can get."

"Yeah, 'specially when he's got a load in the back."

The man in the billed cap turned slowly around. "Whater ya talkin' 'bout?"

"We was sittin' out front and seen that feller there dancing with the blonde in the blue dress come out and slash a tire on a Model A truck with a side door off. I was sayin' it was a shitty thin' to do."

"Sounds like my truck." The big man slid off the stool. "If it was, I'm tearin' his head off. Back in a minute," he said to the barkeep.

Homer and Chester followed the man outside and heard his roar of rage when he saw his tire.

"That's a damn shame," Chester exclaimed.

"Can we help ya change the tire, mister?" Homer asked.

"I'll change the damn tire after I take the head off that son of a bitch!" The big man headed back into the bar.

Homer and Chester followed. The trucker waited until Brady left the dance floor and approached the bar before he stepped out and planted his heavy fist in his face.

The unexpected blow caught Brady flat-footed. He scarcely saw the man as he backpedaled to gain his balance. The next blow knocked him to the floor. He bounced to his feet like a cat.

"What the hell is the matter with you?"

Brady threw up an arm to weather the windmilling attack of arms and fists. He sidestepped and swung a jarring right to the mouth of his assailant. The blow would have stopped a bigger man, but it merely slowed down the trucker, who let out a bellow of rage and came at Brady again.

"Out! Get the hell out!" The shout came from the barkeep, Booger, who waded in between them swinging a shotgun. "Take your fight outside."

"I don't know what's got his ass up, but if he wants to fight, we'll fight." Brady wiped the blood from his mouth on his shirtsleeve.

"Ya know, ya goddamn tire slasher!" the trucker shouted.

Brady backed out of the doorway and into the space in front of the honky-tonk. While he eyed the man who wanted to whip him, a fierce love of battle welled up inside him. It had been a year or two since he had a good fight, and he was in the mood for it. He didn't know and didn't care what the man's bitch was. If he wanted a fight, he'd get one.

The trucker, tall as Brady but outweighing him by forty pounds, rolled up his sleeves. His friends gathered around him shouting encouragement.

Deke, Jody behind him, spilled out the door and hurried to him. "What's going on?" Deke asked Brady.

"I've no idea. The man wants a fight."

"Get outta the way, Deke. No need you gettin' hurt."

"Brady's with me, Booger. Ya think I'll stand back and let that bunch beat him up?"

"It'll be one-on-one. We'll see it's a fair fight—fer yore sake, Deke, 'cause he came here with ya." Booger cradled his shotgun in his arms. "If it was my tire he slashed, I'd stomp his ass in the ground."

"Whatta ya mean? Slashed whose tires?"

"The low-down polecat was seen slashin' Miller Evans's tire."

"That's a damn lie." Brady stepped out and pushed Deke behind him. "Who says they saw me?"

"Two fellers came in and told me they saw ya doin' it," Evans said, "and I'm taking the price of that tire outta yore hide."

"They lied, but if you want a fight, come on, ya big blowhard." Brady's eyes blazed with a leaping light, and his teeth bared a little.

"Wait, Brady! Wait!" Jody was tugging on Brady's arm. "Your tires have been slashed too."

"What?" Turning his back on the trucker, Brady went to where he had parked his car. All four tires were flat. The car was sitting on the rims. "Son of a bitch!"

"Here's the sheriff. Take over here, McChesney," Booger called. "I've got to get back inside."

"What's the problem?"

"How ya doin', Rex?" Deke said. "Miller Evans come plowin' into my friend here accusin' him of tire slashin'. His truck wasn't even here when we got here. Brady was in the PowWow with me all the blessed time. 'Sides, his tires were slashed too."

"What makes you think this fellow slashed your tire, Evans?"

"He was seen doin' it, Sheriff. Some fellers came in the bar and told me."

"Loaded pretty heavy tonight, aren't you?"

"No more than usual. Got some feed to take to the ranch."

"Got anything under the feed, Evans?"

"Ah, hell, Rex. Maybe a bottle or two. Ain't nothin' to get in a sweat over."

"Where are the men who told you they saw this man slash your tire?"

"I don't know. 'Round here somewheres."

"Find them."

"Hell, Rex. You takin' his side?"

"I'm not takin' any side. Find the men." The sheriff, a tall, thin man with sharp blue eyes, focused them on Brady. "Who are you?"

"Brady Hoyt. Just passing through."

"He's staying at the campground, Rex," Deke said.

"Yeah? Don't suppose anyone saw who slashed *his* tires. It isn't likely he did it himself."

Miller Evans came out of the bar. He eyed Brady but

spoke to the sheriff. "The fellers who told me left when the fight started."

"Someone around here got a grudge against you, Mr. Hoyt?"

"I only got here today. I don't know anyone except Deke."

The sheriff took off his hat and scratched his head. "What'd these fellows look like, Evans?"

"I don't know. One was young, other'n a little older. Offered to help me change the tire. Seemed nice."

"If they were pulling a fast one, they would be. It appears to me that they wanted to stir up a little excitement, and both of you got suckered into it."

"Suckered, hell! I'm out four good tires and tubes," Brady said angrily. "And I owe that hotheaded dungheap a sock in the mouth." He glared at the trucker, who stood slightly behind the sheriff.

"Then come on and give it your best shot!" Evans stepped out, stood on spread feet and glared at Brady.

"Calm down." McChesney stepped between the two men. "You should have asked a few questions, Evans, before you started swinging your fists."

"Well, hell. You'da done the same. Fellers said that they saw him do it."

"I wouldn't have gone off half-cocked like you did. You owe the man an apology."

"Apology? Hell, I'll not be belly-crawlin' for nobody. But . . . I'll help ya change the tires if ya got any to change to."

"I'm not be needin' help from the likes of you," Brady growled.

"Evans, I'll help ya put your spare on, then ya can take

me back to the garage," Deke said. "We'll pick up some tires for Brady."

"The son of a bitch even ruined my spare," Brady exclaimed.

Now that the excitement was over, the onlookers wandered back into the bar. The sheriff was speaking to his deputy, who had driven up. When he finished, he turned to Brady.

"My deputy said that two fellows in a coupe hightailed it out of town a while ago. If they are Evans's witnesses, they're long gone by now. Sorry this happened to you in our town, Hoyt."

"Yeah, well, so am I."

McChesney turned to the trucker. "This settled, Evans?"

"Hell no. It won't be settled till I get my hands on those two shitheads that did this."

"Good luck."

While Deke helped Evans get his spare tire and wheel out of the truck, Brady squatted beside his front tire and wondered if any of the tires would be usable even with a heavy boot placed inside over the hole. If he had to buy four new tires and four new tubes, it was going to take a big bite out of his travel money. When he stood, Margie was beside him holding out a wet towel.

"Thanks." He held it to his face, wiped his cut chin, then his hands. Margie avoided his eyes. He continued to wipe his hands and look at her.

Thinking that she must say something, she said, "I asked the bartender for it."

"You went up to the bar?"

"Sure," she said, raising her chin. "I know my way around bars and speakeasies. Even brothels."

In spite of his cut lip, Brady had to grin.

"Don't go back in there by yourself." He waited a minute, his eyes holding her defiant ones. "You're not going to argue?"

"No. I've taken care of myself for a long time. I don't need your advice."

"Where's Mona and Rusty?"

"Over there." She jerked her head to the side of the building where the couple were standing face-to-face, Rusty's hands on her shoulders.

"Smoochin'?"

"And if they are?"

"I'm jealous."

"Of . . . Rusty?"

"No, because I'm not smoochin' with you. Don't," he said when she turned away. "Give them a little time alone. Do you want to wait in the car?"

"We're goin' back to the garage, darlin'," Deke said before she could answer. "Do you want to go or stay here?"

"I'll stay with Mona and Rusty."

"Keep an eye on her, Brady. I'll bring back boots for the tires and tubes that will get you back to the campground."

"I'll jack up the front end and get the wheels off."

"The trucker is taking Deke back to the garage. Jody's helping Brady take the wheels off the front of his car."

"Anyone paying attention to us?" Rusty whispered close to Mona's ear.

"Brady and Margie looked our way a while ago. But he's busy now, and she's watching him and Jody."

"Will you scream if I kiss you?" Rusty leaned against the building, drew her close and buried his nose in her hair.

"You won't know unless you try."

"I think I will."

"I'll not argue . . ." Her voice was a mere whisper against his mouth.

The warm pressure of his lips sent her senses spinning. They covered hers lightly, his tongue caressing the edge of her mouth. Her arms slid around his neck.

"Soft, sweet, delicious." His voice was no more than a sigh.

"Hummm . . ." A sweet, almost unbearable pain unfolded in Mona's stomach.

"Did you like that, sweet girl?"

"I love it. I've only kissed one other boy, and I . . . didn't like it much."

"He probably wasn't as good a kisser as I am."

"I suppose you've had a lot of practice."

"Yeah, lots." He laughed. "One time. I missed the mark and kissed her eye."

She giggled softly. "I'm glad you're not an expert. I might not be able to stand it."

"I never thought I'd ever meet a girl like you. I hoped I would."

She lifted her palms and caressed his face. "Then you like me . . . a little?"

"More than a little, sweet girl. But I don't want you to get too fond of me. I'm never going to see, Mona."

"I wish you could, even though you might not like me if you could see me and compare me to other girls."

"Don't say that," he scolded, and hugged her tightly to him. "I see you in my mind. Sweetheart, fifty years from now when I'm bald and have lost my teeth, you'll look the same to me."

"Do you think we'll know each other then?"

"I would like to think so. Do I dare kiss you again? Is anyone looking?"

"Jody, but he knows—"

"Knows what?"

"That I . . . like you."

"Do you go around kissing fellows you *don't* like?"

"All the time."

They laughed joyfully and decided that this was the happiest night of their lives.

"Let's get out of here. If that cowboy sees yore face, he'll know it was you who slashed his tires." Chester drove down the dusty road and pulled out onto the highway five miles west of town.

"All right. I've had my fun for now. We'll wait for them in Amarillo."

"I'm not going to Amarillo," Chester said angrily. "I've got to get this car home to Mama."

"We'll send her a telegram. Tell her that you had a call to come to Amarillo. Gordon needed you."

"Gordon? Hell, we've not heard from him in ten years."

"That's why I said Gordon. She said at Grandpa's burial she had a longin' to see her oldest boy."

"Gordon's probably dead by now."

"Don't matter. It'll give us time in Amarillo to hit a few places and wait for the cowboy. Granny'll think yore out doin' good work helpin' her long-lost boy."

"I shouldn't've took her car."

"You still moanin' 'bout that?"

"I ain't anxious to be robbin' more stores either. I ain't wantin' to do no jail time, and I ain't wantin' to get shot."

"Christ, Uncle Chester. What money we got in Elk City ain't goin' to last hardly no time a-tall."

"Ya got more'n fifty from that grocery store."

Homer laughed. "That was slicker than snot. The fool never knowed what hit him. I was in and outta there like a scalded cat."

"Ya'd better not hurt nobody too bad. I ain't for hurtin' anybody."

"Shitfire, Uncle Chester. Ya got no more guts than a crawly worm. Ya got to hurt folks once in a while, or they ain't goin' to respect ya."

"Yo're crazy."

"Might be, but I'm havin' a hell of a lot of fun. After I get a bit more money in my pocket, I'm goin' to find me a woman and have me a high old time. I ain't forgot the cowboy's blonde babe, mind ya. I can wait. When the time is right, I'll screw her into the ground."

"All ya got on yore mind is that cowboy and screwin' women. Beats all I ever did see."

Chapter 15

SHE HEARD A ROOSTER CROWING.

Margie flipped the sheet up over her head. She didn't want to open her eyes and start another day. They had returned to camp last night after midnight, and sleep hadn't come until several hours later. She had lain wide awake for what seemed hours trying to sort out the emotions that were pressing down on her. The events of the past few days were crushing her spirit.

She was disgusted with herself. She was a fool. She was so mad she could scream. She stifled a groan as her mind began summoning back, in feverish detail, the feel of Brady's breath on her face, his arms and how she had melted into them, letting the music wash over her. She had wanted to stay there in his arms forever.

How she could have these thoughts about a man who thought so little of her was the most demoralizing of all.

Margie's common sense told her what she should do, but she seriously doubted that she had the nerve to do it. When they reached Amarillo, she should ask Elmer to let her off in the downtown area. She had no doubt that he would do it. She'd take a bus to California. Then let him explain where she was to the Putmans and to Brady, if they should ask.

She thought briefly of asking Deke if she could stay a few days, help his mother in the garden, then take the bus to California. On second thought, she realized that she couldn't impose on their hospitality.

Right now she had to figure out how to get through the day while avoiding Brady and keeping the others from knowing how really desperate she was.

After breakfast she approached the back of Deke's house, where Alvin was heating water in the iron pot for Grace to do her washing. Margie was relieved to learn that Brady had driven with Deke and Foley to Elk City to find a radiator for Foley's car and tires for his. Jody and Rusty had been left in charge of the gas pump and sat on a bench in front of the garage. Rusty was brushing the burs out of Blackie's thick coat of fur.

After washing her own clothes in a bucket and hanging them on the line, Margie pitched in to help Grace, who had not only her family's wash but Anna Marie's and Brady's as well.

Grace washed the clothes in the iron tub with a scrubboard, all the while chatting with Mrs. Bales.

"My watermelon pickles are good. I won a blue ribbon at the fair one year, a red the next. I'll be hornswoggled if I know what happened that time. Do you soak the rind in lime and cold water to crisp them up before you cook them?"

"Always. Do you add ground cloves or whole?"

"Whole. Stick cinnamon too."

The two talked as if they had known each other forever.

After she had washed a piece of clothing, Grace wrung it out and dropped it in the rinse water. Margie rinsed each piece, wrung it out and hung it on the line.

Anna Marie played happily on the porch, basking in the attention of Mrs. Bales, who had cut a string of paper dolls out of newspaper.

"I saw the chicken with three legs," Anna Marie called out to Margie. "One leg is little and just hangs down. Wanna see? I know where it is."

"As soon as we get through here, honey, we'll take a look at it. Are these yours too?" Margie asked Grace, indicating a pile of clothes on the end of the porch.

"They're Mona's. She's washing for herself and Jody. There was a fuss raised when *Miss Sugar* tried to add hers to the pile. Mona told her daddy in no uncertain terms that she was not washing Sugar's clothes. That man has sure got himself into a mess with that one."

"Good for Mona. I've not seen Sugar lift a hand to do anything but primp."

"She was honeyin' up to Brady this morning. I think she wanted to go to Elk City with the men."

"Did she go?"

"No. For once Foley put his foot down."

Margie rinsed one of Brady's shirts, then took it to the far end of the line and hung it up by the tail so that it would flop in the breeze. It was the blue one he wore the night they sat on the blanket and listened to the music.

"It's a shame about Mr. Hoyt's tires," Mrs. Bales said when Margie came back to the porch. "Deke seems to think it was someone wanting to cause a fight to create a little excitement."

"It did that, all right. When Brady hit the floor, Deke shot out of the booth yelling for Jody to come on and for Rusty to stay and take care of us girls."

"Oh, my. Did he really say that?" Grace asked. "I thank God for men who don't make my son feel useless."

"When everyone went outside, Rusty, Mona and I went along to see what was going on. Deke was right in the middle, between those two big men."

"That boy will tackle anything if he's mad enough. When he's mad, he thinks he's six feet tall," Mrs. Bales said with a click of her tongue.

Margie smiled. "I remember how he went after the man who took my money. He didn't wait for help from anyone."

"Uncle Brady was mad about his tires. He even said a . . . nasty word. He didn't know I was listening."

Grace caught Margie's eye. "Big ears," she mouthed.

"She doesn't miss much," Margie murmured.

"She's smart as a whip." Grace followed Margie to the pump, where she was filling a bucket of water to pour into the iron pot. "I wish I could keep her."

"He'd probably give her to you if you ask. He's going to palm her off on a woman he doesn't even know."

"Brady said he was taking her to her mother's sister."

"Yeah, he said that and that he doesn't know what kind of woman she is. Hasn't he told you about Anna's mother?"

"Not much."

"She wasn't much of a mother, according to Brady. The sister may be the same."

Grace frowned. "He wouldn't leave her with someone unless he was sure she really wanted her and would take good care of her. He cares a lot for that child."

"He puts up a good front. I'll give him that."

"Forevermore! Why do you say that? You liked him . . . at first."

"Never trust first impressions. It takes a while to get to know a person, especially a smooth-talkin' man. I've been burnt before. It'll not happen again."

Margie dumped the bucket of water into the iron pot, then poked a few sticks of wood in the fire beneath it.

"The water will be hot for Mona in no time at all."

"Aunty Grace, Margie—I gotta go."

"Come on, puddin'." Margie grabbed Anna Marie's hand, and they ran toward the outhouse.

When they came out, they were both laughing. "We made it just in time," Margie called to Grace. "We'll go tell Mona she'd better shake a leg and get her wash on the line so it can dry." Swinging hands, they headed for the campground.

At first Margie didn't notice, but when she did, she stopped dead still and a feeling of déjà vu washed over her.

Elmer's truck was gone.

Was history repeating itself? Had he left her here and taken everything she had in the world except the sixty dollars she had pinned in her brassiere and the clothes she had drying on the line?

"Honey," she said to Anna Marie, "go to Mona. She's there in front of the garage." Feeling as if a rock had fallen into the pit of her stomach, she hurried down into the campground where Alvin was tinkering with the motor on his truck. "Mr. Put . . . man?" Her voice cracked.

"Hello, Margie." Alvin brought his head up from under the hood of the car.

"Where did Elmer go?"

"He didn't say." Alvin wiped his hands on a rag. "I heard the truck start up and thought he was working on the motor. Then he pulled out and headed down the highway toward Sayre."

"He didn't say anything?"

"Not to me. And as far as I know he didn't go near Rusty and Jody. He probably went into town to get a few groceries or some ice."

She shook her head. "He heard Deke say the iceman comes today."

"Are you thinkin' he might not come back?"

"I'd not put it past him. He'd think it's what I deserved."

"For what?"

"For being born," she said bitterly.

"He'll be back. I can't believe he'd just go off and leave you or us without some explanation."

"You don't know him like I do."

"I guess I never knew him at all. He was very congenial while we were planning this trip. I haven't been able to get a decent word out of him since that first night up in Missouri. I decided that the best way to get along with him was to leave him alone."

"Everyone probably heard me screaming at him last night. I just lost my patience."

"We heard and . . . frankly Grace and I wanted to give you a pat on the back."

"I'm taking my things out of the truck. That is, if he comes back. Deke will help me get to a bus station. I can't continue on with him. His constant disapproving silence and his sly remarks are making a nervous wreck out of me."

"You could make arrangements to ride with Brady—"

"No!" Margie shook her head vigorously. "Elmer told Brady that I'm a . . . a thief. I'm surprised he hasn't told the rest of you that I'm not fit company for decent folks."

"Brady hasn't said anything. I'm sure he didn't believe—"

"Oh, but he did. But that's . . . Never mind about that. I'm sorry I interrupted your work. I'd better go look after Anna Marie so Mona can do her wash."

"There's a cloud bank building in the southwest. It could mean rain or could be a dust storm."

"Grace has her clothes on the line. It won't take long for them to dry."

"Don't worry, Margie. You've got friends here."

"Thank you, Mr. Putman."

As she passed the Luker tent, she glanced in to see Sugar sitting on the mattress plucking her eyebrows. She was leaning back against a box, her feet on the mattress and her thighs spread, exposing herself all the way up to her crotch. A large bottle of NeHi soda pop sat beside her. Shocked at the vulgar display, Margie hurried on by.

Margie was sitting on the bench with Rusty and Jody was putting gas in a car that had pulled in off the highway, when Brady's car turned in and stopped in front of the garage. His eyes caught hers as soon as he stepped from the car. His bitter stare made the color rise to flood her face. Margie managed to turn and smile at Rusty, although she didn't have the slightest idea what he had said.

"Howdy, darlin'. How's my girl?" Deke came and nudged her chin with his fist.

"Did you get what you went after?" She felt that she had to say something. Brady was listening.

"Sure did. Brady's fixed up with tires, and we got a radiator for Foley's car. It'll take us the rest of the day to put it in."

"We sold ten gallons of gas, Mr. Bales." Jody dug into his pocket and brought out a few bills and some change.

"Tell you what, son. Keep a dollar of that and hang here for the rest of the day so I can work on your pa's car."

"No, I'll watch the pump and do anything else I can to help, but I'll not take your money."

"Well, hold on to it for now."

Margie, feeling out of place among the men, inched by Deke and slipped around the side of the garage. Once out of sight, she walked faster. Then a hand on her arm pulled her to a stop. She knew who it was without turning around.

"Where'd Elmer go?"

"How would I know?" She tried to pull away from him. "Let go of my arm. I need to help Grace get the clothes off the line."

"Deke told me what happened when you were here before."

"So? I'm supposed to be thrilled about that?"

"I didn't believe what Elmer said."

"That just plumb tickles me to death." She drew in her lower lip, her face stiff with brittle cynicism.

"How many times do I have to say it?"

"Actions speak louder than words, Mr. Hoyt."

"I was rough when I kissed you. I admit it."

"I've forgotten all about *that*. Now, let go of me." Her voice had savage, raw feeling in it.

"You haven't forgotten it, and neither have I."

"Why would I remember the kiss of a footloose cowboy? I've kissed hundreds—"

"Shut-up lyin'. You've done no such thing."

"Ask Elmer. He'll tell you, if he comes back, about all the men in Conway, Missouri, that I serviced. I had a real good business going, but decided business would be better in California."

"I could shake you." He looked at her set face and blazing eyes for a long time. Then he muttered, "To hell with it."

The instant his hand left her arm, Margie walked quickly away before the tears she fought so hard to hold back disgraced her.

Noon came, and still Elmer hadn't returned. Embarrassed to be at loose ends while everyone was preparing the noon meal, Margie found a hoe in the shed and went out to Deke's garden patch. She was sure Grace would invite her to eat with them, and she didn't think she would be able to bear the clicking tongues, the pitying glances and the unspoken questions about what she would do if her father had gone off and left her.

She had cleared weeds from one row of beans when Deke came to the edge of the garden and called to her.

"Darlin', whater ya doin' out here?"

"Clearing out some weeds. I love working in a garden.

When I was here before, Leona and I canned a bushel of beans and one of tomatoes from this patch."

"Mama sent me to find you. She's cooked up some ham and beans and made a bread puddin'."

"I had a big breakfast, Deke."

"I ain't takin' a no, darlin'. Come talk to me while I eat."

She batted her eyes continually as she walked back down the row toward him. The closer she got to him, the harder it was to keep the tears at bay.

He knew, and held out his arms.

"Oh, Deke, what'll I do?" It was all she could get through the sobs that clogged her throat. She leaned her forehead on his shoulder and let the tears flow. He stood silently holding her, his hand stroking her back.

Neither of them was aware that Brady had come around the corner of the barn and was watching them, his eyes hard, his mouth grim.

"I'm sorry, Deke."

"Don't be sorry, darlin'. Do you think your pa has gone off and left you?"

"I don't know. He's so . . . ornery."

"Tell ya what, darlin'. We'll cross that bridge when we come to it. Come on now, let's go have a nice cold glass of tea."

Deke carried the hoe and put it in the shed on their way to the house. The cozy kitchen was as she remembered it. The table was set for three, and Mrs. Bales was taking a pan of corn bread from the oven.

"You can wash up there at the washstand, Margie. Deke washed on the porch."

Margie ate. She enjoyed the meal after a week of food cooked over a campfire. When it was over, Deke went back to the garage and Margie stayed to help Mrs. Bales do the dishes.

"If you have anything you want to iron, dear, we'll just set the sad iron on the stove and put up the ironing board."

"Thank you. I'm grateful to have washed clothes; to have ironed ones will be a real treat."

"I'll be surprised if we don't get a storm out of those clouds." Mrs. Bales came in after throwing the dishwater off the end of the porch. "It's been trying to storm off and on for a week."

"I hope not. It's not even rained since we left home."

"We've got a good storm cellar. We've been in it once already this spring."

Deke came into the house in the middle of the afternoon to get a rag to tie around a cut on his hand. Margie held it over the washdish while his mother dabbed it with iodine.

"That hurts!"

"Too bad." Mrs. Bales continued to dab. "I keep this on hand because he's always getting cut. He'd just tie a dirty rag around it and go on if I didn't watch him," she scolded.

"Mama likes to fuss." Deke looked at Margie and winked.

"How's the work going?" she asked.

"Good. That big cowboy knows about as much about it as I do. He's a big help. We'd be farther along than we are if Foley's wife would stop prancin' around gettin' in the way. I wasn't surprised a-tall to learn she ain't the mother of his kids. They're two damn nice kids."

"Why, Deke, I thought you'd be bowled over by Sugar," Margie teased.

"You know better'n that, darlin'. She flirts with Brady right under her husband's nose."

"Brady could put a stop to it if he wanted to."

"He's between a rock and a hard place, darlin'. The woman's a barracuda."

"What's that?"

"It's a little fish that eats everything in sight."

"Ugh!" Margie made a face. "If he keeps messing around with her, her husband will knock his block off."

"Darlin', I didn't say that *he* was doin' the flirtin'."

"Now, don't let that come off." Mrs. Bales finished tying a clean cloth around Deke's hand.

The afternoon wore on. Margie did her best to stay busy. She ironed a couple of dresses for Anna Marie and a blouse for Mona. Every so often she would look toward the campground to see if Elmer's truck was there.

By late afternoon she had resigned herself to the fact he was not coming back and that when the caravan left tomorrow she would not be with it. She knew that she would be welcome to stay with Deke and his mother until she could get a small suitcase for her meager possessions and make arrangements for a bus ticket. It hurt to think of the box of treasured keepsakes in Elmer's truck. But, she reasoned, they were only *things*.

Knowing that Brady was still in the garage with Deke, and wanting to get the dresses she'd ironed for Anna Marie to Grace before suppertime, Margie folded them over her arm and left the kitchen. She rounded the end of the house to see Elmer's truck turn into the drive and proceed on to the campground and park.

Margie stopped beside the garage. Her feet refused to carry her any farther. Sudden anger raged through her like a forest fire scorching everything in its path. She began to tremble.

The lousy, conniving horse's ass had deliberately stayed away all day in order to worry her. He wanted to make her so angry that she would stay here when they pulled out in the morning.

He wanted to be rid of her without his losing face with the others.

Chapter 16

Elmer was sitting in his canvas chair beside his truck, his hands tucked into the bib of his overalls, his feet stretched out in front of him, when Margie passed by carrying the dresses she had ironed for Anna Marie. Refusing to give him the satisfaction of even looking at him, she went on to the Putmans' camp and placed them on the back of the straight chair.

"He came back." Grace spoke in low tones. "Alvin wasn't sure he would."

"Neither was I. Where's Anna Marie?"

"She and Mona went to look at the chicken again. She thinks it's grand."

"It is strange. Several carloads of people stopped today to look at the snake, the chicken and the buffalo. All but one of them bought gas."

Grace's laugh was soft . . . and nice. "Mona won't go near the snake. She made Jody lift Anna Marie up so she could see it."

"Mona and Rusty danced last night. You would have been so proud of him."

"I am proud of him. It's been good for him to be with young folks."

"I guess you know that Mona has a crush on him."

"Yes, and I hope to God she don't break his heart."

"Or he hers. Young girls can be hurt easily."

"I know."

Grace watched Margie walk back past her father without giving him as much as a glance and wondered how she could put up with that cantankerous man.

Under lowering clouds darkness came early. It was nearly dark when Margie returned to the truck with her neatly folded clean clothes. She laid out the clothes she would wear the next day and repacked her suitcase. After mulling it over in her mind she had decided to ride with Elmer until they reached a town where she could catch a bus. It would be a clean break from the others in the caravan. There would be no explaining to do and no good-byes.

She would ask Deke to keep her box of "keepsakes" until she could send for them. She sat on the bunk and waited for the light to go off in the garage and for Brady to go to the Putman camp before she carried the box up to the house.

Weariness overcame her. After a while she lay down and pillowed her head on her bent arm. She was tired not only in body but in mind. It had been a stressful day, not knowing if she had been abandoned here . . . again. She dozed fitfully, aroused briefly, then fell into a deep sleep.

She awakened with a startled cry and became instantly alert. Strong gusts of wind rocked the truck, and she heard the insistent rumble of thunder. She sat up in total darkness clutching the edge of the bunk. The back flap had been let down and tied. As a rule she was not afraid of storms, but sitting here alone in the darkness unable to see what was going on outside, she was desperately afraid and began to tremble violently as she dressed.

It seemed to her that she had been sitting there for hours when she heard a voice over the roar of the thunder.

"Margie! Margie, are you in there?"

"Yes, I'm here." She made her way to the end of the truck and began to claw at the rope holding down the flap. A corner of it opened suddenly. Brady stood there.

"We're going to the cellar." He reached for her and lifted her out over the tailgate, then quickly retied the flap.

Glancing upward, Margie glimpsed during the flashes of lightning a blanket of dark, rolling clouds. A gust of wind came up under her full skirt and wrapped it around her thighs. She fought to hold it down while the wind whipped her hair around her face.

"Anna Marie?" The wind whipped her words away, but he must have heard them.

"With Alvin," he shouted. "Deke is taking his mother to the cellar, and the Lukers are on their way. Where's Elmer?"

Margie pointed toward the cab of the truck, where she supposed he would be unless he had put up his pup tent in this wind. Holding her hand tightly, Brady pulled her around the truck until he could reach the door of the cab and yank it open.

"Come to the cellar," he shouted over the rumbling thunder, the roar of the wind and the rippling of the canvas covering the truck bed. "There could be a twister up there."

Elmer shook his head.

"Come on. We'll be safe in the cellar," Brady shouted angrily.

For an answer Elmer reached over and pulled the door shut.

Brady cursed. "Damn stubborn fool."

Wrapping an arm around her, Brady urged Margie up the path. Drops of wind-driven rain lashed them like pine needles. The door to the cellar was open, and the glow of a lantern came from within. Alvin stood on the steps, took Margie's arm and helped her scramble down the stairwell.

"Did you find Elmer?" Alvin shouted over the deafening noise of the approaching storm.

"He won't come."

"Darn fool. Where is he?"

"The cab of his truck."

"I'll go."

"He won't come, Mr. Putman," Margie said quickly.

"I'll go anyway."

Grace got up to protest, but Alvin was up the stairs and out, running toward the campground.

Benches lined the walls of the cellar. The Lukers sat on one of them; Grace, Rusty and Mona sat across from them on another. Anna Marie was cuddled in Rusty's lap, Blackie at his feet. Mrs. Bales sat on a wooden folding chair beside a box that held the lantern.

"Where's Deke?"

"He went to see about his animals," Mrs. Bales said calmly. "He'll be here."

And he was. Minutes later the little man, his hair swirling wildly around his head, bounded down the uneven steps as agilely as a young fawn. And on his heels came Alvin.

"The stubborn fool wouldn't come," he told Margie.

"Thank you for trying."

Brady and Deke battled to close the door. Summoning all their strength, they managed to get the door up off the ground, then ducked into the stairwell as the wind caught it and slammed it shut. Deke produced a flashlight so that he could see to shoot the bolt that would keep it closed.

Now the noise of the storm was muffled.

Margie sat down on the end of the bench where the Lukers were. Alvin went to sit by Grace and put his arm around her. Brady, stooping to keep his head from hitting the cellar ceiling, sat beside Margie. Deke hung the lantern on a nail in one of the ceiling beams and sat down on the box.

Anna Marie slid off Rusty's lap and went to Margie, bringing a scrap of blanket with her. Margie lifted her up to sit on her lap, put her arms around her and snuggled her close.

"Are ya scared, Margie?"

"No, puddin'. I'm not scared. We'll be just fine down here." She covered the child with the blanket, tucking it in around her legs.

"I was scared. Uncle Alvin carried me so Uncle Brady could go get you. Then Rusty held me. Rusty likes me."

"Of course he does. We all like you, very much."

"*She* don't." Anna Marie lifted her head so she could see Sugar Luker. "She said, 'Go away, pest.' "

Margie's eyes collided with Sugar Luker's. If looks could kill, Sugar would have dropped dead.

"We don't pay any attention to her," Margie was goaded to say loudly enough for all to hear.

Silence followed. A chunk of something hit the cellar door.

"Let's hope that's not a limb from your peach tree, Mama." Deke put a reassuring hand on his mother's shoulder. "I thought we were only going to get a good thunderstorm until the wind came up and I saw those rolling clouds. They're the kind a twister could drop out of."

"I've heard that this is tornado country," Foley said. "Ever been in one?"

"Close, but not head-on. We sight a few every year; usually in late summer."

"I'm glad we're here and not in some other campground," Alvin said. "We thank you for invitin' us down here."

Deke shrugged and after a long silent period, looked at Margie. "How ya doin', darlin'?"

"All right." She couldn't think of anything else to say. She hated the quiet within the cellar. She wished someone would say something so that she wouldn't be so conscious of Brady's hard body close to hers, or the big hand resting on his thigh, the hand that had cupped her head when he kissed her. She tried to concentrate on something else.

Mona, sitting close to Rusty, was glaring at her stepmother, daring her to make one of her sarcastic comments. Sugar was cuddled against Foley, her hand clutching the front of his shirt. Tension between Mona and Sugar was sharp as a knife.

Then Alvin began to sing.

> *"Give me that old-time religion,*
> *Give me that old-time religion,*

Give me that old-time religion;
It's good enough for me."

Grace joined the singing, then Rusty and Mrs. Bales. Soon the others joined in. After several hymns Jody urged Rusty to sing alone.

"What do you want to hear?"

"One of the ballads you sang the other night."

Even without the accompaniment of his guitar Rusty's voice was low and haunting.

"Standing by the water tank,
Waiting for a train.
I'm a thousand miles away from home,
Sleeping in the rain.
My pocketbook is empty,
Not a penny to my name . . ."

He sang with such feeling you could almost see in your mind's eye the lonely figure waiting for the train. He sang several ballads, then after coaxing from Mona, sang her favorite.

"In a little rosewood casket,
Sitting on a marble stand,
Are a package of love letters,
Written by my true love's hand."

Rusty's hand reached for Mona's. Her fingers interlaced with his, and tears filled her eyes. He continued to sing.

"While I listen to you read them,
I will gently fall asleep,
Fall asleep to wake with Jesus;
Oh, dear sister, do not weep."

In the quiet after he had finished, Sugar exclaimed, "Oh, my God! That's the silliest song I ever heard. Don't you ever sing anything happy, or about good times?"

"Sure," Rusty said calmly. "How about this:

"Happy days are here again.
The skies above are clear again.
So let's sing a song of cheer again.
Happy days are here again."

"If that's the best you can do, I prefer quiet."

"Sugar!" Foley removed his arm from around her. "That wasn't called for."

"She's got no more manners than an alley cat," Mona said staunchly.

"Mona, that's enough." There was a warning tone in Foley's voice. "This is not the time or the place for a family squabble."

"Then hush *her* up!" Mona said, and whispered an apology to Rusty.

"Thank you for the songs, Rusty," Margie said. "I enjoyed every one of them."

"I've heard a lot worse than that on the radio," Deke added. "You should be on the *Grand Ole Opry*. Don't you think so, Mama? Mama and I listen to Nashville every Saturday night."

Rain pounded on the slanting plank door of the cellar.

"Could be a little hail mixed with the rain," Alvin commented.

"Yeah," Deke said. "The wind may have gone down some. The thunder seemed to be moving farther away."

Margie had no idea how long she had sat there. She knew that her bottom was numb. Anna Marie had fallen asleep while Rusty sang.

"Let me hold her for a while." The softly spoken words came suddenly. Margie turned and found Brady's face close to hers. She looked down quickly.

"All right. My arms are tired."

Brady leaned into her to lift Anna Marie from her arms. When she was settled in his lap, Margie lifted the child's feet and legs across hers and adjusted the blanket around her.

"Are you cold?" Brady asked.

"No, I'm all right."

Silence. Even Deke didn't have anything to say. Sugar's rude remarks seemed to have dried up the conversation and placed a blanket of unease over the group in the cellar. Grace's head was against Alvin's shoulder, her eyes closed. Mona and Rusty whispered in each other's ears. Margie closed her eyes and dozed.

She awoke with a start and sat up quickly when she realized her head was against Brady's shoulder. Vowing to stay awake—and in order to whip up her anger against him—she recalled to mind the night he manhandled her like the loose woman he thought she was.

But instead of thinking of the hateful kiss and the hateful words that followed, she remembered the tender kisses they shared before Elmer poisoned Brady against her. Even after their quarrel at the PowWow, he had held her gently while they danced and had pressed his cheek against hers.

After tomorrow morning she would never see him again. Thinking about it made her want to cry.

"The rain has let up." Deke was at the cellar door. He shot the bolt back, lifted the plank door and let it fall back. "It's only a light drizzle now." He stuck his head out and looked around. "It looks like the wind has tore up jack. Branches are down all over."

"Take her, Margie." Brady shifted Anna Marie to Margie's lap. "I'll go out with Deke and Alvin and look around."

Foley left Sugar's clinging arms and followed the men out, stopping to put a hand on Jody's shoulder with the unspoken request that he try to keep peace between his daughter and his wife.

The damp breeze blew from the open door, and Margie shivered and hugged Anna Marie close, welcoming her warmth.

Deke went to the barn to check on his animals, the others to see what, if any, damage had been done to their cars and trucks. Then Brady saw sparks dancing along the ground in the middle of the campground.

"Hold it," he said. "The electric wires are down. Watch where you step. If you come in contact with a hot wire on this wet ground, you're a goner."

"I'll go for the lantern." Alvin backtracked quickly.

He was back in less than a minute. "I hated to leave the women in the dark."

Brady picked up a long leafless branch, one of many strewn about. They proceeded cautiously toward the downed wire that was sending sparks over the wet ground.

"There! Good Lord!" Alvin exclaimed. "That's—that's—Elmer!"

The light from the lantern shone on the body of the man who lay crumpled in the puddle of water. Nearby, the end of the live electric wire lay on the ground.

"Stay back. I'll try to move the wire away from him." Brady, using the branch, carefully lifted the deadly wire a few feet from the end and moved it a good six feet before it slipped off the end of the branch.

Alvin and Foley knelt beside the still form, turned him over and stared into his open, vacant eyes.

"Mother of Christ," Foley murmured. "He's dead!"

"No doubt about that."

Shocked into silence, the men looked down at the man who had rejected their attempts to be friendly.

"It looks like he may have decided to come to the cellar after all. The limb from one of those trees broke off and snapped the wire. It caught him out here in the open."

The beam of Deke's flashlight danced along the ground as he approached.

"I see we got a downed wire."

"That's not all that's down." Alvin moved aside and held up the lantern.

"Godalmighty!" Deke peered closer. "Is he dead?" The question was moot, he knew, even as he asked it.

"We should get him out of this puddle," Brady said.

"Put him in the garage. I'll hop on my cycle, get the sheriff and someone out here to take care of that hot wire."

"We can take my car." Brady moved to lift Elmer beneath his arms. Foley took his feet.

"Better leave it as it is. The wind could come up and whip that wire around. I'll go on my cycle."

"Hadn't thought of that."

Deke led the way and had the garage doors open by the time they reached it. They laid Elmer down on the floor beside Foley's car. Deke covered his face with a towel.

Alvin shook his head sadly. "Poor stubborn fool. I don't know what got into him this past week."

"His stubbornness got him killed," Brady said without feeling. "I urged him to come with us to the cellar, but he'd have none of it."

"Will the sheriff bring the undertaker?" Alvin asked Deke while he was filling an extra lantern with kerosene.

"I suspect he will after I tell him what's happened. Before I go, I'll light the lamps in the house. Mama won't stay in that cellar any longer than she has to." He lit the lantern and set it on a box beside the door.

"I'll bring the women up. Do you mind if they sit on your porch?"

"Lord, no. Bring Mama and the women up to the house, Mr. Putman. Mama will fuss over 'em."

"Margie has to be told." This came from Brady after Deke's cycle had roared off down the highway toward town.

"Do you want to tell her?" Alvin asked.

"No. She'll take it better coming from you."

Chapter 17

Margie took the news of her father's death quietly. It was almost as if Alvin had told her of the death of a stranger. She was sad that it had happened, but she felt no heart-wrenching grief. The implication of what this meant for *her* would take a while longer to sink in.

Everyone had been kind. Grace had told her how sorry she was and hugged her, as had Mona and Mrs. Bales. The men had removed their hats when they spoke to her. Margie knew they were sincere in their expressions of sympathy. She also knew how each of them had felt about her father while he was alive. He was not a likable man.

The midmorning air was fresh and cool—not that she noticed as she walked down to the campground. It hit her, as she approached the truck, that now she was without kin. Elmer had not been much of a father, but he had given her life. As far as she knew, he was her only blood relative. Her half brother's family, if he had one, probably didn't even know that she was alive and wouldn't care if they did.

Earlier, feeling detached, she had sat on Deke's porch and watched the undertaker take the body away. Shortly afterward, Brady came to the porch with the contents he had taken from Elmer's pockets tied in a handkerchief.

"I told the undertaker that I'd bring down clean clothes sometime this morning."

"He kept the box locked where he kept his things."

"You have his keys. Do you want to bury him here or send him back to Conway?"

"Here. There's no one back there."

"Do you want me to take care of it?"

"I don't want to put you out—"

"I want to help."

"I'll go look for something to bury him in."

"I thought you would want to know, so I asked the undertaker how much this was going to cost. He said the grave space is five dollars, and his fee plus the casket is forty. There is money there in Elmer's billfold. I didn't count it, but I believe it's enough."

"I guess we'll need a preacher."

"Not necessarily. Alvin will conduct a service if you want him to. The undertaker suggested ten o'clock in the morning."

"The families won't want to wait until noon to leave. Mrs. Luker is wanting to go today."

"Foley put the kibosh on that. Alvin will stay. So will I."

"I'll go to the truck and see what I can find for the burial."

"The undertaker will need some information about Elmer for the records."

"I'll write down what I know." She left the porch and

started down the path toward the truck. Brady kept step with her. When they reached the truck, he took her arm.

"Margie . . . I'm sorry about what happened the other night. I shouldn't have been rough with you."

"It's all right."

"I've no excuse except to say I was frustrated . . . because you seemed to think that I would take more than I was offered."

"It doesn't matter."

"It matters to me."

"Once a stink is out of a box, it can't be put back in."

"What do you mean?"

"I understand you thought I was a silly, starstruck girl who would welcome that kind of treatment. Forget it."

She fumbled to untie the wet ropes on the flap on the back of the truck. Brady reached over her, blocking her in with his body, and pushed her hands away. He untied and rolled up the flap.

"Thank you. I appreciate your help with . . . the funeral. But if you'd rather not, I'm sure Deke would—"

"I'm sure he'd do what he could, but he doesn't need to, because I'm here." He let down the tailgate and took her arm when she stepped up onto the box to climb into the truck. "I'll be back in a little while to get whatever you want to send to the funeral home."

She nodded.

"You look worn-out. Why don't you lie down and sleep for a while?"

She nodded again, stepped up into the truck and sat down on the bunk. When she was sure that she was alone, she covered her face with her hands and allowed the tears to run between her fingers and down her cheeks. She cried silently, not from grief over Elmer, but because she felt as if she were floating on a river of unreality and there was a waterfall just ahead.

A wave of fatigue washed over her. She loosened the top buttons at the neck of her blouse and lay back on the bunk. Her spine straightened painfully. She flexed her shoulders and rolled her head from side to side to ease her tense muscles. Her body was tired to the point of collapse.

"What will happen next?" she whispered into the silence that gave no answer.

Alvin had tried to assure her that something would be worked out so that she could continue on with the caravan. Knowing how Brady felt about her made it all the more humiliating to have to accept his help.

Sometime later she heard the sound of voices coming from the Luker camp. Then a car passed on the highway. It was time to face what had to be done.

She sat up and reached for the bundle of things taken from Elmer's pockets. Inside she found a ring of keys, pocketknife, worn billfold, pocket watch and some loose change. In the billfold was fifty-eight dollars. Thank goodness it was enough for the burial. She was sure that Elmer had the money from the sale of his house and the ice company put away somewhere, but it didn't matter: She wasn't entitled to it.

When Goldie, his wife, was notified of his death, she would search out every nook and cranny for whatever he had left. Everything he had, including the truck, now belonged to her even if she had gone off and left him.

Margie removed the pad from the box she had been sleeping on and tried each of the keys in the padlock until she found the one that opened it. Feeling jumpy, as if Elmer might come around to the back of the truck and catch her searching through his private possessions, she opened the lid.

In one end of the box were several pairs of neatly folded overalls and shirts, a black serge suit and black shoes with socks stuffed in the toes. Margie wondered if this was the suit he'd worn when he and Goldie were married. On the top of his underwear was a white shirt with a black string tie in the pocket.

At the other end of the box was a mantel clock wrapped in a piece of blanket, a square metal box secured with another padlock, a handgun and several boxes of shells. Tucked down alongside of the clock was a red Prince Albert tobacco can.

She took out the black suit, shook the coat and held it to the light. The suit appeared to be new. The white shirt was wrinkled but clean. She refolded the suit and shirt and set the shoes beside them.

Margie had the feeling of invading Elmer's privacy when she fitted a key in the lock of the metal box to open it. There wasn't much in it: two flat, round snuff cans with something heavy in them, apparently coins. A half dozen letters were tied with a string; an envelope held a cameo necklace. There was also a lady's lapel watch and a pair of baby shoes.

She pulled one of the envelopes from the stack, opened the flap and gasped in amazement. Instead of a letter, the envelope held four fifty-dollar bills. When she recovered from the surprise of finding the money, she looked in the next five envelopes. Two one-hundred-dollar bills were in each.

In the last envelope was a two-sheet letter. She put the sheets back in the envelope still so shocked she didn't bother to read the letter. With shaking hands, she retied the envelopes, put them back in the metal box and locked it.

She had never in all her life seen so much money at one time. She closed the lid on the wooden box and replaced the padlock. It didn't even occur to her to claim the money. Elmer had married, so, of course, it belonged to his wife.

Goldie would be overjoyed. Damn her!

Margie had never seen her father in anything but overalls. The shiny black shoes she had placed beside the suit that she had laid out for Brady to take to the funeral parlor looked as if they had never been worn. She pulled a sock from a shoe. Rolling the top of the sock down to turn it right side out, she felt a hard lump in the toe and pulled out two fifty-dollar bills folded in a small tight square. She stared at them dumbfounded for a long moment, then looked in the other sock and found the same. Two hundred more dollars.

Margie tucked the money in her skirt pocket and quickly searched the pockets of the suit. She found nothing but a stick of Juicy Fruit gum. She was refolding the trousers when Brady appeared. He stood at the end of the truck, his hat pulled down over his eyes.

"Margie?"

"He had a suit."

"Do you want to go to town with me?"

"No."

"I think you should. The undertaker will want to know a few things."

"I don't even know how old he was," she said irritably. "He didn't think enough of me to even tell me he had married—for the third time. I had to find it out when someone came into the café where I was working."

"The date of his birth would be on his driver's license if he had one. Did you look in his billfold?"

She held out the billfold. "I only looked to see if there was enough money to bury him." She turned her back and picked up the stack of folded clothes.

"He was born in '85," Brady said, slipping a card back in the billfold. "That makes him forty-eight."

"That sounds about right. Granny said he was twenty-five when I was born and he had already buried one wife."

"Was he born there in Conway?"

"As far as I know."

"I wish you'd come with me. You don't have to get out of the car if you don't want to."

"I don't want to go," she said stubbornly. "If you don't want to take the burial clothes, I'll ask Deke."

"It isn't that I don't want to go," he said patiently. "I think it would be good for you to get away from here for a while."

"Well, I don't. I've got thinking to do. I can do it better here by myself. I've got to decide what to do."

"Are you worried that we'll all pull out and leave you here by yourself? We'll not do that."

"I won't be by myself. Deke will help me sell the truck. The sheriff will help me locate Goldie. She'll come running if she thinks she's getting some money."

"Is that what you want to do?"

"It isn't a matter of wanting. It's what I've got to do."

Brady saw the fatigue in her face, the dark circles beneath her eyes. "Why don't you lie down and sleep for a while? I'll give the undertaker the information."

"Pay him with the money in the billfold."

"You've got friends here, Margie. Don't push them away."

"I appreciate your staying for Elmer's burial."

"We're not staying for Elmer. We're staying for you."

"When he's in the ground, your obligation will be over. I've always taken care of myself, paid my own way. I've never been a burden on anyone and don't intend to start now."

Brady looked at her long and steadily. He saw her quivering lips, her chin tilted defiantly, the overbright eyes that were trying to hold back tears. She was tired and scared and, Lord, how he wanted to take her in his arms and tell her that she wasn't alone. Instead he reached for the clothes and backed away.

He had taken only a few steps when he heard the back flap on the truck drop down.

When Margie awoke, she realized that the sun had gone down and that she had slept the day away. She could smell the smoke from the supper fires. While she slept, someone had stepped up into the truck and covered her with a sheet.

She sat up on the side of the bunk and ran her forked fingers through her hair. Her stomach growled, and she had to use the outhouse. Dreading to leave the truck but knowing that she must, she ran a comb through her hair and held it back from her face by slipping a ribbon beneath it, tying it in a bow and moving the bow back to be covered by her hair.

She made it to the outhouse without being intercepted, but she wasn't so lucky on the way back. Foley Luker stopped her to invite her to eat supper with them.

"Thank you, but I've got something laid out."

"If there's anything we can do, let us know. Would you like Mona to come over and stay with you?"

"No, but thanks." Margie shook her head and looked directly at Sugar, who had come to stand beside her husband. "I'll manage just fine." She walked away, her head high.

"She don't want Mona. She wants to sleep with Brady," Sugar said spitefully and loud enough for Margie to hear.

Foley turned on his wife. "Shut up! Don't you have anything nice to say about anybody?" He stalked off and left her standing.

Margie climbed into the truck and looked in the icebox. The day before, Elmer had bought ice as well as eggs, a ring of baloney and milk. In the cupboard were bread, crackers, pork and beans and canned peaches. Margie buttered two slices of bread and cut the baloney in chunks. She sat on the bunk and ate slowly.

"Darlin'? Are you all right?" Deke came to stand at the end of the truck.

"I'm fine, Deke. I was tired and slept the day away."

"It's what ya needed, darlin'. Why don't ya come up to the house and stay with Mama? I'd stay here with ya, but I'm goin' to be workin' on a motor that was brought in from the ranch where I used to work."

"I don't need anyone with me, Deke. I'll stay right here. I've got to decide what I'm going to do."

"Ya know yo're welcome to stay here long as ya want. And if I can help in any way, ya only got to ask."

"I know that, and I'll not hesitate to ask."

"Get some rest, darlin'."

When she finished eating, Margie put the back flap down, filled the washdish with water from the barrel, washed herself from head to toe and felt considerably better.

From where he sat eating supper with the Putmans, Brady had seen Margie leave the truck, go to the outhouse and talk with Foley on the way back. He couldn't hear the conversation, but he was certain that Sugar said something after Margie had left that didn't sit well with Foley. He had stalked off leaving his wife standing with her hands on her hips glaring after him. It was about time he got that woman in line. She was a walking, talking troublemaker.

Brady brought his attention back to what Alvin was saying.

"It's too bad that Elmer went the way he did. The man turned sour the last week or so. I was having my doubts about going partners with him in the ice business when we got to California. Luker said the same."

"You don't have to worry about that now."

"Margie is as nice a girl as I've ever met, and Elmer treated her like dirt." Grace passed around boiled eggs. She had bought several dozen from Mrs. Bales. It was a treat to eat them. She usually had to save them for cooking.

"Rusty, will you take the shell off mine?" Anna Marie put the egg in Rusty's hand. It was amazing to Brady how the child had adapted to Rusty's blindness.

"Sure, little puddin'." Rusty peeled the egg and ran his sensitive fingertips over it to make sure it was free of shell pieces. "There's salt here on my plate if you want to use it."

"Thank you, Rusty. Can I give Blackie a bite of my bread?"

Once again Brady thanked his lucky stars he had met up with the Putmans. But Anna Marie was becoming so attached to them that he feared her reaction when they parted company in California.

"I'll go over and talk to Margie." Alvin placed his empty plate on the table. "Tomorrow after the service we should get on down the road."

"What will we do if she refuses what we've talked about?" There was concern in Brady's voice. He didn't understand Margie's hostility toward him. Nor did he understand why he was so concerned about that hostility. He only knew, deep down, that he wasn't going off and leaving her to flounder around by herself.

"There isn't anything we can do. She's a grown woman. Do you want to come with me, hon?" he asked Grace.

"I'll come if you want me to, but it might be better if you talked to her alone." Grace slipped her hand under his arm and hugged it to her. "You can talk the skin off a rabbit when you set your mind to it."

"Bein' able to talk comes in handy once in a while. I talked you into marryin' me even though your pa said I wasn't worth the powder it would take to blow me up. He said that if you hitched up with me, you and a passel of younguns would end up in the poorhouse."

"He was wrong, and I've not been a bit sorry I chose

you over that sissified corset salesman he wanted me to marry."

Alvin laughed and hugged her. "You could have had free corsets for life."

"Who needs 'em?"

"You sure don't. Even after twenty-three years you're as trim as you were at eighteen."

"Sweet-talkin' me, ain't ya? You're not getting another egg no matter how you rattle on, if that's what you're anglin' for. They're for the noon meal tomorrow."

"You're a mean, cruel woman, Gracie Louise Putman," Alvin said affectionately, and dropped a kiss on the top of her head.

"Go on with you. Just don't forget that Margie's got pride she hasn't used yet. Tell her I'm expecting her for breakfast in the morning. After I finish with the dishes Anna Marie and I are going up and sit on the porch with Mrs. Bales. I'm sure glad we stopped here. I've taken a likin' to that woman."

Brady watched the couple, seeing the loving, comfortable way they were with each other. It brought back deeply buried memories of his mother and father. They had loved each other, and their love had included their sons. He remembered how his father would pull his mother down on his lap and nestle his face in the curve of her neck. Poor Brian had thought he was going to share with Becky what their parents had. But it hadn't worked out that way.

Brady vowed, then and there, never to marry until he found a woman who would love him with all her heart and soul. One who would stand beside him through good times and bad, be his best friend as well as his lover.

Loud voices jarred Brady from his reverie. At the other end of the campground Sugar was arguing with Foley. He had moved the car from the garage and parked it beside their trailer. His hands were on her shoulders trying to restrain her. Suddenly she swung her hand and slapped him. When he released her, she tried to hit him again. He caught her arm and pushed her away.

Sugar stood still for a moment. Low, angry words streamed from her lips, then she turned, left the campground and walked down the highway toward town.

Chapter 18

FOLEY STOOD AT THE BACK OF HIS CAR and watched Sugar leave. This trip had been an eye-opener. It suddenly occurred to him that her actions didn't hurt nearly as much as they would have a few weeks ago.

Sugar was showing an altogether different side of herself from the one she had presented when they first met and during the first few weeks after they had married. Good Lord, how can a woman be so sweet and loving one minute and a real bitch the next? Foley had begun to wonder if his loneliness and his desire for sexual satisfaction had caused him to make a complete fool out of himself. Now he no longer had to wonder.

Let a pretty young thing make up to a sex-starved man, and he loses what few brains he ever had.

"Pa?" Jody had come up beside him. "Do you want me to go get her?"

Foley didn't answer for a moment, then said, "No, son. Let her walk off her snit. I'll go get her in a little while." He turned a tired, almost defeated face to Jody. "Thank you for your patience. My marrying her hasn't turned out like I thought it would. I know this has been hard for you and Mona, and I'm sorry, son."

"Harder on Mona than on me."

"Well, what's done is done," Foley said with resignation. "I'll keep my eyes open from now on."

"She was so different from Mama that it was hard for me and Mona to warm up to her."

"It's true. She's nothing like your mother. I wasn't looking for someone to take her place. No one will ever do that." Foley's voice became rough, and he walked quickly away.

Margie always liked the early evening hours. She loved to watch the setting sun change the colors of the sky and to inhale the cool, fresh air, with the smell of the greening pastures, as it swept across the land.

When she was younger and her granny was alive, everything had been easy. She had never imagined that life would be so hard, so lonely, so full of disappointments, and could end so quickly. Like any young girl, she had dreamed of meeting a strong man who would love her with all his heart. And, as couples did in the movies, they would build a life together, fill a home with children and laughter and live happily ever after.

She supposed that was what was the matter with her now. There was an emptiness within her, a yearning that still begged for that fairy-tale dream. She was a woman with a woman's love to give; and in her ignorance she had reached out to Brady Hoyt because he was handsome and had been kind and attentive when she so badly needed a friend.

She had been blinded by loneliness. What a fool she was, and how he must have secretly laughed at the naive small-town girl with the big dreams.

"Evenin', Margie." Alvin approached as Margie stepped down from the truck.

"Hello, Mr. Putman."

"We would have had you come to supper, but Brady said you were sleeping. Grace sends an invite to breakfast in the morning."

"That's nice of her."

"Can we talk a little?"

"Sure. I'll get Elmer's folding chair for you." She reached in the truck for the chair, took it to the front of the truck, then perched herself on the fender.

"Nice evening." Alvin sat down and stretched his legs out in front of him. "I thought Missouri's weather changed fast. It can't hold a candle to Oklahoma weather. The storm we had last night was a real tail twister. I only wish Elmer had come with us to the cellar."

"It was a freaky thing that happened to him. He was in the wrong place when the electric line broke."

"I've heard of electrocution by hot wires. I never thought I'd see it firsthand. Being in water when around electricity is about the worst place you can be."

"Is this going to ruin your plans to set up your ice business?"

"I don't think so. Luker and I have talked it over. It'll mean that there will be two of us instead of three, and we'll have to try for a bigger loan from a bank."

"Elmer had a wife. She left him a few months ago and

went out to California. I thought that was his reason for going out there."

"He never mentioned a wife to me. She may have already left when we started talking about a partnership a couple months ago."

"Everything he had now belongs to her." She glanced toward the Putman camp and saw Brady squatting on his heels beside Rusty, but he was looking toward her.

"Do you know where his wife is?"

"No." She brought her attention back to Alvin. "I'd only seen her a couple of times—from a distance. The town was full of rumors about them. They married suddenly but were not together very long. I can't think that my father would be easy to live with. The joke around town was that he was so miserly he'd skin a mosquito for the hide."

"He may have been different with her."

"Something caused her to leave." Margie was aware that Brady was still watching. It made her nervous. "Deke will help me sell the truck. I'll give the money and what I found in his locked box to the sheriff. I don't think it's my place to find her."

"Then what will you do?"

"Get myself a bus ticket." Margie touched the two hundred dollars still in her skirt pocket. "I'm going to keep out enough money to get me to California and a little more to last until I find a job. I think he owes me that much."

"Have you considered taking the truck on to California and turning it over to Elmer's wife out there?"

"I may not be able to find her. Besides that, I can't drive this truck all the way to California."

"You can hire Jody Luker to drive. He's been drivin' Foley's ice truck for several years."

"If I pay out my money for a driver, I won't have much when I get there."

"Pay him out of Elmer's money. You'll be taking the truck to his wife. It'll save you bus fare."

"I've not the slightest idea how to take care of a car of any kind. All I know about them is that they need water and gas and air for the tires."

"We want you and your truck in the caravan, Margie." Alvin spoke earnestly. "It will be safer for all of us. Brady and I will see that the truck is kept in running order."

Margie shook her head. "I don't like having to depend—"

"You'll be doing us a favor. If you decide to come along, you can take your meals with us. Grace would welcome your help."

"No. You've already got Brady and Anna Marie."

"He pitches in on groceries. You could do the same."

"No. I thank you, but I'd rather be on my own." Margie put her hand in her pocket and fingered again the bills she had taken from Elmer's socks before she sent his clothes to the funeral home. "It would be different if I could drive."

"You can learn by doing. Along the way there will be places where there is little or no traffic. We'll help you in the evening. Then the first thing you know you'd be an old hand at it. We're all hoping you'll stay with us."

"You and Grace?"

"Me and Grace, Brady, Rusty, the Lukers."

"I don't know, Mr. Putman. I'm afraid I'll slow you down."

"Elmer, Foley and I made an agreement when we started that we would hang together—for safety. It has proven to be a good idea. If one or even two of us had been in that campground the other night, we'd have been easy pickings for the robbers."

"What about Mr. Luker? Mrs. Luker doesn't like me at all."

"Mrs. Luker doesn't like any of us. Foley may be waking up to the fact that he's got to take a strong hand with her."

"I wouldn't know what to pay Jody even if his father let him drive for me."

"He may not want pay, but if he does, I'd suggest not more than a dollar a day. I figure it'll take us a little more than three weeks to get there if we don't rest on Sundays. That's somewhere around twenty-one dollars. And you'd get a better price if you sold the truck out there."

"I'm not interested in getting more money for Goldie."

"Can't say that I blame you for that."

"Elmer was tight with his money, but I can't believe that she left empty-handed."

"I'm surprised Elmer wasn't wearing a money belt."

"He had his money locked in a stout box. It would take an ax to open it without a key."

"I don't think it's wise to put all your eggs in one basket, Margie. Someone could come along and steal the truck."

Alvin took out his pipe, lit it and watched Rusty and Mona walking arm in arm out to the fenced pasture where Deke kept his buffalo and his horse.

Lord, please let my boy find a woman who will love

him as I have loved his mother. If Mona isn't the one, I'm
still grateful for the happiness she's brought to him.

After a while, Alvin said, "It wasn't my intention to
put pressure on you, Margie. You're a grown woman and
know what you want to do. Whatever it is, we will do
what we can to help you."

"I'll have to talk to Jody before I know if I have a
choice or not."

"All right. Let me know what you decide."

"Mr. Luker is leaving. I suppose he's going after his
wife. She had one of her little tantrums, left him and
walked down the highway toward town."

"The man's got his hands full with that one."

Inside the Ford coupe at the top of the hill, Homer Persy
and his Uncle Chester surveyed Deke's campground.

"They still ain't got electric down there. In a while it'll
be darker'n inside a blackbird's ass." Chester sent a quick
look at his nephew. "You could sneak in there, cut up the
cowboy's tires again, then we could go home."

"Stop bein' a nervous Nellie. Grandma's got your wire
about goin' to help Uncle Gordon and won't expect us
back for a month."

"She'll want news of him."

"We'll give her news. In a day or two we'll wire her
and say that he's come down with somethin' and we have
to take care of him till he's on his feet. Don't ya have any
imagination a-tall?"

"I hate lyin' to Maw."

"Why? She'll never know the difference. Gal-damn!

Looks like one of the women is takin' off down the highway."

"What's she doin' that for?"

"Might of had a spat with her old man. Hot dog! We'll wait a bit, then follow 'er."

"You're goin' to get us hung," Chester moaned.

Homer was too excited to listen to his uncle's mutterings.

"Wait till she gets on down past that clump of woods."

"I'm tellin' ya, Homer. We ain't takin' no woman! We could get hung for kidnappin'."

"Trust me, Uncle Chester. It's near dark. We'll offer her a ride, politelike. She ain't goin' to recognize us."

"She will too."

"Them birds in the campground don't know this car either. So ease on down there."

Muttering that Homer had no more sense than a pie-eyed mule, Chester started the car and drove on down the hill.

"Get up to twenty-five when we pass the garage. We don't want them to think we're pokin' along. Then slow when we get by."

"Do this, do that. Yo're good at givin' orders."

Homer paid no attention to his uncle's grumbling. His eyes were on the woman walking at the edge of the road.

"Ease up on her—by damn, I think it's the hot-blooded, black-haired bitch that give us supper. Howdy," he said when they were even with Sugar. "You needin' a ride somers?"

"What's it to you?"

"Nothin'. Just offerin' ya a ride. Be glad to take ya where yo're goin'."

"I'm goin' to town."

"So are we, ma'am. No sense in a lady walkin' when she can ride."

Sugar stopped. The car moved past her before Chester could stop. Homer opened the door, stepped out and made a courtly bow.

"We're harmless and at yore service, pretty lady," he said with a charming grin.

"You'll take me to town?"

"Sure will. It's just down the road a mile or two."

Sugar hesitated only a moment, then stepped up onto the running board. She sat down, then moved over into the middle of the seat. Homer got in and slammed the door.

"My name is Homer. His is Chester. He don't talk much."

"My name is Selma, but I'm called Sugar."

"Fittin' name for a pretty lady." Homer put his arm across the back of the seat. Chester stepped on the gas, and the car shot off down the highway. "Whyer ya goin' to town, Sugar?"

" 'Cause I'm sick and tired of being in an old campground with a bunch of old farts whose idea of havin' fun is singin' hymns. Hey, wait a minute. You're . . . you're—Godalmighty! The other night you had a cap on!" To the surprise of both Homer and Chester, Sugar laughed, loud and long. "Now, ain't this rich? Water you doin' here?"

"We wasn't goin' to rob ya, ya know. We was just havin' us a little fun when that cowboy poked his nose in." Homer's arm on the back of the seat slid down and hugged her to him. When she offered no resistance, he hugged her tighter.

"How come you're here? Are you goin' to California?"

"To tell you the truth, sweet little Sugar, we're pokin' along to get even with that cowboy who tied us up all night. The sheriff let us go 'cause we hadn't done nothin'. What do you think of that?"

"You rascals you! You slashed his tires the other night!"

"Now, why would you go and think a thin' like that?"

"Because it's what I'd have done."

"Whee! Hot doggie-dog-dog! Uncle Chester, this is the woman I've been lookin' for all my life." He hugged her briefly with both arms.

"Hey, look. I've not forgotten what you said about me that night at the campground." Sugar stuck her lip out in a pout.

"About ya being a bitch and all? I was tryin' to rile yore old man and the cowboy into doin' something fool-ish. I knew they both thought ya was the cat's meow. Honey, ya got to use yore old noggin when yo're in a fix like that. I knew sayin' that 'bout you would rile 'em more'n anythin', and they might drop their guard so we could get the hell out of there."

"You're as full of shit as a young robin."

Homer's laugh rang out. Sugar tilted her head so that she could see his face. He was young and full of life. Not bad-looking either.

"Where ya been all my life, sugar teat?"

"Lookin' for someone to put a little fun in mine."

"Ya found him, sweet thin'."

"That depends . . . sweet thin'." Her voice was a breathy whisper. She leaned forward to look out the windshield "We're in town. God, what a dead place."

"We can go on up to Elk City. There's a couple hot honky-tonks up there. Have we got enough gas, Chester?"

"Yeah. But I don't think we ort to go there."

"Go to Elk City? Why not? We got us a good-time lady here who wants to go honky-tonkin'."

"You know why we shouldn't go there."

"Forget that. I want to show this sweet little thin' a good time. How 'bout it, sugar doll?"

"Got any money?"

"Some."

"Then let's go!"

"Will yore old man be after ya?"

"Probably."

"I would too, if'n ya was mine."

"He *adores* me! Take me someplace where he can't find me. I've had 'bout all of him and his damn kids I can take."

"Why'd a good-lookin' woman like you marry a clod like him?"

"Money, honey. He's got some, but he's not turnin' loose of it till he gets to California."

"A lot of it?"

"Enough."

"Maybe we can help ya pry some of it away from him."

"Maybe." Sugar looked at him and made a kissing movement with her lips. "I'll think on it."

"By damn, Uncle Chester. I'm fallin' in love with this woman."

Chapter 19

DO YOU WANT ME TO GO WITH YOU, PA?"

"No, son." Foley slid in under the wheel of his car. "I'll go get her. She's goin' to be madder than a wet hen. You don't need to listen to her rant and rave. Hopefully she'll be calmed down by the time we get back."

Margie joined Jody. They stood together and watched his father leave the campground.

"Is he going to get Sugar?"

"Yeah. She got mad and walked off. It don't take much to set her off."

Margie walked beside him back to the Luker camp.

"Mona and Rusty are out walking," Jody remarked.

"Does that set all right with you and your father?"

He turned to look at her. "Because Rusty's blind?"

"Almost every time I see them they've got their heads together."

"Yeah." He smiled.

"You approve?"

"Sure, but it isn't for me to approve or to disapprove.

It's all right with me as long as Mona is happy. If they love each other, it'll work out."

Margie tilted her head and looked up at the tall boy. "Mona is lucky. If I'd had a brother, Jody, I would want him to be just like you."

Jody laughed nervously and kicked a dirt clod with the toe of his shoe.

Margie took a deep breath, then said, "Jody, I've got to decide what I'm going to do. As I see it, I could turn the truck over to the sheriff until my father's wife can claim it. Or, as Mr. Putman suggested, I could hire a driver and take the truck to Goldie in California, if I could find her."

"I didn't know Mr. Kinnard was married."

"He married Goldie Johnson. It didn't last. She ran off and went to California, or so her cousin said. What Elmer left is hers now."

"I take it you don't drive."

"No. I've not had a reason to learn."

"I taught Mona to drive a few years ago. She would go on ice deliveries with me, and I'd let her drive some until she got pretty good."

"Would you be interested in driving the truck? I would pay you of course."

"Drive you to California?"

"Uh-huh. Mr. Putman suggested that I pay you a dollar a day."

"I'll drive the truck for you, but I won't take your money."

"Oh, but I couldn't let you do it otherwise."

"We can talk later about pay."

"Shouldn't you talk it over with your father before you decide?"

"I don't think so. Pa wouldn't object."

"Would you be able to stand my company all day, every day, for more than three weeks?"

"That won't be any trouble at all." Jody smiled. "Could Mona ride with us part of the time? It would make things a little easier for Pa."

"Why not? And, Jody, will you teach me to drive? Of course, I'll not have anything to drive once I turn the truck over to Goldie."

"Sure. If we stop at a campground where there's room, I'll show you how to start and stop and use the hand signals. The rest is just steering."

"Oh, thank you." Margie was so relieved she put her hand on Jody's arm and smiled at him. When she became aware that Brady and Anna Marie had come up beside them, her first smile of the day faded.

"Margie, Uncle Brady is going to get me a soda pop."

"That's nice. What kind?" Margie's eyes went down to the child. All she could see of Brady was from his knees to his dusty boots.

"I don't know. Strawberry or orange."

"Both are good."

"He'll get one for *you*." Anna Marie giggled. "If you've been good."

Margie's eyes flew up to collide with squinted green ones, then back to Anna Marie.

Margie's pretty and proud and has had more trouble this past week than some women have in half a lifetime. These thoughts went through Brady's head as he looked at her. Her face, he noticed, had tanned from the sun, and her hair was becoming sun-bleached. She was capable and strong-minded, despite looking so fragile that a man would automatically want to protect her. She had demonstrated that strength when told of her father's sudden death.

Edgy under Brady's scrutiny, Margie stooped and straightened the collar of the child's dress.

"I just finished a big glass of iced tea, honey."

"I haven't thanked you for ironing Anna Marie's dresses." Brady's voice was a little rough.

"I had nothing else to do." Margie turned and headed for the truck. "I'll talk to you later, Jody," she called over her shoulder.

Brady waited until Margie reached the truck and sat down in the canvas chair before he spoke to Jody.

"Did she ask you to drive?"

"Yeah. She wants to pay me, but I couldn't take her money."

"Maybe you should. That way she'll feel that she's paying her way. She's doesn't want to be obligated to anyone." He said the last dryly.

"She wouldn't be."

"She would think she was, and that's what counts."

"Mr. Kinnard wasn't a nice man, but at least she wasn't alone. I feel sorry for her."

"Don't let her know that," Brady was quick to suggest. "That would get her back up in a hurry. She'd take off like a wild goose if she thought we asked her to come along because we feel sorry for her."

"Why else do you want her along?" Brady heard a small note of irritation in the boy's voice.

Uh-oh. The frown on Jody's young face triggered a

warning signal. Did the boy have a crush on Margie? God, he hoped not. At his age unrequited love was painful.

"We don't have to pity her to want to help her. But it'll not hurt at all to have another truck in our caravan." When Jody said nothing more, Brady asked, "Did Foley go after Sugar?"

"Yeah. She wanted him to take her honky-tonkin'. He told her he was tired from working on the car all day and that when we got to Amarillo they would go out one night. She got in a snit and walked off down the highway."

"That wasn't too smart. There's nothing between here and town but woods on both sides of the highway."

"Can we get the pop now?" Anna Marie tugged on Brady's hand.

"Sure, Punkie. Let's go get it before Deke locks up for the night."

Brady and Anna Marie were sitting on the bench in front of the garage when Foley Luker drove in. Jody hurried to the car when he saw that he was alone. Foley got out and spoke to his son. Snatches of words drifted to Brady.

"Can't find her."

"Did you look in the PowWow?"

"Not many there. It's early."

"She couldn't have walked to town in that length of time."

"Are you sure she didn't come back through the woods? I looked all over town. I don't know what the hell to do."

"Is this all the pop you want, Punkie?" Brady held the bottle of NeHi.

"I'm full."

"Mind if I have the rest?"

"Huh-uh."

Brady emptied the bottle in a few gulps and left it in the wooden case. Picking up the tired little girl, he carried her to where Foley was leaning against his car.

"I'll be glad to take my car and help hunt for her."

"I'd be obliged, Brady. I don't know where to look next."

"Deke might have an idea," Jody suggested.

"We should let Alvin know that we're leaving."

"While you're letting him know, I'll leave Anna Marie with Margie and be right back."

He stopped a few feet from where Margie sat in the canvas chair. "Can Punkie stay with you while I help Foley look for his wife?"

"Sure. Stand her in the truck. I'll wash her face and hands, and when she gets sleepy, she can lie down on the bunk."

"Grace and Alvin are visiting with Mrs. Bales and Deke. Mona and Rusty are out spoonin'."

"And I'm all that's left."

"I didn't mean to imply that," he said sharply.

"I don't care how you meant it."

When Margie climbed into the truck and turned to take the child, she found her eyes locked with a pair of startling green ones. Brady looked at her as if he were reading each and every thought that passed through her mind. She kept her features composed, but a little shock went through her when she realized how hardened she had become since she left home.

She wasn't bowing her head to anyone ever again.

"I don't know how long I'll be gone."

"It doesn't matter. She can sleep here. Come on, puddin'." Margie turned her back to Brady and lifted the child to sit on the bunk. "We'll wash your face and hands and take off your shoes."

"I got mud on 'em."

"That's all right. We can take care of that."

Brady lingered for a few seconds, then walked away.

Anna Marie whispered, "Is he gone?"

"He's gone."

"I got to pee-pee. Real bad."

"That's no problem, honey." Margie climbed out of the truck and held up her arms. "Everyone is gone. We'll just go around here on the other side of the truck where no one can see us." She unbuttoned the back of the child's underpants and held up her dress while she squatted beside the truck.

"I like you, Margie."

Every time Anna Marie said that, Margie wanted to slap the mother who had told her child she didn't like her.

"I like you too, puddin'. I more than like you. I think you're the sweetest, prettiest little girl I've ever known."

"You do?"

"I sure do. Let's get back in the truck. I'll light the lantern, and after we take off your muddy shoes I'll wash your face and hands. Then we'll look at the pictures in a movie magazine."

"Can I see a picture of the little girl with the curls?"

"I know right where to find one."

"Where's the man who sat out there in the chair every night? He didn't like me. I said hello to him and he went like this." Anna Marie drew her eyebrows together and turned down her lips.

"It wasn't that he didn't like you, honey. He was unhappy and . . . thinking about things."

"Is he comin' back?"

"Ah . . . no. He went to where your mama and daddy went."

"Oh. I'm glad he's not comin' back," she said with a child's honesty.

Sometime later Anna Marie fell asleep cuddled against Margie. Putting aside the magazine, Margie eased the child down on the bunk. Poor little girl, going to live with strangers. Margie wished with all her heart that she had the means to keep her and give her the love she never had from her mother.

Margie made a pad of blankets on Elmer's strongbox at the front of the truck and moved Anna Marie there so she could lie down on the bunk. After covering the child with a light sheet she stooped and kissed her cheek.

A wave of fatigue washed over her. She blew out the lantern and sank down on the bunk. She felt her stomach drop away when she thought of the burial tomorrow. She had tried, really tried, to grieve for her father. Long ago she had relegated him to a special place in her mind— the place where she put unpleasant things she didn't like to think about. Now she was ashamed to admit that she would grieve more if it had been Alvin Putman who came in fatal contact with the electric wire.

What kind of a person have I turned out to be?

Lying there in the dark, she would occasionally hear a car pass on the highway. She didn't allow herself to think about Brady Hoyt. Giving in to him had been an even bigger mistake than thinking that Ernie Harding was an honorable man and going off with him. She vowed silently never to put her blind trust in anyone again.

The people who thought they knew her had the notion that her big dream was to see Hollywood. She had wanted to see it since she saw her first movie, but more than that, she wanted a home and to belong to someone who needed her as much as she needed him. She wanted to love and be loved. She wanted a man who thought she was grand, the way that Alvin thought Grace was grand. She wanted *roots*. She wanted a little girl like Anna Marie to love and fuss over. She wanted, she wanted—

She made no attempt to wipe away the tears. She would indulge herself tonight . . . tomorrow would be another day.

It was near midnight when Brady stopped his car in front of the post office and waited for Foley to pull alongside.

"Jody and I went as far west as Texola. There wasn't anything there. I doubt that whoever picked her up would have backtracked to Elk City."

"Deke talked to the bartender at the PowWow. He said there had been very few ladies in there tonight and none fitted her description. Do you want to notify the sheriff?"

"If she isn't back by morning, we'll have to. I believe

that she was picked up on the highway by someone she thought would show her a good time. She hadn't had time to get very far before I went out looking for her." Foley rubbed his hand over his face. "She has a suitcase in the trailer. She may come back for it."

"Are you thinking that she got a chance to go with someone and left you?"

"In the back of my mind I knew it would happen someday. I just didn't expect it so soon."

"Hell. I'm sorry."

"Let's get on back," Foley said tiredly. "No use burning up more gas looking for her. It would be like her to worry me by hiding out all night, then come trottin' in in the morning."

On the way back to the campground Deke said, "It didn't take long for me to figure out that woman wasn't ever goin' to be anythin' but trouble to Luker. I'm a-wonderin' why he married her."

"He was lonely and horny." Brady looked at the little man and grinned.

"Godalmighty. There's easier ways of gettin' your rocks hauled than marryin' up with a floozy."

"I agree. My brother married a woman who gave him a merry chase. I learned a lesson there. I'm going to be damn careful who I tie up with."

"You said young Luker was goin' to drive Margie's truck. I'm right glad she's not goin' to strike out on her own. She's too nice, too trusting."

"We'll look after her."

"Hell I hope so. Mama'd be glad for her to stay here till she got on her feet, but she didn't want to put us out.

As if having that little thin' around would be anything but pure pleasure."

"She wants to see Hollywood," Brady said irritably.

Deke glanced at Brady's set features. "I hope she sees it and gets it out of her system. Then she'll settle down."

"To what? Workin' in a laundry washin' someone's dirty drawers?"

"She's pretty enough to be in the movies. Maybe some high muckety-muck will take one look at her, sign her up, and we'll see that pretty little face on the screen."

"More than likely she'll take up with some no-good jelly bean who'll use her like the bastard that left her here last year."

Deke turned his head and smiled when he heard the irritation in Brady's voice. *The man had a yen for little Margie!* He decided to goad him a little.

"Yep, that's about what'll happen to her. She'll find herself tied down with a bunch of kids and a life of pickin' oranges or hoein' cotton to feed 'em. A lot of no-good bums out there are just waitin' to latch onto a woman like Margie who's sweet and loving and loyal. She deserves more, by golly."

Brady's silence spoke louder than words. Hearing Deke's prediction of Margie's future had set his teeth on edge and a muscle dancing in his jaw. Deke kind of wished they'd stay around so he could find out what would happen between them.

When Deke and Brady turned into the campground, the car headlights shone on Mona, Rusty and Jody standing beside the Lukers' trailer. Jody, no doubt, was telling them of the search for Sugar. Brady let Deke out, then parked his car behind the Kinnard truck. He sat there for a minute or two before going to the end of the truck to get Anna Marie.

"Did you find her?" Margie's voice came out of the dark interior.

"No. Foley says she'll either come back or she won't."

"I suppose he's all torn up about her leaving."

"Didn't seem to be. I think he finally got his eyes opened to the kind of woman she was."

"I'm glad. I hate to think of him hurting."

"I'll take Anna Marie."

"Don't wake her. She's all right."

"Sure you don't mind?"

"Would I have said, 'Don't wake her,' if I minded?"

"Guess not. Well, thanks and good night."

Margie stared into the darkness. Sleep now evaded her. After a while she heard Jody's voice just outside the truck telling Mona to go on and that he would wait for her.

Mona was walking Rusty to the Putman camp, and Jody didn't want his sister coming back through the darkness alone. Margie decided that although Foley Luker hadn't used much judgment in choosing a second wife, he must have done something right. He had two really nice kids.

In a motor court cabin near Elk City, Sugar and Homer Persy lay in a tangle of bedsheets. Sugar giggled happily.

"Spread yore legs, slut!" he demanded.

"We've done it three times, you horny little stud!"

"I can go three more." Homer sucked on a spot beneath her ear and rocked himself against her naked thigh.

"Save some of it, lover. I don't want you to go dry on me."

"Don't worry about it. You've got the hottest little pussy I've ever had. Know that?"

Sugar sank her teeth in his shoulder. She loved it when he called her a slut, a hot pussy. She loved it when he drank bootleg whiskey out of her navel.

"Whater we going to do about Uncle Chester? He didn't like having to sleep in the car."

"Nothin' right now. I got other things on my mind."

"He don't like it that you're in here with me. I heard him call me a bangtail."

"Well, ya are, ain't ya? I aim to bang yore tail all the way to California."

Sugar giggled, wiggled against him and stroked his erection.

"I'll send him back home." Homer worried her earlobe between his lips. "Then it'll be just you and me, baby doll. We'll honky-tonk, screw and raise holy hell all the way to California."

"I want to get my suitcase—"

"We'll get it." Homer moved over between her spread legs. "Is yore old man goin' to kick up a fuss?"

"What if he does? There's nothin' he can do."

"Godalmighty. You musta been desperate to wed up with a clod old enough to have grown kids."

"It seemed like a good way to get to California."

Homer slid into her. "Goddamn. I been waitin' all my life for a hot-and-ready woman."

"Ya found her, Stud."

"We'll make a damn good team. Stud and Sugar. Sugar and Stud."

"Whater we goin' to do, Stud, after we get rid of Uncle Chester?" Sugar wrapped her legs around him.

"We'll get us some money. You said you could drive."

"Anything that's got four wheels. Will we—"

"Shut up talkin' and move yore ass! Ya've got me big as a fence post and harder'n a rock—"

Chapter 20

Sugar Luker had not returned when the group gathered to go to the cemetery for the burial. Foley looked haggard and tired after spending a sleepless night. He and Jody had gone on ahead to report to the sheriff that Sugar was missing, and would meet them later at the cemetery.

Alvin suggested that he and Grace go in his truck and Brady's car would carry the rest. Anna Marie would stay with Mrs. Bales. When Brady brought the car around to the front of the garage, Margie got in the backseat with Deke. Mona sat in front between Brady and Rusty. Rusty put his arm on the back of the seat. His hand cupped Mona's shoulder and pulled her close to him.

"You all right, darlin'?" Deke asked Margie as they pulled into the lonely-looking treeless cemetery where two workers in overalls stood back from a mound of red Oklahoma dirt. The casket containing her father's body sat on the ground beside an open hole. Deke reached for her hand and held it tightly.

"I'm all right. It was good of you to come, Deke. You'll lose business with the garage closed."

"Only for an hour, darlin'. Ole Deke wouldn't let ya go through this without bein' with ya."

"Both times I've been here, I've been trouble to you."

"It wasn't of your makin', darlin'. None of it."

"Thank you for being with me today."

When Foley and Jody drove up and parked behind them, they got out of the car. Somberly they walked through the sparse prairie grass and stood at the grave site. Before the service began Alvin asked Margie if she wanted the casket opened so that she could see her father for the last time. She shook her head. Deke stayed beside her, his arm around her.

Alvin spoke about how they had started on this trip and how Elmer's life had ended before they completed a third of it. After a sketchy background of Elmer's life, Rusty began to strum on his guitar, then sang "Rock of Ages." Alvin read from his Bible. When he closed it, he, Grace and Rusty sang "Nearer My God to Thee."

The service was short but decent and respectful. When it was over, Deke turned Margie away from the grave and led her back to the car while the casket was being lowered into the ground. Brady watched Deke lead Margie away and felt a surge of primitive jealousy. *He* should have been the one to be with her when they buried her father.

Brady hid his feelings when Alvin moved up beside him, but that didn't make them go away. He knew what was the matter with him, but it didn't make it any easier to tolerate. This plucky, little blond woman had gotten under his skin. He wanted her for his own. The need to have her was burning a hole in his gut. He didn't like the feeling and was impatient with himself for his restlessness.

Foley, who was the last to arrive at the cemetery, led the way back down the highway to the garage. As soon as they pulled into the campground, he saw that the ropes holding the cover on his trailer had been cut and the canvas thrown back. He knew before he looked that Sugar's suitcase would be gone. She and whoever she was with had sneaked in here to get it, knowing that he would be at the cemetery burying Elmer Kinnard.

Now he felt like a fool for reporting her as missing to the sheriff. She had left him for someone who had picked her up on the highway. Foley was relieved in a way that she hadn't been kidnapped, that she was evidently where she wanted to be. He didn't wish her to be harmed. But, Lord, what a chance she was taking. Didn't she have any sense at all? Then he thought that he had no right to question *her* reasoning when *he* hadn't shown any at all when he married her.

He glanced at his children. Jody and Mona were waiting to see what he was going to do. He owed them far more than he owed the woman he had known only a couple of weeks when he took her for his wife. He would try to make it up to them for the time they'd had to spend with Sugar.

"Daddy?" Mona came to look in the trailer, then up at her father. "She took her suitcase. I'm sorry, Daddy."

Foley put his arm around his daughter. "I'm the one who's sorry, honey. I knew even before we started on this trip that I shouldn't have married her."

"You were lonesome and . . . missed Mama." Mona put her arms around her father and hugged him. "What will we do now? Do we have to stay here and wait for her?" she asked anxiously.

"Well . . ." Foley loosened her arms and stepped back. "There's not much use in hanging around here. We'll go on. Jody is going to drive for Margie. If we don't go on, she won't have a driver."

"We can stay if you want to. Margie will wait with us." Mona was compelled to say it even though it would break her heart to have to part from Rusty.

"No. Sugar broke from us. She won't be back."

"But what if you never see her again?"

"Right now, honey, that would be all right with me."

"But you'll still be married to her."

"That worries me. If something happened to me, she would get everything. You and Jody would be left in the same fix as Margie." Foley knotted the cut rope and tied down the canvas.

"Isn't there something you can do?"

"I've already given Jody some of my cash money to keep. As soon as you can rig up a way to carry it, I'll divide what I have left with you. It's what Alvin did. He divided his money between the three of them. He said that way if he's robbed, they wouldn't lose everything."

"Do you think we might be robbed?"

"I don't know, honey. Sugar has hooked up with someone. I can't think a decent sort would pick a woman up off the highway, keep her out all night, then sneak her in here to get her suitcase. She may have dropped a hint that I'm carrying money."

"Pa." Jody came to where Foley was checking the air in his tires. "I need to tell Margie if we're goin' or stayin'."

"We're going."

"You don't want to wait—"

"No. We'll go on."

"Deke talked to his mother. She didn't see anyone drive in while we were gone."

"I'm not surprised they didn't drive in." Foley kept his head down.

"Brady is filling his gas tank. Margie wants me to move the truck up to the gas pump. She's wondering if she should buy extra tubes or anything before we go."

"Tell her to ask Deke. He'll know."

A knowing look that said "stay with Pa" passed from brother to sister before Jody hurried away.

He drove the truck up to the gas pump, and while he was putting gas in the overly large gas tank, Deke was checking the water and the oil. Brady with a pump in his hand was inspecting the tires with a gauge he put on the air valve.

"Ever'thing's up to snuff, darlin'," Deke said to Margie.

"Is there anything I should get now to have on hand?"

"I'm not tryin' to make a sale, but you should have an extra fan belt in case you get off in the desert and break one."

"Do I need tire tubes?"

Brady spoke up. "She's got two that haven't been used and extra boots in case she gets a hole in a tire."

"Then you don't need 'em now, darlin'. I'll get you a spare fan belt." He spoke to Brady as he passed. "Y'all got the tools to put it on?"

Brady nodded, then called out to Jody, "Look in the tool-box and hand me an oilcan."

Margie followed Deke into the garage. "Deke, do you know what it would cost to put some kind of marker on my father's grave?"

"Honey, it'd cost fifteen or twenty dollars to put a marker there that would last."

Margie looked apologetic as she pulled a twenty-dollar bill from her pocket.

"Do you know someone who would do it? I hate to impose on you once again."

"The undertaker will take care of it. Just write down what you want on the marker. I'll see that he gets it, and I'll see that it's done." He tore a sheet from the back of a tablet and handed her a pencil.

"I'll write down his name, his age and the date. I think that will be enough, don't you? I hate to think of years going by and no one knowing who is buried there."

"Don't ya worry none about it. It'll be done."

"Oh, Deke," she said after she had put the note and the money on the shelf beside the tablet, "I've never had such a good friend." Margie put her arms around his neck and laid her head on his shoulder.

"Now, now, darlin'. Yo're goin' to be all right. Mr. Putman is pure hickory, and Brady's a man to ride the river with. They'll look after ya."

"I don't want to be looked after as if I was a little kid. I have to feel that I'm pulling my own weight."

"Now, darlin'." Deke saw Brady come to the garage door. "Don't ya go and get all stiff-necked with pride. Hear? These is good folks yo're with, or I'd not let ya go off with them."

"I'm afraid that I'll be nothing but trouble."

"When the time comes that ya think yo're holdin' them

back, just peel off, leave the truck settin' and take the bus."

Deke was watching Brady over Margie's shoulder. Brady's scowling face spoke volumes; his eyes were so narrow Deke could scarcely see them. The big galoot was jealous of him! Deke turned his face and kissed Margie on the cheek. When he looked up, the door was empty.

"I want to tell your mother good-bye."

When Margie left the garage, Jody moved the truck to make room for his father to pull up to the gas pump. After Alvin had gassed up and was ready to go, Jody got in line behind him.

"I'm sure obliged for what you've done," Foley said as Deke filled his gas tank. "Alvin figures that we should be in Flagstaff, Arizona, in about a week and a half. If you hear anything from my wife, I would appreciate it if you'd send me a card General Delivery. Or send it to Bakersfield, California. We are going there to scout out places for our ice business. I think Alvin has relatives there. I'll ask at both places."

"I'll do that, Foley. I'm sure sorry about what happened."

"Yeah, so am I. I just hope that Sugar's with someone who will look out for her. She lived all her life in a one-horse town up in Missouri. For all her flirty ways she's dumb as a stump when it comes to taking care of herself."

When the caravan was lined up and ready to leave, they all got out to tell Deke good-bye. He squatted down so Anna Marie could hug his neck.

"We'll not forget you," Mona said, and waved to Mrs. Bales on the porch.

"And I'll not forget you, darlin'. Y'all send me a card

from time to time and let me know how yo're makin' out. Just send it to Deke's Garage, Sayre, Oklahoma, and we'll get it. Bye now. Be careful with my girl, Jody."

"I will. I'm going to teach her to drive."

"Well, now, I ain't so sure *that's* a good idea," Deke teased, and winked at Margie. "Take care, darlin'. Write to me."

"I will, Deke. I promise."

Margie had tears in her eyes when they pulled away from the campground. She waved at Deke until he was lost from sight.

Margie soon discovered that Jody handled the truck even better than Elmer had. He maintained a steady speed, not speeding up, then slowing down as Elmer had. At the end of the day Margie used to feel as if she had been on a roller coaster.

When they passed the prairie cemetery on their way out of town, Margie could see the fresh mound of red dirt that was her father's grave. He would remain there, far from home, throughout all eternity.

Good-bye, Daddy. I wish we could have loved each other like a father and daughter should.

Shortly after they had crossed into Texas they hit a patch of dirt highway. Choking dust boiled up. Jody slowed to allow the Putmans to get farther ahead. Margie rolled up the window, making it terribly hot in the truck.

"Oh, my. This is the first dirt road we've hit in a while. You're a good driver, Jody."

"Pa taught me when I was twelve. Mama had a fit. She thought I was too young. Pa put the truck out in a field and told me to go at it." He grinned at her proudly. "I started delivering ice when I was thirteen."

"Is your father heartbroken over losing Sugar?"

"He doesn't appear to be. Pa's usually very level-headed. Marrying Sugar is the one time that I can remember when he went off kind of half-cocked."

"Most of us do that sometime in our life. I've already done it a couple of times, and I'm younger than your father."

"He's thirty-seven. He was my age when he and mama married. They were in school together. It 'bout killed him when she died. He might have thought he'd have something like he had with mama when he married Sugar."

"Some things don't work out like we plan."

"*That* sure didn't."

"Having someone to talk to makes the time go fast, Jody. How far to Amarillo?"

"From Sayre, Alvin figured about a hundred and twenty-nine miles. We won't make it tonight. None of us want to be on the road at night."

"I heard Alvin say that the trucks are loaded too heavily to make good time."

"Yeah, and they want to get them to California in good shape so they can be used in the business."

In the middle of the afternoon they came to a place where men were working on the highway. Jody slowed the truck to a crawl. Farther on down they had to stop and wait for a scoop, pulled by a team of mules, to get across the road.

Margie sat on the edge of her seat and watched the road construction with interest. The crew used big machines that belched smoke from smokestacks, a water wagon that was pulled by horses and drags pulled by mules. Men in overalls worked with scoop shovels and rakes.

"That's a relief," Margie said an hour later when they pulled up onto the new paving. "We're spoiled." She smiled at the boy behind the wheel.

"Sure is easier driving."

"Want a drink of water out of the fruit jar?"

"Uncle Brady." Anna Marie pulled on Brady's arm. "I'm hot. I want a drink of water."

He reached over and rolled down the window. "That better? Move over away from the door, honey."

"I still want a drink."

"Hold on just a minute, Punkie. It looks like we're going to be stopping." Brady watched Alvin pull over onto a wide shoulder of the road, and Jody stopped behind him. Brady parked behind Margie and Jody.

Rusty and Grace stood beside their truck while Alvin climbed into the back. The rough road had caused some pans to fall, and they were bouncing around. Holding Anna Marie's hand, Brady walked up to where Jody and Margie stood. Jody was drinking from a fruit jar.

"Margie!" Anna Marie cried.

"Hello, puddin'."

Anna Marie pulled on her hand. Margie bent over so the girl could whisper. "I'm thirsty but . . . I got to pee-pee first."

"Well, let's see." Margie looked around the flat, treeless area conscious that Brady was watching her. Finally she said, "We'll get in the truck."

Before she could untie the ropes holding the back flap, Brady was there. He let down the tailgate, then reached in for the box Margie used to step up into the truck.

"Thank you."

She climbed up and reached for the child. Brady lifted her up. Her eyes were snared for several seconds by his, and she was surprised to see that a sadness was reflected there.

"Thank *you*," he echoed her words softly.

As soon as the flap was dropped down, Margie took the washdish from where it was wedged next to the water barrel. It was the only thing she could think of for the child to use. She would wash and scald it tonight before it was used again.

Anna Marie giggled. "I've not pee-peed in a washdish."

"Hurry, puddin'. We don't want to keep them waiting for us."

When the child was finished, Margie lifted the canvas flap. Brady stood a few feet away talking to Foley and Jody. He came and lifted Anna Marie down.

"Go to Mona, Punkie. She's waiting with a drink of water for you."

He offered his hand to Margie and helped her down. He clasped it tightly and seemed reluctant to let it go. She tugged on it, and he suddenly realized what she needed to do and went to the side of the truck. Margie reached for the washdish, emptied it quickly and shoved it back into the truck.

Brady was there seconds later, lifting the box and rolling down the flap.

"I can do it," Margie said.

"I know you can. I think you can do most anything you set your mind to, but you don't have to do this when I'm here." He finished tying the flap and turned so that his big frame blocked her view of the others. "You're still mad about . . . that night, aren't you?"

"What . . . ah . . . night?" She hated herself for stammering. "Oh, that. I've forgotten all about that."

He reached out a finger and looped a strand of hair over her ear. Time ticked away as they looked at each other. His warm fingertips touched her cheeks. Something inside Margie began to melt, spreading warmth to her toes. Finally he pulled his eyes away from hers and swung them to watch a car that passed them on the highway. When his eyes returned to hers, they held a quiet, serious look.

"Did you get all shook up on that bad stretch of road?" He drank in the sight of her pretty face.

She met his green stare with all the poise and self-control she could muster. His eyes were so narrowed she could hardly see the green glint between the thick lashes. She was more scared of his effect on her than she wanted to admit.

"Yeah, I did."

"Did what?" Watching her, he had forgotten that he had asked her a question.

"Get shook up on that rough road."

He couldn't stop looking at her. "Are you and Jody doing all right?"

"He's a good driver."

"I'm glad you didn't stay behind."

"So am I."

When she smiled, her eyes moved over him like a soft caress. Watching her lips spread and her eyes light up, he was so fascinated that he couldn't look away. His hand reached for hers and held it in his large rough one. He glanced down at their clasped hands. Hers was small, her wrists fragile. His eyes moved to her face, and he wished desperately to know what she was thinking, if she was still remembering his rough treatment of her. The thought made him weak inside.

The silence between them was beginning to be embarrassing when Anna Marie called.

"Uncle Brady. Can I ride with Aunt Grace? Rusty is goin' to ride with Mona."

"Did she ask you, honey, or did you ask her?"

"She asked me."

Before answering Anna Marie he squeezed Margie's hand and murmured, "I'll see you this evening."

Chapter 21

CHESTER WAS ANGRY.

He drove the Ford coupe at breakneck speed toward Amarillo and hardly slowed over the rough, unpaved patch of highway. The workers jumped out of the way, cursing and shaking their fists at the car as it disappeared in the cloud of dust.

Homer and Sugar didn't appear to notice Chester's recklessness. They cuddled on the seat beside him, hugging and kissing and . . . more. At times Homer's hand was up under her dress and hers was rubbing his crotch.

The woman was a bitch.

Chester seethed with indignation. Homer had gone too far this time. Some of the men in their family were a little wild, he thought, but all of the women were decent. Every blasted one of them! Chester wanted no truck with this woman who called herself Sugar. She was the type who would eat a man alive.

Chester intended to dump Homer and his whore the first chance he got and head back home. He admitted to himself that he had done a lot of mean things, but taking his mother's car bothered him the most. He shouldn't have let the stupid little horsecock talk him into it.

He drove into Amarillo at sundown.

"Find a motor court, Uncle. We'll wait till dark, then go out and find us some money. We got to have us a good time while we wait for the road-hoppers to get here."

"They won't get here tonight," Sugar said. "Foley piddles along following the trucks and won't drive at night."

"Good. That'll give us some time. This is a good-sized town. With yore looks, baby, we ort to do pretty good here."

"I'm not goin' to rob any more stores," Chester said flatly.

"You didn't rob them, Uncle. I did. It was as easy as fallin' off a log. But I got me a idey how we can get more money faster without takin' such a risk."

"We've got enough gas money to get home."

"You still singin' that tune? I'm not through with that cowboy yet. I ain't goin' till I am."

"Homer, honey, you said we'd go to California—"

"I ain't goin' to California either!" Chester broke in angrily.

"Don't get it in yore head to run out on us, Uncle Chester." Homer's voice held a threat. Then he laughed nastily. "I bet I know what's got yore tail over the line. Yo're randy as a ruttin' moose and mad cause ya ain't gettin' any of what my Sugar's puttin' out."

"I ain't wantin' *her*."

"Well, la-di-da! You wouldn't get it if you was rich as Rockofelter—or whatever his name is," Sugar jeered.

Homer laughed and kissed her soundly. "He ain't gettin' any if he was Alfalfa Bill Murray, the great know-it-all governor of Oklahoma. This's all mine." He grabbed her between her legs.

Sugar giggled. Chester grimaced and muttered under his breath. Homer ignored him.

"Ya know what that crazy son of a bitch did?"

"Who?"

"Alfalfa Bill. He plowed up the yard at that statehouse where he lived and planted taters. Don't that beat all?"

"Why'd he do that?"

"Hell, who knows? Whater ya mutterin' about, Uncle? Stick with us till we get enough money to get us a car and you can hightail it back to the sticks, run a little booze and take handouts from Grandma while me 'n' Sugar is livin' high on the hog."

Chester turned into a motor court with six tiny cabins lined up behind the main office.

"Find out what they got, Chester. If they got one with two beds, ya won't have to sleep in the car."

Chester got out and slammed the door.

"I don't like him none a-tall." Sugar snuggled her hand inside Homer's shirt and ran her fingernails over his chest. "And I don't want him in the room with us tonight."

"Why not, pretty little puss? If ya get him hot enough, he'll drive this car to hell and back for ya. Wouldn't ya like that?"

"Naw, I want it to be just you and me."

"We need the car right now, little pussy," he whispered in her ear, then grabbed her earlobe with his teeth and nibbled on it.

"He left the keys. We could just drive off and leave him."

Homer chuckled. "Yo're a real pisser, sugar teat. He'd call the sheriff, and we'd have to hole up somewhere."

"He'd do that?"

"Wouldn't put it past him. Tell ya what. Get all dolled up tonight, sweet pussy, and we'll go out huntin'. Now that I've got you to partner up with, it's time we got another car. If that old lady back at the garage saw this one, she's told the cowboy and yore old man. They'll be on the lookout for it."

"She couldn't of seen it. We parked down the road and went through the woods."

"I got it all figured out how we can get our hands on some money and buy our own car."

"Foley had money, but he wouldn't give me any. He wore a money belt around his waist and wouldn't take it off for anything. No chance of us getting that."

Homer grabbed her face and turned it to his. "He wouldn't take it off even to get naked with ya?"

"No." Her lips formed the word. He was holding her face so tight she couldn't speak.

"The poor, stupid son of a bitch!" His fingers dug into her cheeks to force her to open her mouth before he kissed her as if sucking the life out of her. "Yo're a wicked little bitch with the face of an angel" he breathed. "Ya like it rough, don't ya?"

Her fingers dug into the back of his neck. She pinched the small nipple on his chest so hard that he grunted.

"Yeah, and so does my horny stud."

Chester jerked the car door open. They broke the kiss, and Homer said, "Well?"

"Far end. Bed and a cot."

Sugar groaned.

Homer laughed. "Don't worry, little puss. Uncle's a sound sleeper."

Later, after they had eaten at a diner, they went back to the cabin so Sugar could put on what Homer jokingly called her working clothes—a modest blue dress with a round low neckline. She brushed her hair back and fastened a blue bow at the side with a bobby pin. When she was ready for Homer's approval, he took a cloth and wiped off some of the rouge and lipstick.

"Yo're just a sweet little girl. Remember? Now, ya know what to do. We'll let you out a block from that fancy hotel. When one a them well-dressed dudes comes out, turn that sweet innocent little face up and let out a little groan. Act like yo're hurtin' real bad. He'll take ya past that alley like he had a string tied to his pecker." Homer kissed her, careful to not smear her lipstick.

"I'd like to tie a string to your pecker and lead you into a dark alley," Sugar whispered seductively, and heard Chester snort. The freedom to talk dirty was one of the things that excited her most.

Acting as if setting up a man to be robbed was something she did every day of the week, Sugar, looking beautiful and seductive, her black hair tumbling around her face and shoulders, got out of the car a block from the hotel.

She was nervous about what she was about to do but was determined that Homer not know it. She had learned a lot about herself during the past twenty-four hours. This was the exciting life she craved, far removed from that hick town in Missouri and from poor, dull Foley Luker and his two equally dull and stupid kids.

Sugar walked confidently down the street until she reached the hotel, where she pretended to stumble. She let out a little cry of pain and hobbled to the side of the building, where she stood on one foot and rubbed her ankle.

"Oh, oh!" she cried as a well-dressed man came out of the hotel.

"Miss? Miss, are you hurt?"

"I've sprained my ankle." Sugar grabbed his arm as if she were about to fall and looked pleadingly into the face of a man with gray hair who wore an expensive suit and a brown felt hat. "Oh, dear. Oh, me. I've got to get down the street to the car. If my husband comes back and I'm not there, he'll . . . be so . . . mad . . ." She let her voice fall away.

"Where is your car?"

"It's . . . it's right down there."

"I'll help you. Hold on to my arm."

"Thank you, sir. Oh, thank you." Sugar held tightly to his arm and took hopping steps.

"Will you be all right until your husband comes?"

"Yes, but it . . . hurts."

"We'll take it slow."

When they reached the alley running alongside the hotel, Homer stepped out and rapped the man smartly on the side of the head with a sap, caught him as he fell and then dragged him into the dark alley. He quickly stripped him of his wallet, a pocket watch and a ring. He stuffed them in his pocket, took Sugar's arm and walked with her leisurely down the street to where Chester waited in the car.

"How'd I do?" Sugar said after they had sped away.

"You're a natural, little puss. Let's see what we got. Whee," he said after he had counted the money he took from the billfold. "Fifty-two dollars, the ring and the watch."

"Did you kill him?" Chester asked.

"Naw. I just gave him a little tap on the head. He'll wake up in the alley with a whale of a headache, wondering what hit him."

"It was exciting," Sugar exclaimed. "And easy. Where are we going now?"

"Ya ort to be in the movies, little puss. Head for that speakeasy we spotted a while ago, Chester. Then we'll hit a honky-tonk. Before the night's over we'll have enough money to buy a car and you'll be shed of us."

Jody and Margie followed Alvin into a treeless area at Alanreed, Texas. The ruins of a burned-out house sat in the middle of the campground. A half dozen campers were there and looked to have been there for some time. Clothes hung on lines stretched between dusty cars and trucks. Children played barefoot in the dirt while women tended campfires. Several men pulled their heads out from under the hood of a car to watch the newcomers drive in.

"They look like a real down-and-out bunch," Jody said as he followed Alvin's lead to the far side of the burned-out house. Nearby, a privy that had survived the fire leaned precariously to one side.

"They've left their homes looking for a better life. I

hope they find it." Margie thought that they at least had one another. It was more than she had.

Jody drove the truck close to the Putmans', then backed up and parked, leaving no more than a car length between the two trucks. Elmer had always made sure that there was a good distance between his camp and the others. Brady stopped close beside Margie on the other side, making it plain to the campers that watched that this caravan was a close unit, probably family.

Mona and Rusty came by as Margie was working the kinks out of her shoulders.

"Eat with us tonight, Margie," Mona said. "Daddy is getting out the kerosene stove. We're going to have fried potatoes and onions."

"All right. I'll bring a can of corn."

"I haven't had fried potatoes and corn since we left home."

"She's tired of my company, Margie. She didn't ask *me* to eat with her." Rusty's hand on Mona's shoulder moved across the back of her neck to cup the other shoulder and pull her closer to him. She turned on him.

"Bullfoot! Shame on you, Rusty Putman. I did too ask you to eat with us, and you said not until I came to eat with you. You said that, and I said I didn't want to leave Daddy and Jody alone tonight."

"She's tellin' a windy, Margie." He laughed happily, his face turned to Mona. It was hard to believe that he was not seeing her.

"You certainly did, you . . . you clabberhead."

It was a pleasure, Margie thought, to see how happy they were together.

"Hi, Rusty. Hi, Mona." Anna Marie and Blackie, glad

to be out of the car, came running toward them. "Guess what? Aunt Grace is goin' to let me draw faces on the eggs before we peel them."

"You can't draw a face," Rusty teased, and stooped to scratch Blackie's ears. The dog was glad to see him and had whined to let him know he was there.

"I can too. I've got a red crayon. I'm goin' to get it. Uncle Brady," Anna Marie called as she ran away.

"See what I mean, Margie? He's gettin' to be a regular smart aleck."

Margie laughed. "But he sings like a bird."

"More like a buzzard." Mona giggled and tried to move away. Rusty caught her, reached down and swung her up into his arms.

"Is there a muddy hole around here, Margie?" He swung Mona around, and Blackie, wanting to join in the merriment, raced around them and barked.

"Put me down, you knucklehead!"

"Not a muddy hole in sight, Rusty. You might consider dropping her in the ruins of that burned-out house."

"Where is it?"

"To your right."

Rusty took a few steps, stopped and let Mona slide down until her feet touched the ground.

Their laughter reached Margie as they walked away, Blackie frolicking alongside, Rusty's arm across Mona's shoulders, hers around his waist as if it were the most natural thing in the world. Without her stepmother glaring at her, waiting to find something to criticize, Mona was free to act like a young girl in love.

Suddenly Margie felt old. It had been a long time since

she was young and carefree and did silly things just for the fun of it.

Since Elmer had gone to a store the day he spent away from Deke's campground, the cupboard was well stocked when Margie looked in it to find a can of corn. There was even a box of Cream of Wheat and syrup for pancakes. She made a mental note to get milk when next they stopped for ice.

She took the corn, the canvas chair, a plate and eating utensils with her when she went to the Luker camp. The get-together was enjoyable. Even Foley appeared to be more relaxed without Sugar's cloying, overpowering presence. Mona and Jody were certainly more at ease. Foley cooked the meal of fried potatoes and onions on a small kerosene stove and heated the creamed corn, Margie's contribution, right in the can.

While she and Mona washed the supper dishes, Foley, Brady and Alvin squatted on their heels with a map spread out in front of them. Jody and Rusty came from the Putman camp with Anna Marie hanging on Rusty's hand. Blackie, as usual, trailed them.

Later when Margie went back to the truck with her chair, Brady's head and shoulders were beneath the hood.

"Is something wrong?"

He raised up to look at her. "No. I was checking the oil. The motor is in good condition. It doesn't use much oil." He wiped his hands on a rag he pulled from his back pocket and shut the hood. "Alvin thinks that we should leave at dawn and make as much time as we can tomorrow on the flatland. After we get over into New Mexico a ways, it's up one hill and down another."

"Have you been there?"

"I've been down around Albuquerque."

She could feel his gaze, hot and questing, on her face and was grateful for the evening shadows that hid the blush that crept up her throat to her cheeks. The silence between them went on and on. She was only half aware of the sound of Anna Marie calling to her.

"Margie! Margie!" Anna Marie ran to her from the Putman camp. "Aunt Grace let me keep an egg. Look." The egg had two round circles for eyes, a dot for a nose and a curved line for the mouth.

"Who is it?" Margie asked after looking at it closely.

"Uncle Brady. See his ears?" She turned the egg in her small fingers.

"It does look like him." Margie looked from the egg to Brady's smiling eyes. "When he loses his hair, you won't be able to tell them apart."

Anna Marie giggled and pulled on Margie's hand so that she would bend over.

"Ask Uncle Brady if I can sleep with you again," she whispered.

"You ask him," Margie whispered back.

"I'm 'fraid he won't let me."

"You won't know until you ask him."

Brady's eyes darted back and forth between his niece and the woman who had been in his thoughts all day.

"I'm beginning to feel like the skunk at the picnic. What are you two whispering about?"

Anna Marie had put the egg in the pocket of her dress and was holding on to Margie's hand with both of hers.

"All right. Out with it," he pressed. "What are you two hatching up?"

As his eyes roamed her face, strange feelings stirred in

Margie. Her heart fluttered. She drew the tip of her tongue across dry lips.

"We-ll," she stammered. "I was just about to invite Anna Marie to sleep in the truck with me again."

Brady's eyes were fixed unwavering on her.

She has a wistfulness about her tonight. She's a woman, yet she's a girl.

She was looking at him with wide, clear eyes. And in the flickering light of the Putmans' campfire her face appeared infinitely soft and beautiful. An unexpected twinge of yearning stirred deep inside of him. Brady tore his eyes away and looked down at his niece.

"Do you want to accept Margie's invitation?"

"Does that mean yes?"

"It means yes if Margie really wants you to stay."

"She wants me. Don't you, Margie?"

"Sure I do, puddin'. You can sleep on the box again. I like the company."

"Goody, goody. I can stretch out my feet."

"You could stretch your legs out in the car."

"Huh-uh. I kicked the door."

"I didn't realize that. I'll get the mattress for you."

"Margie likes me," Anna Marie said brightly, smiling up at her uncle.

Margie saw his jaw tighten and knew that he was remembering the cruel words that Becky, the child's mother, had said to her.

"Of course I like you." Margie hugged the child to her. "Everyone likes you. You're pretty and sweet and . . . smart to draw your uncle's face on the egg."

"I gave him big ears."

"By golly, you did." Margie lifted the child up into the

truck. "You've got to be washed before you can go to bed. I've got a bar of scented soap I've been saving. We'll use it and some powder to make you smell good."

Margie lit the lantern and set it on the icebox.

"I wish you were my mama." Anna Marie cuddled the boiled egg in her hand and looked at Margie with big, solemn eyes. "She was pretty, like you, but she didn't like me."

"Oh, honey. You must be mistaken."

"Huh-uh."

Wanting to change the subject, Margie said quickly, "We should have told your uncle to bring a nightgown."

"I brought one." Brady was standing at the end of the truck with the small mattress from his car. "I'll slide the mattress in. Can you take it from there? Otherwise you girls will have to get out before I can get in."

Margie had cleared off the things that rode on the box during the day. She moved the mattress over and tilted it onto the box.

"Just fits. Does she have a pillow?"

"I'll get it."

Later Brady sat beside the dark truck, smoked a cigarette and listened to Margie talking to his niece.

"When I was a little girl, my grandmother used to read to me. I liked the fairy tales best. Want me to tell you about Cinderella and the prince?"

"I like stories. Daddy told me about the three bears."

"Once upon a time there was a beautiful girl who lived with her cruel stepmother and stepsisters. They made her work from morning until night . . ."

Brady found himself listening to the story with rapt attention. It dawned on him for the hundredth time how foolish he had been to attempt to drive across the country with a five-year-old girl. God must have been watching out for the child and arranged for him to meet Margie and the Putmans. It had not even occurred to him to tell her a story. He didn't know if he even knew one.

"The prince tried the glass slipper on every girl in his kingdom, but it fit none of them. He feared that he would never find the beautiful girl who came to the ball. Then he came to the house where Cinderella lived with her step-mother and stepsisters . . ."

Silence. Brady tilted his head to listen. Would Margie come out? God, he hoped so. The heavy hand of loneliness gripped him, wrapping its icy fingers around his heart at the thought of the journey's end and never again seeing the slim, brown-eyed girl with the sweet, soft lips and the sad, shy smile.

Dear God! He was in love with her!

How had it happened? He knew that he liked her. Liked her a lot and enjoyed being with her. He hadn't intended to fall in love until he was on his feet and could provide for a wife. Hell and damnation! He had learned that love was an intimate, gut-wrenching experience that turned a reasonably intelligent man into a blithering idiot.

Is this how poor tortured Brian felt about Becky? Is this why a sensible man like Foley Luker married a floozy like Sugar?

Inside the truck Anna Marie had gone to sleep. Margie sat on the bunk and debated about what to do. She knew that Brady was out there. If she went out, he would think that she was running after him. If she didn't, he would think that she was avoiding him because she was still angry. She wanted him to believe that she was indifferent to him, that she was no more interested in him than she was in Jody or Rusty, which meant not going out of her way to avoid him.

She climbed out of the truck.

Chapter 22

BRADY GOT TO HIS FEET when Margie appeared. With a flick of her hand she motioned for him to sit down and went to sit on the fender of the truck.

"Does Anna Marie have a toothbrush?"

"She did when we started out. I looked for it this morning and couldn't find it."

"Even though she'll be losing her baby teeth, she should brush them at least once a day."

"I know. Brian was a stickler for that and for keeping her hands clean."

"Another thing. She's outgrown her shoes. Her little toes are red from being squeezed."

"Good Lord. I hadn't noticed that. She hasn't said anything. She's barefoot while in the car, but she puts on her shoes when we get out, because of cockleburs, nails and glass in the campgrounds."

"She wanted me to put her egg in a safe place so it wouldn't be broken."

"Not much chance of that. It's been boiled." He got to

his feet. Margie thought he was leaving, but he came to where she sat on the fender and held out his hand.

"Sit in the car with me for a while. We'll leave both doors open so we can hear Anna Marie if she wakes."

She ignored his hand and said, "No," shaking her head at the same time.

"Please." The softly spoken word coming from him shocked her. She looked up at the dark blur that was his face. "I want to tell you about Brian and Becky and how I came to have Anna Marie."

"You can tell me here. I don't think it's a good idea to get in the car with you."

"Do you think that I'm going to force myself on you? I've told you that I'm sorry about what happened that night in Oklahoma City. Don't you believe me?"

"Yes, I believe that you're sorry now, but that doesn't mean it won't happen again."

"Oh, Lord. I didn't realize that I had hurt you so much."

"The words hurt more than the rough treatment."

"I don't even remember what I said. Whatever it was, I said it in the heat of anger."

"Oftentimes people blurt out their innermost feelings when they are angry."

"Can't you forget it so we can start over?"

"I can't forget it. But if you like, we can start over. I don't want to be at loggerheads with anyone as I was with Elmer all my life. And I do appreciate all that you've done to help me these last few days."

"I need no thanks for that."

"You might not need them, but I need to offer them anyway."

"Deke said that you are one of a kind, and I believe him. If we are going to let the sleeping dog lie, come sit with me. You can call it a test . . . of sorts."

She was as surprised as he was when she accepted the hand he offered. She found herself walking beside him, her hand engulfed in a large, warm one.

"What else did Deke tell you?"

"He said that you had a lot of love to give someone and the man who got it would be a lucky son of a bitch. His words exactly."

"I wish I could have loved him the way a woman loves her special man. He is one of the most caring, unselfish people I've ever known."

"He'll meet someone someday who will realize that. My mother said that God made a woman for every man and that he made her for my father."

"What a sweet thing to say."

"He loved her very much and didn't last very long after she died."

Brady opened the passenger side of his car and left the door open after Margie had gotten in. He went around to the driver's side and slid in under the wheel.

"If it gets too windy, close the door."

"I hadn't visualized the land here in the Texas Panhandle as so flat and treeless."

"It is that. I prefer mountains and valleys."

"Is your ranch on a mountain?"

"It's in a lush, green valley. The grass at times comes up to the horses' bellies."

"Who do you sell your horses to?"

"Mostly other ranchers. Some go to the army. I also

run a few hundred head of steers. They are what pay the bills."

Margie was surprised that she was so comfortable with him. They were quiet for a long while before Margie spoke.

"It's been strange without Elmer. Somehow I keep thinking that he'll show up and tell me to get out of his truck."

"I know the feeling. I kept thinking that Brian would walk in the door. It wasn't until Anna Marie and I drove away from the house that I felt that it was over, that he was really gone." He put a cigarette in his mouth, flipped the head of the match with his thumbnail and lit it.

"When we get to a town that's big enough to have a shoe store, will you help me pick out shoes for Anna Marie?"

"Sure. She's a smart little thing . . . for her age."

"Is she? I've not been around enough children to know."

"The people I worked for had a boy and a girl. They were six and eight. Anna Marie is very bright. She acts as mature as the eight-year-old."

"She talks about you a lot. She's not been around many young women her mother's age. The woman Brian hired to take care of her was a grandmother. When Anna Marie wasn't with Brian, she was with her. She may have thought all young women were mean like her mother."

"Well, for crying out loud. I certainly hope that your brother set her straight about that."

"He tried. When I think of how he died, it almost tears me apart." Brady rushed on, hurrying to say what he wanted to say. "He was my twin. We looked exactly alike except for the scar in Brian's eyebrow. That's how the teacher told us apart. We even fooled our pa sometimes. We were always together. After the folks died it was just the two of us. We worked together, had fun together, without a thought that someday there would be only one of us left.

"Then he married Becky."

Margie watched Brady's large hands grip the steering wheel and knew that talking about his brother was painful. When one of his hands left the wheel and groped for hers, she put her hand in it.

"He loved Becky with all his heart from the time we were fourteen. He could see no other girl but her. She led him a merry chase through school and afterward. She was a good-time girl: loved to go to parties, dances, smoke cigarettes and drink bootleg whiskey. But she always kept Brian on the string. I think she married him to get away from home. Her folks were clamping down on her. Brian thought that she would settle down once they had a family.

"She did for a while. She hated being pregnant. Brian did everything for her. He was thrilled over Anna Marie. Becky never wanted to have much to do with her. Brian named her Anna after our grandma and Marie after our mother."

"Was your brother a rancher?"

"No. With the money we got from our parents and grandparents he bought a newspaper in a little town in Kansas. Becky didn't want to move, but she did; and it wasn't long until she had a circle of wild friends and fell back into her same old pattern. Foley's wife reminds me of her, but Becky wasn't as pretty or as flirty. If Brian knew she was messing around with other men, he never let on."

"What about you at that time? Did you go to Kansas?"

"No. I took my money and went west. It meant that Brian and I would be separated for the first time. But he had a wife who didn't like me much, and I couldn't abide her. It was best that I go my way and Brian go his. During the four years I was in Colorado I came back several times.

"Then I got a letter from Brian saying that he was about to lose the paper because he couldn't give it the time it needed. He didn't mention Becky, but I knew by the tone of the letter that she was at the root of his problems and that he was in a terrible state of depression. I got on the train the day I received the letter and got there an hour too late."

Margie didn't know what to say. She heard the pain in his voice and desperately wanted to say something to comfort him. She took his hand in both of hers, drew it into her lap and held it tightly.

"Brian went home and found her in his bed with a man he thought was his friend. He killed both of them. I met him coming out of the house with Becky's body in his arms. He went to the barn and killed himself." Brady drew in a deep breath. "I never knew anything could hurt so much. It was like a knife had cut out part of my heart."

"I can imagine. It must have been unbearable."

"He asked me what he had done wrong that would cause his Becky to hurt him so. What could I tell him? He had wasted his life loving a woman who wasn't worth spit."

"Was there no one else to take Anna Marie?"

"Becky's folks had washed their hands of Becky and didn't even come to the funeral. She had one old-maid aunt. But after I looked her over I wouldn't leave a sick pup with her. So I wrote to Opal, Becky's sister. She wrote back and said to bring her out."

"She may be just the thing for Anna Marie."

"And she may not. If I remember correctly, she was a year or two younger than Becky and had left home before she did. The aunt who gave me her address seemed to think that she was all right, although I heard Brian say something to the effect that her husband was a scalawag who couldn't hold a job. I've grown so attached to the little mite that I don't know if I'll be able to give her up even if Opal is a saint."

"When the time comes, you'll do what's best for Anna Marie."

"I'm afraid that I'll be selfish and want to keep her with me, even if I can't give her the life someone else could give her."

"Do you think someone else will love her more than you do? Take better care of her?" Margie could feel each time he looked at her and then away.

"No. She's all I have left of my brother . . . my family. But I've learned on this trip that I don't know much about how to take care of a little girl. She's even embarrassed to tell me when she needs to go to the outhouse."

"Couldn't you hire someone to take care of her? Her father did."

"I live ten miles from town. Two Indian families and one Mexican family live there on the ranch. My house is just a rough cabin. I was going to fix it up this year, but I've spent my money going back to Kansas and on this trip to California. After paying Brian's bills, all that was left was this car."

"Anna Marie might prefer living in a rough cabin where she is loved to living in a nice house where she is an outsider."

"But she's too young to make that decision."

The logic of his statement left Margie with nothing to say. The silence between them stretched into frozen moments in time—two people sitting in the dark. She looked out the car window into a sky studded with a million stars. The moon, looking like a big yellow balloon, was hanging high above the burned-out house. The crying of a child from one of the other camps, then the barking of a dog, broke the stillness. Brady brought her hand to the seat between them and laced his fingers with hers.

"My ranch is about three hundred miles north of Albuquerque." He finally spoke, leaving his statement hanging in the air.

Margie hesitated, then said, "You could turn off there. It would save you miles and . . . time. Alvin and Grace would take Anna Marie on to her aunt in California. They are going to Bakersfield."

Slowly he turned his head and looked at her. "If I turn off at Albuquerque, Anna Marie will be with me." He continued to look at her.

Margie with the big sad eyes, I wish that I dared to ask you to go with me. But in a way you are like Becky. She had her heart set on having a good time. You've got yours set on seeing Hollywood and would laugh if I asked you to live with me on an isolated horse ranch.

"You've got two or three days to make up your mind."

She wiggled her hand out of his and slid out of the car. "I'd better turn in if we're going to leave at dawn."

Brady met her in front of the car and took her arm. "Thank you for being with me and being such a patient listener."

She wasn't sure what to say, so she said nothing. At the end of the truck they stopped and looked steadily at each other. Even though it was dark, the force of his eyes held her as firmly as if he held her with his hands. It had been pleasant being with him. She had not felt in the least threatened.

He was a hard man, but he had soft spots too. He had loved his brother, and, whether he was aware of it or not, he loved his brother's child.

"Would you like me to light the lantern?"

"No." She laughed lightly. "My night vision has improved lately."

"Well, good night."

"Good night."

Margie lay awake for a long time thinking about Brady Hoyt and what had made him the kind of man he was.

Margie was up and dressed when dawn began to light the eastern sky.

Anna Marie was still asleep when Brady came for her. Margie held her while he put her mattress back in his car. She wished with all her heart that she could keep this child with her forever. How wonderful it would be to have someone of your very own to love and to watch grow. She was unaware that Brady stood at the end of the truck until she lifted her head after placing a kiss on Anna Marie's forehead.

He stepped up on the box and reached for the child. It was too dark to see his eyes, but Margie felt them on her face. He gently lifted the little girl out of her arms, then stood for a long moment looking at her, the sleeping child between them.

"We'll stop for gas in Amarillo," he said.

"All right."

"See you then."

The headlights shone on the back of Alvin's truck as Margie and Jody left the campground. As soon as the sky was light enough that Jody could see, he turned them off.

"Brady said the lights were a drain on the battery."

"How is your father doin'?" Margie asked.

"All right. He's worried about Sugar. He doesn't want anything bad to happen to her."

"Elmer's wife ran off and left him too. I don't know what made her go, but I do know that he must have been hard to live with."

"Pa was too good to Sugar. He tried hard to give her everything she wanted. He thinks now that she was just using him to get to California."

"But he's married to her. She could step in and take everything he has if anything happened to him."

"Pa knows that. He said that when we get to California, he'll see if he can get something called an annulment because she ran off and left him."

*   *   *

Sugar woke to find herself alone in the small cabin. Light was streaming in through the window. She crawled out of the rumpled bed and went to look out. The car was gone!

"The dirty, low-life son of a bitch!"

She quickly searched the room. He had taken everything except her suitcase. He'd not left her a dime! She fumed as she dressed. He'd not get away with it. She'd go to the police and tell them that he not only kidnapped her, he forced her to help him rob those people. She'd see his sorry ass in jail!

She was putting on her lipstick when she heard a car stop, then the slamming of a door. A key rattled in the lock, then the door was flung open.

" 'Lo, sweet thing. Didn't expect ya to be up." Homer came to her, grabbed the hair at the back of her head and kissed her. "Why ya got them clothes on for?"

"Where the hell have you been?"

"Takin' care of a few things. Did ya think I run off and left ya? I took all the money so ya'd be here when I got back all warm, naked and sweet-smellin'—"

"Where's Chester?"

"Gone home."

"You talked him into lettin' us keep the car?"

"Yup. We'll get us another car license to put on it in a day or two."

"It's just you and me now?"

"Uh-huh."

Sugar laughed. "Glory be! I bet old Chester didn't want to get on that bus. Did he put up a fight?" She snuggled against him, bit him on the chin and rubbed against him.

"Not much of a fight at all. We gotta be out of here in

an hour, or we'll have to pay again. Get outta them clothes, pretty little bitch. I'm horny as a rutting moose, hard as a rock and randy as a two-peckered mountain goat."

"I got just what ya need, my lusty stud," she said, squeezing him.

Homer put her away from him, shed his coat and unbuttoned his shirt. He took the gun that was tucked in his belt and laid it on the scarred table, then placed a pocket watch and a wad of bills beside it.

Sugar hurriedly removed her dress and slip and sprawled naked across the bed.

"Isn't that Chester's watch?"

"Yeah. He gave it to me."

Sugar waited until he was naked and crawling on top of her before she asked, "Did you do something to Chester?"

"Whatta ya care? Ya didn't like him."

"I didn't like him and I don't care."

"Then shut up and open up."

Later he lay on her, breathing heavily, and whispered, "Get up, ya damn beautiful bitch. We've got to get out to the highway so we can follow that cowboy when he comes through."

Chapter 23

THE SMALL GAS STATION OWNER, on the western edge of Amarillo, couldn't believe his luck when two trucks and two cars lined up and waited patiently at the pump.

After giving Jody money to pay for their gas, Margie got out of the truck and walked back and forth to limber her legs after the long ride. Brady was getting out of his car. Anna Marie was sitting in the front seat. As Margie neared, she saw that the child's little face was wet with tears. Margie's eyes caught Brady's troubled gaze over the top of the car before she spoke to the child.

"What's the matter, honey?"

"Nothin'."

"Want a drink of water?"

"No. I want . . . I want—"

"Want what? What do you want, punkin?"

Before Anna Marie answered, Brady said, "She wants to ride with you. I told her that she should wait until she was invited."

"I'm inviting her," Margie said quickly, opened the car

door and lifted the child out. When Anna Marie wrapped her arms around her neck and her legs around her waist, Margie discovered that the child's nightgown was wet. She hid her wet face against Margie's neck and sobbed out something Margie didn't understand.

"Now, now, punkin. Don't cry." Margie turned her back to Brady, hugged and murmured to the sobbing child. "What is it, darlin'? What do you want?"

"I want . . . my dad . . . dy . . ."

The tearful words tore at Margie's heart, and big tears sprang to her eyes. After a heart-stopping moment she went to the truck, which was now at the gas pump. Brady met her there, a concerned look on his face.

"Her dress is in there," Margie said, unable to hold back the tears that leaked from the corners of her eyes.

"What's the matter? Is she sick?"

"She's wet and . . . she wants her . . . daddy." Margie spoke with trembling lips.

"Oh . . . God," he breathed huskily.

Through her blurred vision Margie saw the stricken look on his face and knew that she would remember it forever. It was the look of a man in almost unbearable pain. He turned and untied the back flap on the truck.

"Do you want to get in?" he asked Anna Marie. "I'll tell Jody to go easy when he leaves the gas pump."

When she nodded, Brady pulled the box down for her to step on and lifted her from Margie's arms so she could climb into the truck. He held the little girl close, his head bent, his cheek against hers. His green eyes were shiny when he lifted his head. After setting his niece up into the truck, he quickly walked away.

By the time Anna Marie was dressed, she was in a bet-

ter mood. It was exciting to her to be in the back of the
truck while it was moved to make room for Brady and
Foley at the gas pump. When they stopped, Margie got
out and reached for the little girl, but Brady was already
there.

"Feel better, Punkie?" He lifted the child in his arms,
held her for a minute, then carefully set her on her feet.
"Stay right here or you may step on a cocklebur. I'll carry
you after I make sure the canvas is tied down."

"Margie's goin' to brush my hair."

"We'll get you some shoes the first chance we get."

He finished tying the flap, picked up Anna Marie again
and set her on his arm. He looked at Margie. His gaze
swept the area, then settled back on her face.

"Ride with us for a couple hours. Rusty will ride with
Jody." His tone of voice revealed a touch of anxiety.

Margie tilted her head to look up at him. His face was
different, uncertain. His green eyes were shadowed with
sadness.

"Well . . . all right. I'll brush Anna Marie's hair. Has
she had anything to eat?"

"Some dry toasties. The man here says there's a store
ahead and just beyond that an ice dock."

"She should have milk."

"I'll get it at the store."

"You can put it in the icebox after I get ice."

By the time they reached Brady's car, Anna Marie's
eyes were anxiously going from one to the other.
"Margie?"

"She's going to ride with us, Punkie." Brady spoke
with a happier note in his voice. He stood her on the seat.
"Move over and make room for her."

"Goody, goody!"

Jody and Rusty had been to the outhouse behind the station. Jody left Rusty at the passenger side of the truck and went around to the driver's side. Mona ran up to say something to Rusty, laughed, hit him on the arm and ran to her father's car. Rusty called out to her that she'd better behave or he'd tell Jody something she had said.

The caravan moved down the highway a half mile and stopped between the mercantile store and the ice dock.

"I'll carry Anna Marie to the porch, then go get your ice. I take it your box will hold twenty-five pounds."

"The last melted out last night. The tongs are in the toolbox there on the side of the truck. Jody has the keys."

Grace was in the store exclaiming over the variety of goods when Margie and Anna Marie entered.

"I haven't seen this much stuff since we left home. There's everything in the world over there." She had come from the dry goods side of the store.

"Do they have shoes?"

"Didn't see any. Oh, mister, do you have any dried apples? I've got a hankerin' to make fried apple pie." Grace went to the grocery side of the store, leaving Margie and Anna Marie to explore the dry goods side.

They paused at a table of dress goods and fingered the pretty prints. There were hats, gloves, stockings, ribbons and buttons. At the far end, as they were turning to come back up the aisle, Margie spotted a table of Indian moccasins. They were different from the ones she had seen in Missouri.

"These are nice. Look at the beadwork. Do you think we could find a pair that would fit you, honey?" Margie lifted Anna Marie up onto the end of the table. "I had a pair when I was little."

"I like blue ones."

"Here's a pair with blue beads." She measured the sole of the moccasin against Anna's foot. "Too little." She delved into the pile and came out with another pair. "These look just right. Shall we try them on?"

"They're pretty."

After slipping the moccasins on Anna's small feet and tying the thong, she lifted the child down.

"How do they feel?" Down on her knees, Margie pressed her thumb on the end of the shoe to test the fit.

"Good. Can I have 'em?"

Margie looked at the sign: CHILDREN'S MOC 75 CENTS. OTHERS 1.00. She got to her feet. A dollar seventy-five if she got a pair for herself. She made the decision.

"Yes, you can, and I'll get a pair for myself."

"Like mine?"

"Like yours."

"Goody, goody!"

She wouldn't have dared to spend the money before, but she had kept the two hundred dollars she had found in Elmer's socks. It was worth every penny of the money to see the smile on Anna Marie's face and see her dance up the aisle of the store.

Grace had left before they reached the counter. Margie asked for a bottle of milk, a loaf of sliced bread and a pound of sliced meat.

"I'll have to charge you a nickel deposit on the bottle."

"Can I turn it in down the line if I buy more milk tomorrow?"

"You should be able to."

She was paying for the purchases when Brady came into the store. She hurriedly put the change in her pocket.

"Looky, Uncle Brady. Looky what I got. You don't have to carry me. They're Indian shoes."

"So they are." He knelt down and lifted her foot. "That's just the ticket, Punkie."

He stood and went to the counter, his eyes on Margie. She avoided looking at him and picked up the sack with the milk, bread and meat. He didn't say anything until they reached the store porch.

"I'm glad you found the footwear. I'll pay you for them and for the milk."

"I'll pay you for the ice."

"It was all of fifteen cents."

"Well . . . the shoes were ten dollars," she said with a cocky smile.

At first he was taken aback, then a slow smile covered his face and his eyes lit up.

"Is that all? You should have bought two or three more pairs."

"I did buy one more." She held up the pair she had bought for herself. "I'm going to sit down right here on the steps and put them on."

"Take your time. We've decided this will be our noon stop even if it is a little early. Stay with Margie, Punkie, I'll be right back." Brady went back into the store.

When he came out, Margie and Anna Marie in their new moccasins stood at the end of the truck. Brady had tied the flap back when he put the ice in the box, but it was still as hot as an oven under the canvas.

"Stay here, honey. I'll get a cup for your milk and butter to go on our bread," Margie said.

"Can I show Aunt Grace and Mona my new shoes?"

"Wait until I come back."

Margie was ready to climb out over the tailgate when Brady reappeared. He set a sack on the ground and lifted her down as easily as if she had been Anna Marie. "Thank you."

"You're very welcome." His eyes smiled at her.

"I got bread and meat. I'll make Anna Marie a sandwich. She's eager to show her shoes to Mona and Grace."

"I got bread and meat too. And a toothbrush for Punkie."

"Put the meat in the icebox. Would you like a glass of tea? I have some made, but had no ice to go in it until now."

"I sure would. Shall I chip the ice?"

Margie glanced at him. The smile he gave her spread a warm light into his eyes. He looked years younger when he smiled. Her pulse leaped, bringing color to her face, and her flushed cheeks made her soft brown eyes seem all the warmer.

They ate the sandwiches while sitting on the fender of the truck and watched Anna Marie run around showing everyone her new footwear.

"I know now why Indians wear moccasins," Margie said, wiggling her toes. "They're comfortable. It's like going barefoot, except you don't have to worry about cockleburs."

Brady dug in his pocket, brought out two dollars and put it in her hand.

"What's this for?"

"The shoes and the milk."

"The shoes and the milk were eighty-five cents. I'll get the deposit back on the bottle." She shoved the bills back in his hand.

"I want to pay for your shoes too . . . for all you've done for Anna Marie."

"I don't expect pay for what I've done for Anna Marie." Her voice was so cold that it sent a chill down his back. "Do you want pay for what you've done for me?"

"No, of course not! Oh, Lord, I've put my foot in it again. I'm sorry. I didn't put it right. I want to give you something, and I used Anna Marie for an excuse."

"We don't know each other well enough for me to accept a present from you." She held her head high, her hard brown eyes refusing to look away from his.

The expression on her face cut him like a knife. He felt a tide of panic rise in his throat. He had to make amends, and fast.

"Margie, for the past four years I've been on an isolated ranch, and even before I went to Colorado I didn't have all that much to do with women. I've lost touch with what's proper and what isn't. If it was forward of me to offer you a gift, I'm sorry."

"After what Elmer said about me I suppose you thought that I—"

"Believe me," he interrupted, "after getting to know you I totally disregarded what Elmer said. He was a bitter, unhappy man, and I think he resented your independence. Be patient with me, Margie. Please."

When she didn't say anything, he said anxiously, "Can't we start over again? Again?"

After a long-drawn-out silence she suddenly let out a little nervous laugh.

"I'm on kind of a short fuse. You can get my back up quicker than anyone I've ever met."

He was too stunned with relief to utter another word; his heart was drumming so hard he could hardly breathe.

"Grace is packing up. I'd better do the same." Margie stood and reached for his glass. "I hate to let this ice go to waste. I'll put it and some tea in the fruit jar. We'll drink it on the way."

He followed her to the truck. After she had filled the jar and before she tied down the flap, she reached inside for her hairbrush.

"I haven't brushed Anna Marie's hair yet."

"I'm hot," Sugar complained. "Are the fools goin' to sit there all day?"

Homer had stopped the coupe beside a cluster of shops several hundred feet from where the caravan was parked. Sugar looked like a boy with her hair up under Homer's cap and in the denim pants and striped shirt they had bought this morning. Homer wore Chester's old felt hat.

Sugar had not mentioned Chester again, and neither had Homer. In the back of her mind she wondered at his sudden leaving after vowing to take the car back to his mother. Homer had handled the situation, and that was enough for her. If he had done away with his uncle, she didn't want to know it. She was happier than she'd ever been. She was free. She was doing exciting things. Now, if only Homer would forget about getting even with that damn cowboy . . .

"I see that sweet little Margie is getting in the car with Brady," Sugar said with heavy sarcasm. "The mealy-mouthed scrawny bitch! She'd been angling to get him between her legs since we started this trip. Now that her papa's out of the way, she'll not have to wait long. A man like Brady's used to getting his poontang. He won't go long without it."

"Scrawny? If I remember right, she had good-sized tits." Homer wore a devilish grin when he looked at her.

"Bullshit! So does a cow. Ya wanta screw a cow?" she asked shrewishly, and flounced over next to the door.

One of the best things about being with Homer was that they spoke the same language. She could use all the forbidden words she had used only in her thoughts. None of this having to be so nasty nice and having to make it right with Foley every time she slipped up. It was great to be out from under that strain and be able to be herself.

Homer let out a hoot of laughter. "Chester screwed a sheep once on a dare."

Sugar looked pained. "I'm not surprised." Then, "How was it?"

"All right, I guess. He shot his wad."

"Piddle," Sugar said with disgust. "He had sheep dung for brains anyhow."

They sat silently and watched the activity going on around the caravan. Then Homer asked, "Is the cowboy hot for the blonde?"

"She's the only one handy beside Foley's kid, and that one went gaga over the blind dummy 'cause he could sing and play the guitar."

"Who's drivin' her truck?"

"Jody, Foley's kid. That's the blind dummy getting in with him. Lordy, but it pissed her for me to call him that."

"If we get the chance, we'll run yore old man off the road."

"Don't do that!" Sugar exclaimed. "I want the money he's carryin'. I'm entitled to some of it."

"He's last in line. Before anyone misses him we'd have the money and be gone."

"He'd know it was me."

"Maybe not."

"You'd kill him?"

"Well, shit! Do you think I'm dumb enough to let him put the finger on me?"

"What about the cowboy?"

"I ain't giving up on him."

"Can't we go on ahead, lover?" Sugar moved over and worked her hand against his fly.

"Cut that out." He removed her hand. "Some jay-hawk will come out of that feedstore and see a boy with his hands in my pants. The shock might kill him."

Sugar's tinkling laugh rang out. Homer gazed at her smiling face. She was about the prettiest woman he'd ever seen, pretty and wicked, and she loved to screw. How in the hell had he had the good luck to find her? Now that they were rid of old Chester, he'd pull off the road whenever they took a notion to have a little fun and go at it.

"Hey, Stud." Sugar waved her hand in front of his face to get his attention. "When are we goin' to get more money?"

"You liked that, didn't you?"

"It was exciting."

"I'm afraid we'll have to wait until we get to a big enough town before I put my pretty little decoy out again. Meanwhile, we'll keep our eyes open for easy pickin's."

Chapter 24

THE COUNTRY WEST OF AMARILLO was big and open as far as the eye could see. The highway cut a path between a sea of short prairie grass, a pale gold carpet, rolled back on each side of the highway. Shadows of the low-flying clouds created dark patches on the open sun-yellowed grassy plain.

Margie thought that they might as well be traveling across a space as empty and limitless as the sky except for the skeleton of a windmill silhouetted against the blue. On the breeze that came from the south was the smell of sun-ripened grass and sage. She had the feeling that she would be like a grain of sand on a beach if she were ever lost in this vast space.

"It's a lonesome country." She spoke for the first time since Anna Marie had fallen asleep, her head in Margie's lap, her feet in Brady's.

"Yes, it is. But hills and valleys can be lonesome too."

"Were you lonesome at your ranch?"

"Most of the time I was so busy that I didn't have time

to think about it. But when I did, I wished to have someone to go home to." He glanced at her profile. "Both of
the Mexicans that work there have large happy families.
Ramon, my partner, married last fall."

"Ramon. Is he a Mexican?"

"No. Cherokee. He has an interesting background. His
father was a teacher at the Cherokee Seminary at Tahlequah, Oklahoma. His mother was a quadroon, which
makes him one-eighth colored. He's one of the smartest
men I've ever known and could be teaching in a university somewhere. But he loves ranching, loves horses,
hates being in town and seldom goes there."

"How did you meet him?"

"While working on a ranch. When I first went out to
Colorado, I signed on to work for bed, board and ten a
month. I wanted to get a little experience under my belt
before I put my money down. Ramon had come out from
Rainwater, Oklahoma, and didn't have a dime to his
name. A few months later his sister, Radna Bluefeather,
and her husband, Randolph, came to visit him. Randolph
insisted on staking Ramon and put up money equal to
mine. That's how I happened to be partners with him. It
was one of the smartest moves I ever made."

"Is Ramon married?"

"He went to Denver to get a load of books and came
back with a wife. They're well suited. Both are educated,
private people and are crazy in love with each other."

"Is she an Indian?"

"No. Do you have anything against a white woman
who marries a man of mixed blood?"

"No." She glanced at his sharply etched profile. He
turned, and she saw a flicker of humor in his eyes as he

swung them away from her and concentrated on his driving. The car picked up speed. There was something terribly attractive about him. He was totally male from the top of his thick black hair to his scuffed cowboy boots. There was no doubt that he aroused her physically. *How do I know another attractive man wouldn't do the same under the same circumstances?*

Brady Hoyt, however, was unlike any man she had ever met. He was efficient, decisive and even brutal when necessary. That was demonstrated by the way he had handled men who would probably have robbed them. On the other hand, he was as gentle and as caring with Anna Marie as if she was the most precious thing in the world. Would he be the same with a woman . . . if he loved her?

Margie longed for someone who would look forward to coming home to *her*. She wanted a man she could stand beside, as a helpmate to share his joy and his sorrows, bear his children and grow old with. She gave a little involuntary shiver. In Brady she had finally met a man she could give her heart to completely, build her life around.

Her lips curled with disgust. She was too much a coward to admit that she was already in love with him, and she was afraid that if she did admit it, it would become real and would hurt much more later on. She had to be realistic about this. Brady was probably interested in her only for the duration of the trip. It would never do to let him know how much she had enjoyed being with him and Anna Marie this afternoon.

The trucks ahead slowed until they were creeping along. When they hit the dirt and gravel road, flourlike dust, stirred by the wheels, swirled up behind them.

Margie rolled up the window. Brady backed away to allow more space between them and the truck ahead.

The going was slow for what seemed to be miles and miles, and the heat inside the car became wicked. Anna Marie's head was wet with sweat. Margie cooled her face with the cardboard fan Brady pulled from under the seat.

"This heat gives me a powerful thirst." Brady wiped the sweat from his forehead with the sleeve of his shirt.

Margie reached for the fruit jar she had wrapped in a towel. "The ice is gone, but there's a little tea left."

"You drink first."

Margie took a swallow and passed the jar to Brady. She watched as he tilted his head to drink. Her eyes took in every detail of his profile. When he finished, he held out the jar. Bright green eyes from beneath a brush of brows as dark as his windblown hair smiled at her. She took the jar from his hand, screwed the top back on and set it on the floor. She hoped desperately that he didn't know how her heart was behaving.

It was a blessed relief when the car bumped over a ridge and onto a patch of newly paved highway.

"I'm glad that's over," Margie said, and rolled down the window.

"We'll hit a lot of dirt roads before we get to Albuquerque."

"Have you been over this road before?"

"Not here. I was on a little patch west of Albuquerque. We should be in Tucumcari in a couple of hours. I hope Alvin knows where to find the campground."

"Will it be dark then? The days are getting longer."

"Just about dark, I think. I was dreading this long day,

but it's gone fast." He looked across the intervening space between them. "You should ride with us every day."

"That would never do, and you know it."

"Why not?"

"Well . . ." She paused and bit down on her lower lip. "Because I've got a lot of thinking to do, and so do you. You've got to decide if you're going to turn off at Albuquerque. We can't do any thinking sitting here chatting."

"What are you trying to decide? I thought you'd made up your mind to see Hollywood."

"That's what I wanted to do when I left Missouri. You think that it's a silly girl's shallow dream, don't you?"

"I don't know about that. If seeing Hollywood is something you always dreamed of, I don't think it's shallow. We all have our dreams. Mine is to raise a quarter horse that is smarter than its rider. At times I've thought that wouldn't be too hard to do." His lips quirked in a smile.

"I dreamed about Hollywood because I lived in a town of three hundred stretched along the highway. I worked in a café and saw maybe two movies a year. I had to have a dream, a goal, or my dull life would have been unbearable."

"And now?"

"Now I'm facing reality. I'm alone in a strange land. I've got to think about a job. Before we left home I had the notion that if I could just get to California, a job would be waiting for me. I'd see the sights and put some excitement in my life. Now I see all these people going there with the same sort of hopes. The place must be as crowded as fleas on a dog's back. It's scary."

Margie drew in a deep breath. She was appalled that

she had revealed so much to this man who would break her heart if she wasn't careful. She was too embarrassed to look at him and kept unseeing eyes turned toward the window.

"So what is it you've got to think about?"

"I've got to think about what I want to do after I find Goldie and give her Elmer's money and his truck. Do I want to stay near Bakersfield? Grace and Alvin said it would be nice if I settled near them. I would know someone. I'm not sure now that I want to use what little money I have and go on to a more uncertain future in Hollywood."

"Elmer's wife left him. Some would say that you are entitled to his money and his truck."

Margie turned, stared at his profile and spoke coolly. "And give proof to what he said about me being a thief? No, thank you."

Anna Marie stirred, then sat up. "Are we there yet?"

"Not yet, honey." Margie smoothed the hair back from her face. "You slept a long time."

"Can I sit on your lap?"

"Sure you can." After she was cuddled in Margie's lap, the child pressed her cheek against Margie's shoulder. "Don't go back to sleep, puddin', or you won't want to sleep tonight."

Brady's eyes left the road to glance at the woman bent over the little girl in her lap. She was murmuring to her and kissing her forehead. He felt a twinge in the region of his heart. Anna Marie had never known a mother's love as he and Brian had. Unlike Becky, Margie appeared to be a woman with mating and nesting instincts who would build her life around her family.

Had he been able to read Margie's thoughts, Brady would have been surprised to know that she was wishing with all her heart that this was her little girl. She would give all the love bottled up inside her to this child and to the man beside her if he wanted it. She would put her heart and soul into making a home for them, taking care of them, loving them.

Good Lord! What was she thinking? She'd better get those notions out of her head, or she was in for a rough time ahead.

She looked up to meet Brady's gaze until he focused again on the road. Each was quiet except for the turmoil going on inside. The late afternoon light illuminated Brady's tired face, showing the dark cast of a day-old beard and, in that one quick glimpse, the hungry, anxious look in his eyes. Her heart slammed against her rib cage so hard she could hardly breathe.

Even when she closed her eyes, Margie could see his face behind her eyelids. *She had to stop thinking about him as if he could even possibly be a permanent part of her life.* The chances were good that he would leave the caravan at Albuquerque and she would never see him again. A feeling of emptiness shot through her at the thought.

It was dusk when Alvin led them into a large field on the edge of Tucumcari. Margie almost groaned when she saw that it was full of campers. Cars, trucks and wagons were spread out over a couple acres. Supper fires that burned in front of some camps were sending up a trail of smoke. Other campers were using small kerosene stoves. Rocking chairs had been unloaded, and women sat in them nursing their babies while men gathered, squatted on their heels and talked of the dust storms back home and their hope of finding a better life for their families in the fertile fields of California.

When Alvin stopped, Jody parked the truck behind him. Brady pulled up and parked parallel to Alvin, and Foley parked behind Brady parallel to Jody. They were a tight group of four vehicles. It was in areas like this that Margie saw the wisdom of traveling in a caravan.

At the far end of the field were two ramshackle out-houses. To reach them, they would have to pass through the camp where men without families lounged beside low rag tents and old cars. After Grace had held a whispered conversation with Alvin, he motioned to the men and they walked a distance away, stopped and appeared to be look-ing things over. Grace took a granite chamber pot and a blanket from the back of the truck.

"I don't like the looks of them outhouses or where they're at." Grace wrinkled her nose. "We'll make our own right here between the cars and the trucks."

Anna Marie thought it was great fun to use the pot while Mona and Margie held up the blanket to give her privacy.

It had been the longest day of their trip. They had cov-ered a hundred and eighty miles. Everyone was tired. It was Brady's idea to pool what they had and have a cold supper. Alvin set up the kerosene stove, and Grace made coffee. Margie and Brady supplied the meat and bread they had bought at the store in Amarillo, and Foley brought out a box of crackers and a large chunk of cheese. It was dark by the time they finished eating.

The caliber of the people at the campground made the men uneasy. They cautioned the women not to go behind the cars unless they all went. Blackie, ever watchful, growled menacingly when another dog wandered too close. Cars came and went. Two men on horseback approached, gave them the eye and moved on.

"I don't like this place." Mona sat beside Rusty on a quilt. Earlier she had described the camp to him in detail. Now, holding his hand in her lap, unconcerned that their parents were nearby, she whispered to him when there was something of interest he couldn't see.

Sneaking sly glances at the couple, Grace thanked God for the girl who was opening up a whole new world for her boy. Since meeting Mona, he seemed to have more confidence and be less self-conscious about his blindness. If they parted when they reached California, he would at least have had this happy experience.

Margie, with Anna Marie on her lap, sat in the canvas chair. Around them were the usual camp sounds: a crying child, a barking dog, drunken laughter and, occasionally, a male voice raised in anger. The group gathered beside Alvin's truck was like a family to Margie, a family she had not had since her granny died. Even then there had been only the two of them.

O Lord, I'm so glad that I'm here and not alone on a bus going to some unknown place.

Her eyes often sought Brady where he lounged on the ground beside Foley. Most of the time when she looked at him, his face was turned toward her. When she realized that he had been looking at her steadily for some time, her cheeks turned warm. She quickly looked away and made a to-do about pulling Anna Marie's dress down over her legs.

"We should keep a watch tonight." Alvin spoke softly

as Blackie stood, his tail straight out, and peered off in the darkness. "Son," he said to Rusty, "better keep Blackie close. He's actin' like there's a bitch in heat nearby. He might decide to go courtin'."

"Sit, Blackie," Rusty commanded.

"There's probably fifty people in this camp, not countin' the kids. We look to be the most prosperous folks here. The trucks could be a mighty big temptation to someone with bootleggin' in mind." Brady struck a match on the sole of his boot and lit a cigarette.

"I've been thinking that we probably shouldn't set up any sleeping tents," Foley added. "I'd rather be out in the open where I can see what's going on."

Margie spoke. "Mona can sleep on the box in the truck, and we'll make a pallet of blankets and pillows beside my bunk for Anna Marie."

"That's a good idea." Grace lifted the coffeepot. "Too bad if anyone wanted more coffee. This is the last of it."

"Mona, Blackie and I will take the first watch," Rusty announced from where he sat beside Mona.

"I know what you're up to, you . . . you masher!" Jody teased. "After we've all gone to bed, you're thinkin' to neck with my sister."

"Just kiss my foot, Jody Luker! And shut up!" Mona glared at her brother, but she was grinning.

"Let the clabberhead talk." Rusty put his arm across Mona's shoulders. "He's just jealous because he doesn't have a girl to neck with unless he can talk Margie into sharing his watch."

"If Margie shares anybody's watch, it'll be mine."

There was a heavy silence after Brady had spoken, and all eyes turned on Margie. Hers flew to him. There was no mistake. He was looking directly at her. When her mind cleared and the words he had spoken registered, she was embarrassed, but elated too. She was also grateful for the dark that concealed her blush. Finally she had enough breath in her lungs to speak.

"I can take a watch—"

"No." Brady, Foley and Alvin spoke in unison.

"Why not? You men are tired from driving all day. I could yell loud enough to wake you, and I have a pistol. I'm not afraid to shoot it if I have to. I need to do my part."

"I'll do your part," Brady said in a no-nonsense tone of voice. Then added as if explaining his statement, "You're looking after Anna Marie."

"I think we should pull out of here in the morning before the camp stirs," Alvin said quietly to fill the awkward silence that followed Brady's statement. "We can stop after daylight and get a bite to eat. We'll have to gas up before we leave town anyway."

"Sounds like a good idea to me." Foley stood and stretched. He felt more like himself than he had in a long time. He would never have been able to be an active part of this group if Sugar were still with him. She would be nagging him to break away, and he would be on pins and needles fearful of what she would do or say.

It had been her choice to take off, and he had been afraid that she might run into something or someone who would hurt her. But sometime during the past couple of days he had come to the conclusion that she had done him a favor by leaving.

*   *   *

Homer waited until the caravan was parked in the camp-ground before he followed it in and stopped as far from it as possible. There were so many campers and so many cars going in and out that a coupe with a couple of young *men* in it was hardly noticed.

"There's yore man, little puss." Homer pointed toward the men who had walked a distance away from the trucks. "Want to wave at him?"

"No, and he's not my man. You are."

"How come ya didn't set yore sights on the cowboy, pussy-wussy? Wasn't he rough enough for ya?"

"I didn't like him; that's why," she retorted testily.

"I hate his guts!" Homer said viciously. He would never forget the humiliation of being tied up, messing in his pants, and the ridicule that followed.

"How long are we staying here? I'm tired and thirsty."

"Now, sugar teat," Homer said patiently. "I'm just get-tin' the lay of the land. In just a little bit we'll go on into town, find us a room and eat a meal. We got money, honey."

"Then whater we goin' to do?"

"I know what I'm goin' to do." The hand on her leg traveled up the inside of her thigh, making his meaning clear. "I'm goin' to strip ya naked as a jaybird and screw ya till yore eyes bug out."

"Promise?"

"Swear to it, little bitch. Then while yo're restin' up for the next go-round, I'll come back here and pay a call on the cowboy."

"I want to come with you."

He grabbed her chin between his thumb and forefinger and turned her face toward him.

"Ya'll do what I tell ya to do, little puss," he snarled. "I'm callin' the shots. Hear?" Then in his usual teasing tone he asked, "Is it that yo're not wantin' to let yore man outta yore sight, huh? Huh?"

"I don't want to miss out on the fun."

"Yo're wantin' to watch me screw his bitch? Is that it?"

"You mess with that snooty bitch that way, and I'll cut your pecker off with a dull knife." She grabbed his crotch, squeezing so hard that he winced. "This is mine."

Homer laughed with delight. "I'd kiss ya, but two fellows are comin' this way on horseback, and I don't want to draw their attention by kissin' a *boy*."

"I could take off the cap."

"Ya leave it on till we get outta here."

"And if I don't?"

"I'll beat yore ass."

"Try it, you'll have a fight on your hands."

Homer laughed and squeezed her cheek between his thumb and forefinger.

"Shucks. Yo're more fun than pinnin' the tail on the donkey at a kids' party. We're goin' to have to have us one of them fights soon, but not tonight, little pussy. I got to think of how I'm goin' to get even with that cowboy."

"Is that all you think about?"

"No. I'm thinkin' how we can get the money off that fool that let ya get away from him."

Chapter 25

BRADY CARRIED ANNA MARIE to the back of the truck and waited for Margie to climb inside, then lifted the child to her waiting arms. She laid her on her bunk and took off her moccasins. It was so dark that she had to feel her way around, but she managed to take off Anna Marie's dress and slip the nightgown over her head. She was very aware that Brady stood at the end of the truck.

"It's going to be hot in there tonight." His low voice came out of the darkness.

"I won't cover her."

"Are you going to come out for a while?"

"I . . . hadn't planned on it. You'd better get some sleep before you take your watch."

"I've got a while. I'm taking the two-to-four."

"Wake me and I'll sit with you."

"No. I don't want you out of the truck at that time of night."

"But you're wanting me out now."

"For purely selfish reasons. I want to be with you for a little while." She couldn't be sure, but she thought he grinned.

"You were with me all day. I'd think you'd be sick of my company by now."

"Are you sick of mine?" He reached for her and lifted her down, but kept her close to him.

She said nothing because she knew that she couldn't tell him that this was one of the happiest times in her life, that she had stored up memories to bring out and replay over in her mind when they were no longer together.

"Are you afraid that I'll be rough with you again?"

She tried to pull away from him, but he locked his hands behind her and refused to let her go. "I'm not afraid of that. I realize that what happened that night was as much my fault as yours."

"How so?" His hands moved to slide up and down her arms. When she didn't answer, he said, "Why do you think it was as much your fault as mine?"

"Well." She licked her lips and wondered where to put her hands. Finally she put them on the arms holding her. "I was easy. You said there was no harm in a few casual kisses, and I just let myself—"

"They were not as casual as I led you to believe."

"It doesn't matter. I'm sorry I made such a to-do over it. I was just . . . overstrung. Elmer had rattled me by saying what he did."

"I've never done such a rotten thing in my life. Our parents raised us to be respectful of women. I want you to know that I'm sorry."

"Let's agree to forget it. We have no future together. At the end of this trip, maybe even when we reach Albuquerque, you'll go your way and I'll go mine. I don't want to do anything during this short time that I'll regret."

"Like what?"

"Like becoming too fond of Anna Marie and . . . you."

"Is there a danger of that?"

"Of course. Anna Marie is a darling little girl. If I had the means to take care of her, I'd take her in a minute and love her as my own."

Brady wanted to know badly if she could love him too, but feared to ask the question. When he hesitated, she rushed into speech.

"You've got your ranch to go to. I've got the sights of Hollywood to see and—"

"I thought you were not so sure about that anymore."

"Well, heck. What else is there for a girl to do?" She tried to keep her voice light.

"You could come and make a home with me and Anna Marie."

Damn his heart for beating so fast and making him feel so inept. Without realizing it, his hands were pulling her closer. This feeling of being totally alive when he was with her, even butting heads with her, and seeing her face behind his closed eyelids was so damn new. Yet here he was asking this lovely, sweet girl to turn her life over to a man that she scarcely knew. It was only natural that she would have some misgivings.

The air in her lungs refused to come out. When it finally did, her voice came in a quivering whisper.

"What does the job pay?" She refused to believe that he was offering any more than a job.

"There won't be much money involved. It will be years before we do more than just make a living." His voice was husky. His hands moved up to her shoulders. "But I can guarantee you a lifetime of . . . devotion. I'll bust my butt to take care of you." He rushed on before she could say anything. "It would not be the kind of life you see in the movies. My house on the ranch is just a rough cabin right now, but it's tight and warm and we'd have plenty of beef to eat."

Margie felt the wild hammering of her pulse as she looked up into his dark face. Her heart was beating in a strange and disturbing way as she struggled to get sufficient air into her lungs. His hands had moved from her shoulders down over her arms. He was waiting for her to speak. *He had not said, "Marry me, I love you." He had offered devotion, food and shelter.*

"Is this so you won't have to leave Anna Marie with Opal?" She asked the question even as she thought it.

"It's true that I don't want to leave my brother's child with a stranger, but I'm not asking you to share my life just for that, although I know you would be a much better mother to her than the one she had. And it would please Brian to know that his little girl was with someone who loved her." He hesitated. His throat worked as he swallowed repeatedly. When he continued, his voice was hoarse. "He asked me to take care of her. I just didn't see how I could do it alone. I planned to send money to her aunt for her keep."

There was a long moment of silence, dominated by the pounding of their hearts. She stood with her head bowed, her forehead a whisker away from his shoulder. A thin thread of panic ran through her. Was she getting in too deeply too fast? Was she setting herself up for living a lifetime with a man who only wanted her to provide a home for him and his niece? It was not the loving relationship she had dreamed about.

When she spoke, it was so softly that he couldn't hear. He lifted her chin with the tips of his fingers.

"What did you say, honey?"

"I said, can I think about it?"

"If you have to think about it, it means that you're not sure that you want to take on the two of us." He looked down into her upturned face and slowly shook his head. "You said that you'd take Anna Marie if you had the means to take care of her. I'm offering you the means. But in order to have her, you'll have to put up with me. Is that what you have to think about?" There was huskiness in his voice as if this was terribly important to him.

"No, that isn't what I have to think about." His words had ignited a spark of anger in her, and she spoke sharply. "I have to decide how having a sweet little girl who, if I'm lucky, will someday think of me as her mother compares against living my life with a man who *someday* may fall in love with a woman and leave me to fend for myself." By the time she finished speaking, tears were rolling from her eyes and she was terribly ashamed of them.

"Ah . . . honey, this can't be easy for you." There was genuine regret in his voice. "Why are you thinking that?" His hands moved to her back and pulled her up against him. The bristles on his chin caught on her hair. Her palms flattened on his chest in an attempt to hold herself away from him.

The intensity with which he longed to make her his was causing his heart to jump out of rhythm. He was sure that he had found the woman who was meant for him. He loved to look at her, to talk to her, to be with her. She had responded to his kisses. He was confident that if she didn't care for him now, she was on the verge of it. She was just confused because things were happening too fast. He had to convince her that they were meant to be together.

"Sweetheart, remember me telling you that my mother said God made a certain woman for a certain man? I'm convinced that you're the woman he made for me. I feel it in my heart, in my bones."

"You never said anything about—you said come make a home with you and Anna Marie."

"I'd not ask you to come with me, share my life, if I didn't care deeply for you."

"I thought you wanted to hire me to take care of Anna Marie—"

"And then I'd fall in love with another woman and leave you?" he finished for her.

"Something like that. I've not known of many truly happy couples except in the movies."

"My mother and father were in love until the day they died. Look at Alvin and Grace. She's the light of his life. I'm sure she feels the same. Are you thinking of my brother and Becky?"

"And Elmer and Mr. Luker and any number of people back home who practically hated each other but stayed together either because they had kids or she had no place to go." Soft brown eyes looked pleadingly into his. "I've got to be very careful that when I give my heart, it's to a man who loves me as much as I love him."

"Honey, I understand that. All of this has happened too fast for you. I can wait for you to think about it." He folded her gently in his arms. "Sweetheart, you're a treasure, a prize at the end of the rainbow. I want to kiss you, but I haven't shaved and I may scratch your face."

"You never let that stop you before," she said on a breath of a whisper.

With a swift look into her face he lifted her chin and fitted his lips to hers. He kissed her as openly and as intimately as a man could kiss a woman. Margie's arm moved up, and her hand caressed his nape. She had never felt anything like the sensual enjoyment she was feeling now.

When he lifted his head, he looked down at the pale, luminous oval of her face. His face was creased with smiles.

O Lord, he is so handsome, so sweet. Thank you, God, for letting me come on this trip and meet him!

"Your eyes glow in the dark. Did you know that?" The softly murmured words sent tremors of joy through her.

He pressed a gentle kiss to her lips. It was over too quickly for both of them. He lifted both her arms to encircle his neck, and his arms closed around her. There was no haste in the kiss this time. It was slow and deliberate. He took his time, with closed eyes and pounding heart. He held her so close against him that she could feel the hard bones and muscles of his body. His hoarse, ragged breathing accompanied the thunder of his heartbeat against her breasts.

With a sigh Margie gave herself up to the pure joy of kissing and being kissed, to the thrill of wanting and being wanted. She offered herself willingly. Her mouth opened under gentle pressure, yielding, molding itself to the shape of his.

He lifted his head. Hungrily his eyes slid over her up-turned face. Their breaths mingled for an instant before he covered her mouth again. When next he lifted his head, he pressed his cheek to hers.

"Ah . . . sweetheart," he murmured, his hand stroking the nape of her neck. "I'm never going to get enough of kissing you." Slowly he moved his head until his lips touched hers again as if, having tasted them, he couldn't stay away. His kiss deepened, and he dropped his hand from her nape to wrap her tightly in his arms, driven by passion, sparked by the touch of her tongue on his lower lip. He wanted it to go on and on but knew it had to end.

She became conscious of his hand stroking her back and his low voice speaking in her ear. "I'll be careful with you, darlin' girl. I want more, much more, than your sweet kisses. But I can wait until you're ready to give it to me."

She tugged on his hand and lifted his knuckles to her lips. They had spoken no words of love, but something wonderful throbbed between them. He pressed her head to his shoulder, and they stood close together, he leaning against the truck and she against him, in companionable silence and sweet intimacy.

Glancing skyward, Brady was jarred out of his contentment when he glimpsed flashes of lightning.

"We may get a rain."

"Where will you go?"

"In the car."

"I don't like to think of you out in the rain. You could get in the truck."

"It would be a mite crowded, honey."

Honey. Sweetheart. Margie closed her eyes and prayed

that this was real, that she wouldn't wake up and find that she had been dreaming.

"Being in this bunk reminds me of when we were first married." Grace giggled softly. "Remember that little half-bed we slept on that first year?"

"Sure do," Alvin whispered. "Some of my happiest hours were spent on that little half-bed."

"We broke the bed slats one night, and the old man downstairs came up and pounded on the door—"

"And I had a heck of a time getting untangled from the bedsheets and climbing over the bed rail to get to the door."

"We were silly happy and didn't have a dime."

"I'm still silly happy when I'm with you, love."

"Almost twenty-five years. I can't believe the time has gone so fast." She kissed him on the chin. "And you're just as randy as you were back then."

He chuckled soundlessly. "Not quite, love."

"Randy enough for me," she whispered.

"I'm glad. I was afraid you were going to trade me in for a new model."

"You were not. You know that no one would put up with me but you." She nestled her face in the curve of his neck. "Alvin? Rusty is so happy. I think he's in love with Mona."

"Puppy love, honey. I was about his age when I fell in love with you."

"She's the first girl he's spent much time with."

"Are you worried that this is just a way to pass the time for her?"

"I'm afraid he'll be brokenhearted if she leaves him." Grace ran the palm of her hand over him in the places she knew he liked.

"Maybe they won't break up, but if they do, he'll have to take it like any other man who is disappointed in love. Now, stop your fooling around, woman. I've got to get some sleep."

"Alvin, I'm afraid Brady has decided to keep Anna Marie and will leave us at Albuquerque. His ranch is straight north."

"I don't think he will unless Margie goes with him. She feels obligated to take the truck and the rest of Elmer's possessions to California and find his wife. That says a lot about the girl's character."

"Brady's crazy about her."

"Yeah, and I'm crazy about you." Alvin yawned.

"Sometimes I long for our old home, but I tell myself that home is where you and Rusty are. I hope that if Rusty ever marries, it will be to a girl who will want to be close to us."

"Honey, we'll have plenty of time to talk about this tomorrow. I've got to get some sleep. I take the watch in about four hours."

Sitting on the blanket beside the truck, with Rusty's arm around her, Mona whispered to him.

"What did you and Jody talk about today?"

"Lots of things. He told me about the time he tied a string on your loose tooth and the other end to the doorknob. He said he slammed the door ten times and every time you ran with the door."

"He was telling a big windy. I ran with the door one time. Then he grabbed the string and yanked out the tooth."

"And you cried because you couldn't find it."

"What else did he tell you?"

"He told me that when you were in the fifth grade, you played Mary in the Christmas play and you pinched the boy who played Joseph because he'd put chewing gum in your hair. He yelled, 'Damn you,' just as the Wise Men arrived."

"That blabbermouth! What else?"

"You don't want to know."

"Yes, I do. Tell me or I'll pinch you."

"I'll pinch you back. I've been wanting to anyway." His hand moved to the side of her breast and stroked gently.

"What did he say?" she asked breathlessly.

"He told me about the time you went to the outhouse and were going to stand up on the seat and your foot slipped." He could hardly talk for the laughter that bubbled up.

"I'm going to kill him," Mona said quietly. "But before I do I'm going to cut him into little-bitty pieces."

Rusty, his hand on Blackie's back, felt the dog tense, then stand. "What is it, boy? Still got the ladies on your mind?" he whispered, and minutes later felt the swish of the dog's tail before he sank back down. "Sometimes us fellas have to just grin and bear it, huh, Blackie?"

"He wasn't thinkin' about *that*. He was looking toward the end of Margie's truck. I think she got in, and Brady went to his car for his bedroll."

"They've been there talking for a long while. I'd bet a dollar Brady's in love with her."

"From what he said tonight?"

"That, and the way he arranged for me to ride with Jody today so she would ride with him and how he's been looking out for her and trying to not overdo it."

"He may be just pretending to be interested in her to get her to look after Anna Marie. He told Daddy he was going to have a hard time parting with his twin's little girl."

"Naw. Brady strikes me as having more integrity than that. I think he's fallen for her. Just like I've fallen for you, sweet girl."

"And like I've fallen for you, sweet man."

They sat silently in the velvet darkness. Mona laid her head on his shoulder. He turned his lips to her forehead. It was quiet except for male voices and laughter coming from in front of one of the rag tents where a group of men had gathered to talk and drink bootleg whiskey. A car came in off the road, its headlights dancing over the array of cars, trucks and tents before shutting off.

"There is a little bit of lightning off in the southwest," Mona said softly.

"It doesn't smell like rain."

"Can you smell rain?"

"Sure. When you can't see, your other senses like hearing and smelling kick in. I know every time you powder your nose. This morning you were wearing a blouse that had been sun-dried and ironed." He buried his nose in her hair. "You washed your hair with castile soap."

"I'll have to be careful, or you'll think I'm dolling up

for you. Rusty, you haven't sung to me since we left Deke's."

"I can't sing to you tonight, sweet girl. I'm trying to keep my ears open for any unexpected sound. If the two of us ride with Jody tomorrow, I'll sing to you all the way to Albuquerque."

"Have you worked any more on your song?"

"Our song? A little bit."

"I'd like to ride with you, even if we have to put up with Jody. It'll depend on whether or not Margie rides with Brady." She put her hand on his cheek and turned his face down to her. "When we started this trip, I hated it. Now I think if not for the trip, I'd never have met you. I'm afraid, now, that after we get to California and you get a job on the radio, you'll be so popular that you'll not want anything to do with a Missouri country girl."

"And I'm afraid that when we get to California, you'll see so many men that you'll not want anything to do with a man you have to lead around by the hand."

Mona's arms went around his neck. "Darlin' Rusty, don't ever think that," she said furiously. "You're the dearest, most wonderful man in the world, and I'll love you forever."

"Forever is a long time, little Mona. And I'm going to be like I am for all that time."

"I don't care! Oh, I do care. I wish you could see—for your sake. But . . . but if you could see me, you might not want me."

"I see you, sweet girl. I see you in my mind's eye. You're young, fresh and pretty as a buttercup. What's more, you'll never change. The years will go by, and you'll never be wrinkled or gray. You'll always be as I see you now."

"Rusty, I'm so glad you like me."

"How glad? Glad enough to kiss me?"

"A thousand times," she whispered.

"Then you'd better get started. I heard my watch chime the hour. We've only got thirty minutes until Jody comes to take over the watch."

Chapter 26

MARGIE WOULD NEVER KNOW what had awakened her.

Perhaps, she thought later, she had not been fully asleep. Instantly alert, she slid off the bunk, slipped her skirt on over her head and buttoned it at the waist. After putting on her blouse she reached for the pistol she sometimes carried in her pocket.

Anna Marie was asleep on the end of the bunk and Mona on the box when Margie eased to the end of the truck and looked out. It was quiet and dark.

Brady had said that he would stay near the back of the truck. She thought of calling out to him, but instead she stepped over the tailgate and eased down onto the ground, holding the pistol close to her side.

Cautiously she moved around between the truck and Foley's car and trailer, wishing she had taken the time to put on her shoes. As her eyes became more accustomed to the darkness, she saw the outline of Brady's car ahead. She stopped near the cab of the truck to listen.

The unmistakable smell of gasoline caused her to

wrinkle her nose. Was Brady's gas tank leaking? Then she heard a sound and recognized it. She had thrown out enough dishwater to know that what she heard was a splash of liquid.

At that moment a man rounded the back of Brady's car. She knew instantly that the short man in the cap wasn't Brady. When he was no more than a few feet away, she saw that he had a can in his hands and was splashing its contents on Brady's car. It was a few seconds before Margie's vocal cords thawed enough for her to yell.

"Stop that!"

Catlike, the man spun around. On seeing her he took a quick step toward her and drew back the can to hit her.

She pointed the gun as she had been taught and pulled the trigger.

Bang!

The man dropped the can and grabbed his arm. "Gawdamn! Bitch!" he shouted, then whirled and disappeared behind the car and down into the ditch beside the road.

Shaken by what she had done, Margie let the hand holding the pistol drop to her side. Seconds later a barechested Alvin was there; then Brady came running. Foley was a few steps behind him.

"He . . . he . . ." Margie tried to point to the car.

"Honey . . . sweetheart"—Brady took the pistol out of her hand—"are you all right? What were you shooting at?" He tucked the gun in his belt and put his arms around her.

"Good Lord! Smell that gas." Alvin picked up the can the man had dropped.

Margie began to shake. "I hit him. In the arm, I think."

Brady held her tightly to him. "What were you doing out here?"

"Something woke me. I was looking for you and smelled the gas before I saw him. He was going to hit me with the can."

Jody came with a lantern. "Stay back with that, son," Foley said. "There's gasoline all over."

Grace, in her nightgown, joined them. Rusty was with her. Mona climbed out of the truck, went to him and took his hand as if her place was beside him.

"Where's Blackie?" Rusty asked.

"I think he went courtin'. Don't blame him," Brady said. "The bitches in heat were too much for him."

"He wouldn't have gone off if Rusty had been out," Alvin said in defense of the faithful dog.

"I was snookered too." Brady continued to hold Margie protectively close. "I heard a woman crying. I walked down alongside the ditch a short way and saw her huddled on the ground. She called out to me, 'Help me. Please, help me.' Before I could get near her she got up and stumbled away. She was bent over and crying and mumbling about someone trying to kill her. She fell down on her knees. And again, before I could get to her she got up and ran down into the ditch. Then I heard Margie's yell followed by the shot."

"Sounds like the woman was drawing you away." Foley scratched his head.

"They probably didn't expect to find anyone up at this time of night."

"Why did they pick your car?" Alvin asked.

"I don't know anyone out this way—"

"What's goin' on? We heard a shot." Two hastily

dressed men approached, the suspenders of one still hanging over his hips. The other man's shirt was loose over his pants. "There's a mighty strong smell of gasoline."

"A man was splashing the car with it," Alvin explained. "From the looks of it he was going to burn him out. As close as we are, it would have burned us all out if we weren't able to move the trucks in time."

"Son of a bitch!" The man pulled the suspenders up over his shoulders.

"A minute or two after I heard the shot, a car took off down the road."

"Did you get a look at it?" Brady asked.

"Naw. But the motor had a soft purrin' sound."

"You fellas travelin' together?" Foley asked.

"Yeah. There was three of us, but one turned back." He stuck out his hand. "Name's Taylor. My trailin' partner here is Harry Wills. We're both from over near Kingfisher, Oklahoma."

The men introduced themselves and shook hands.

"We was a mite leery of this place and glad when you folks drove in." Taylor was the more talkative of the two.

"We were leery too. It's why we posted a guard. Good thing we did," Alvin said.

"We was sleepin' with one eye open."

"It wasn't anyone from inside the camp." Harry Wills spoke for the first time since grunting a greeting when introduced. "He'da knowed that south wind woulda spread the fire."

"Maybe he didn't care," Foley said.

"We'd better get this mess cleaned up if we want to be away from here by daylight."

"Mister," Taylor said, "me and my partner would like to tag along behind you folks for a while, if ya ain't mindin' it. We ain't wantin' to be no trouble, and we ain't askin' for no help."

Alvin lifted his hands palms-out. "We couldn't stop you if we wanted to. We're stopping to gas up before we leave town."

Margie pushed away from Brady. The realization of what she had just done was taking root in her mind.

"You don't have your shoes on." Brady swung her up in his arms. "There's burs and glass and no telling what all out here." He carried her to the end of the truck and guided her feet in over the tailgate. "Put on your shoes."

Margie sat down on the end of the bunk, put her feet in her moccasins and tied them. Brady was waiting. She clung to him for a minute after he'd lifted her down.

"Do you think I killed him?"

"Probably not. It would be no great loss if you did, though. He could have burned down the whole campground."

"Brady," Alvin called, "we're going to use the water we have in the barrels to wash the gas off your car. A spark from a backfire could set off a blaze."

Rusty drained water from the barrels in both trucks and from the small one in Foley's trailer into buckets. Brady and Foley washed down the car, diluting the gasoline with the water. Alvin moved the kerosene stove out into an open space away from the cars and trucks so Grace could make coffee.

"You women stay together," he cautioned. "As soon as it's safe to start the cars, we'll leave here."

Blackie, his tail between his legs and his coat full of cockleburs, came and sank down under the truck.

"Some watchdog you are," Alvin scolded. "Off ramming around when we needed you."

"I'm glad you shot 'em," Mona said as soon as Alvin left them. "I just wish you'd shot him in the head."

"I did it before I thought. I didn't think about anything except that he was going to hit me with the can."

"A can half full of gasoline would've knocked you cold." Mona shivered. "You'd of burnt up with the car."

Brady was wiping the windshield on his car and thinking about Margie shooting at a man holding a can of gas.

"I'm sure as hell glad that Margie hit the man and not the gas can," Foley said as if he had read Brady's thoughts.

"That's the gospel truth."

Foley mopped his forehead with his shirtsleeve. "If she'd shot into that can, it would have exploded, and pieces of her would have been scattered all over the campground."

Brady paled, then said, "I'd rather she didn't know that."

"A half can of gas is more dangerous than a full one because it's half full of fumes. I've heard it's the fumes that explode."

Brady nodded. He felt cold with fear at the thought of her coming out of the truck with that little gun and meeting up with a man rotten enough to start a fire that could have swept through a campground full of poor folk trying to get to where they could make a living. He stopped what he was doing and stared down at the ground.

Dear Lord. He had almost lost her!

Who had picked his car to set ablaze and why? It bothered him that he had been observed without his being aware of it and dumb enough to let himself be suckered away from the camp. The son of a bitch saw him there and used the woman to lure him from the car.

He searched his mind for a description of the woman who had acted as decoy. She had dark thick hair that fell over her face. He was sure of that. She could have been a Mexican, he reasoned. The only Mexicans he knew lived on the ranch, and he got along well with all of them. Something about her voice, though, rang a bell. He was fifty percent sure he'd heard that whine before. But where?

Sugar had come out of the brush and run down into the ditch when she heard the sound of a shot being fired. She ran to the car and started the motor as she had been instructed to do. Looking through the back window, she craned her neck, expecting to see the blaze of the fire. Instead she saw a shadowy figure running down the road toward the car. The door was jerked open. Homer vaulted inside.

"Get goin'! Get goin'!"

The car's wheels skidded when Sugar stomped on the gas and they shot off down the dark, dirt road that ran alongside the campground. A minute later she turned on the lights and found they were perilously close to the ditch on the other side of the road. During that minute

Homer had spewed out a string of curses, some of which Sugar had never even heard before.

"Why didn't you fire the car?" she asked as soon as she got the car in the middle of the road.

"Shut up, gawddammit! Can't ya see I been shot?"

"Oh, no! Oh, Jesus!" Sugar's foot hit the brake.

"Keep goin', ya stupid bitch," Homer shouted.

"Are you hurt bad?"

"How in hell do I know? Turn right at the corner."

"Are we going back to the motor court?"

"Where else? Use yore head, for God's sake."

"You don't have to be so shitty!" Sugar shouted. "I did my part. I got him away like I said I would."

"Turn left."

"I know how to get there. Who shot you? It wasn't the cowboy."

"It was his bitch! I came around the end of the car, and there she was yellin' her fuckin' head off. Then she shot me."

"Why didn't you shoot her back?"

" 'Cause she shot my arm, ya useless fuckhead! I couldn't get my gun out."

Sugar stomped down so hard on the brakes the wheels skidded. She jerked open the door and stepped out.

"I don't have to take your shit! It wasn't my fault that you got shot."

"Get back in here, babe. I'm sorry. I hurt so damn bad."

"Whyer you taking your spite out on me? I did everything you told me to do."

"I'm hurtin' so goddamn bad I ain't got good sense."

Sugar got back in and started the car. "Are you ready to give up on the cowboy so we can go on to California?"

"Not on yore life, sugar teat! I'm gettin' him, and I'm gettin' the bitch that shot me!"

Sugar clamped her mouth shut and said not another word until they stopped in front of the cabin they had rented at the motor court.

"Give me the key," she whispered so as not to draw attention to their coming in at such a late hour.

Inside the cabin she turned on the overhead light and made sure that the blinds were tightly closed before she turned to look at Homer. His shirtsleeve was blood-soaked.

"Oh, honey, we got to get you to a hospital."

"No. Help me off with the shirt so I can see how bad it is."

The bullet had gone through the flesh on the inside of his upper arm, leaving a three-inch gash. Sugar wrapped a wet towel tightly around his arm to stem the flow of blood, then helped him out of his bloodstained britches.

"Don't you want to go to a hospital and let them sew that up?" She was gently washing the blood from between his fingers.

"As soon as the stores open, we'll go get some iodine, bandages and sticky tape. That'll hold it together long enough for it to heal. Bundle up the bloody shirt and pants, babe. We'll dump them someplace."

Homer seemed to have calmed down. He lay on the bed unashamedly naked while Sugar fussed over him. She washed him, paying particular attention to his male organs, which brought a smile to his face. After she had finished washing the bloody towels in the rust-stained lavatory, she hung them on the edge of the tub to dry.

"Come here, little puss." Homer held out his uninjured arm. "Come finish what ya started."

Sugar removed her wet skirt, took off her blouse and looked at the man on the bed. The cocky little bastard wasn't all that much to look at, yet he set her on fire. She had lived more since she met him than in all her life put together. Of all the men she had known, he was the horniest. She didn't doubt that he could screw ten times a day. But, then, he was only twenty-three years old. He hadn't asked her her age, and if he had, she would have lied.

She was made for this kind of life with this kind of man even if he was years younger than she was. She hated to think of the years she had wasted. God, she wished that she had met someone like him ten years earlier.

Sugar had never intended to spend her life with Foley Luker. She had seduced him into marrying her while fully intending to leave him once they got to California. She readily admitted that she was a woman who loved to fornicate, but, with Foley, she'd been lucky to get a rise out of him once or twice a week after the first couple weeks of marriage.

She flashed a smile at the man on the bed and pulled her slip off over her head. She teased him by cupping her breasts before she slowly slid her panties down over her hips.

"You wicked, angel-faced bitch! Get yore sweet ass over here."

Chapter 27

THE SUN WAS PEEKING OVER THE HORIZON when Brady lifted Anna Marie out of the truck and gently laid her on the small mattress in the backseat of his car. She snuggled down and went back to sleep. He covered her and rolled down the windows to allow the air to pass through, thankful that the windows had been rolled up when the gasoline was splashed and that there was none inside the car.

While they were packing up to leave, he had asked Margie to ride with him. She had said she would after they filled up at the gas station if Rusty would ride with Jody.

Since the early morning scare, Brady didn't want to be parted from her. The close call had made him realize, more than ever, how important she was to him, how much he loved her. Was this how Brian had felt about Becky? If so, it was no wonder he went out of his mind when he saw her in bed with another man.

Brady helped Jody tie the canvas down on all sides of the truck, then went to sit in his car until it was time to pull out. It was a hundred and fourteen miles to Albuquerque. If everything went well, they would be there by the middle of the afternoon. He wished he could take Margie and Anna Marie and head for Colorado. But after what they had encountered last night, he wouldn't feel right about leaving Alvin and Foley to finish the trip alone, even if Margie was willing.

It was hard for Brady to believe that he had been picked as the target by the person who tried to set fire to his car. Who would know him in this place besides the Putmans, the Lukers and Margie? It had to be a random act. But if not, was he putting Margie in more danger by keeping her with him? It was a thought he had wrestled with most of the night.

If this camp was an example of what they would run into the closer they came to Bakersfield, he would suggest that they avoid the public camps and camp back away from the highway in an out-of-the-way place.

The gas station where they stopped provided a welcome sight: two nearly new privies. While Jody waited behind Alvin for their turn at the gas pump, Margie came back to Brady's car with Anna Marie's dress and moccasins.

"Wake up, honey. Let's put on your dress and shoes and go to the outhouse." Brady came up behind her and ran his hand lovingly up and down her back. She smiled at him over her shoulder. "We can't afford to pass up this opportunity."

As soon as she was dressed, Anna Marie scooted out of the car and Margie took her hand. Brady's hand was still warm on her back.

"The man says we can fill the water barrels for fifteen

cents. I told Jody to pull over to the hand pump after he gets gas."

"I gave him money," Margie said. "There should be enough left over for the water."'

"Rusty and Mona want to be together. Rusty asked me if you were going to ride with me today. And, if so, would you mind if they rode with Jody."

"What did you tell him?"

"That I was sure you wouldn't mind if they rode with Jody. I told him that I wanted you with me, that I never want to let you out of my sight again, that I like to look at you, touch you and kiss you. I said that I'm so crazy about you that every minute I'm away from you seems like an hour." His voice was husky and tender.

"You didn't say *that*!"

"Yes, I did, and I also told him that I'm thinking about carrying you off someplace where I can have you all to myself for the next hundred years."

"Be serious."

"I am serious, sweetheart."

"Margie, let's go." Anna Marie tugged on her hand.

Margie looked down at the fidgeting child, then back at Brady with eyes that shone with pure happiness.

"Now, this is serious."

"Go on," he said softly. "I'll be waiting." Brady watched her walk away with Anna Marie's hand tucked in hers.

There goes my everything. Lord, help me to keep them safe.

When Alvin's gas tank was full, he pulled up to the water pump. Rusty worked the pump handle while he carried the buckets of water to his water keg. The women, along with those from the two families that were tagging along behind them, were in front of the outhouse.

Jody pulled Margie's truck up to the gas pump. While the tank was being filled, Brady lifted the hood and checked the oil and the water in the radiator.

After the truck had been serviced, Rusty and Jody filled the water barrel and Alvin went over to speak with Brady.

"What do you think about the folks trailing us?" Alvin jerked his head toward the two sedans with carriers on top that were waiting along the road.

"They seem to be decent. I looked them over before we left this morning. I don't think a robber or a boot-legger would be travelin' with a woman and two little kids. The woman with Harry Wills is in the family way."

"They have pretty good outfits."

"Wills had a gun under his shirt this morning. I can't hold that against him. I may start carrying one myself."

"You've got a sharp eye. I didn't notice the gun."

"To my way of thinking, Wills is a man who won't back down. The other one follows his lead, although he does the talking."

"We might be glad to have 'em near if we get into another place like the one last night." Alvin laughed and shook his head. "Grace has the women cornered. She'll know all about them by the time we start up again."

Margie was so happy she was scared. Hovering in the back of her mind was the fear that something would happen to spoil her happiness. *Brady cared for her.* He had not said that he loved her. He'd said that he cared deeply, but he was acting as if he loved her. And he was happy. She could tell by the shine in his eyes and the smile that tilted his lips when he looked at her. And when he touched her, it was gently, as if he feared she would break.

Sitting beside him in the car, her eyes catching his each time he turned to look at her, she would have been happy to keep on going forever. They had entered low, clustering hills that promised mountains ahead. The highway wound around jutting slopes and crossed small rocky streams that divided the hills that rammed each other. At times it clung to the rocky ledges; at other times it passed through meadowland.

There were more stretches of unpaved roadway with huge chuckholes. Brady had to keep his eyes on the road. But his hand caught hers and released it only when he had to shift gears.

Anna Marie was bored and sleepy. She wanted to get in the back and lie down on her bed. Margie helped her climb over the back of the seat.

"Stay away from the door, puddin'," she cautioned. "If we hit one of these big old chuckholes, one of the doors might pop open."

After Margie had turned around, Anna Marie leaned over the seat and wrapped her arms around Margie's neck and whispered something to her.

"Oh, honey. I wish it too." Tears sprang to Margie's eyes. She stared out the side window for a long while, batting her eyes to keep the tears at bay.

Brady held her hand tightly. When she finally looked at him, she saw concern in his eyes.

"Sweetheart?"

She moved closer to him and spoke softly. "Sometimes I think that I had it bad, but I had a mother and then a grandmother who loved me."

"And now me." He lifted the hand in his and rubbed her knuckles across his lips. "What did Punkie say that caused you to cry?"

"She said . . . she said that she loved me and wished . . . that I was her mama." Her eyes filled again, and the tears spilled over to run down her cheeks. "No one has ever said, 'I love you,' to me. Not even Granny, though I know she did."

"*I* love you. I told you last night."

"You . . . didn't say the words."

"I didn't? I thought I'd made my feelings clear. I love you. I want to spend my life with you. Brian was the one good with words. He told Punkie many times that he loved her."

"I love you too. I didn't want to." Her wet eyes blurred her vision.

Brady let out a slow breath. "You didn't want to?"

"I knew that you could break my heart." Her words came out on a strangled sob. "If you didn't love me back."

He looked at her, then had to jerk the wheel to avoid a chuckhole when his eyes went back to the road.

"This is a hell of a place to have this conversation." He held her hand to his lips.

The realization that except for chance he would never have met this woman, never have known that she existed, sent a surge of emotion through him that was both tender and fierce. He longed to pull her into his arms and tell her again and again that he would never break her heart. He would guard it as carefully as he guarded his own. He loved her with a cherishing kind of love. He wanted to hold her in his arms, plant his child in her warm, fertile body and keep her at his side forever.

Dear God, help me to find the words to tell her how I feel about her.

It wasn't until they had neared the outskirts of Albuquerque that Brady spoke about his ranch being only two days north.

"You'd rather turn here than go on to California." Margie wished that she hadn't brought to light her fear. *Dear Lord, I couldn't bear to lose him now.*

"I'm going to do whatever it takes to keep you with me."

"You want me to go to Colorado?"

"More than anything in the world."

"Deke told me to just leave the truck with the authorities and let them find Goldie. I'd hate to do that. I'd never be sure if she got it or the money in Elmer's box." She tilted her head to rest for just a minute against his upper arm, then looked up into his face. "I took two hundred dollars of it. I'm calling it payment for delivering the truck."

"He was your father. He brought you on this trip and owed you enough money to see you through. How are you going to find his wife?"

"Her cousin said she went to Bakersfield."

"Was there an address book or any letters in Elmer's things?"

"There's a packet of envelopes. Money is in some of them."

"Maybe you should look again. You might find something that would make the hunt for her easier. Honey, I don't have money to stay in Bakersfield but a few days unless I find work."

"I have the two hundred dollars."

"Don't you want to use that to see Hollywood?"

"I want to use it to buy curtains, rugs and doodads for our cabin."

"Sweetheart! Are you giving up your dream?"

"It was a little girl's dream. Now I have a bigger, better one. To be a helpmate to the man I love. To make a home with him, have his children. I can get all the Hollywood I want in the movie magazines."

"Sweet girl. I don't want you to be sorry."

"I plan to be too busy to be sorry. If your ranch is ten miles from town, I'm going to have to be mother and teacher to Anna Marie for the first few years—that is, if we can get the books and the other things I will need."

"You can do that?"

"Sure I can. When I got out of high school, I helped the teacher one year because the school system was so broke they couldn't hire another teacher. I got half her pay. I thought I was rich."

He glanced at her with love and pride. "Wait till I tell Ramon I've got a teacher for the kids."

"Kids? I don't speak Spanish."

"They all know a smattering of English. Uh-oh . . . I'd better pay more attention to my driving. Jody is pulling over."

Brady parked along the highway behind Jody, got out and waited for Alvin, who was walking toward him from up ahead, and Foley, coming from behind.

"The public campground ahead looks about like the one we came out of," Alvin said. "Are you willing to go on to another place even if we have to pay fifty cents or a dollar to camp?"

"Do you know of another camp?" Foley asked.

"No. But if we don't find one, I'm willing to move on out of town and find an out-of-the-way spot."

"Fine with me," Brady said.

Foley nodded.

"I'll walk back and—no need, here come Taylor and Wills." Alvin spoke to the men. "I was just coming to tell you that the public campground is ahead, but we're going on."

"Glad to hear it," Taylor said. "Harry has been warned about this place. He has directions to a place where we can camp for two bits a car. It has water and toilets. The man runs a good place, so he was told."

"Is it far off the highway?"

" 'Bout a mile." Harry was stingy with his words.

Alvin looked for approval from both Foley and Brady before he spoke.

"Sounds good. Move out in front and lead the way."

While they waited for the other two cars to pull ahead, Brady, with his arm around Margie, explained the situation.

"If this is a good place and Grace will look after Anna Marie for a while, we'll go into town and take in a picture show."

"Really?" Margie's eyes went wide with pleasure.

"Really. Just the two of us, pretty girl." He hugged her and placed a kiss on her nose. "We'll eat supper at a restaurant and go to a picture show to celebrate. It isn't every day a man meets the woman he wants to keep beside him for the rest of his life."

"Can we afford it? We've got to have money to get back to Colorado."

"This will be our one and only splurge, honey."

The campground was a shady acre enclosed with barbed wire. A man in overalls had a little stand at the gate where he was selling oranges and a few garden vegetables. After Alvin had pulled through, Jody stopped. Brady was about to get out and pay for the truck when Jody drove on into the campground.

"Howdy. Welcome to Shady Acres. Stayin' long?" The man was middle-aged, big and brawny. He looked them over, glancing at Anna Marie in the backseat.

"Just overnight." Brady dropped a coin in his hand.

"This is the best place we've stayed," Margie remarked as they passed the man at the gate. "Even if we do have to pay."

"I liked that place up in Oklahoma where I met a sassy little blonde with pretty brown eyes." Brady stopped the car alongside the truck.

Margie's eyes devoured his smiling face. She wouldn't have believed it if she had been told when she met this stern, unsmiling man who had just buried his twin brother, that in only a few short weeks he would become so dear to her.

"Margie." Anna Marie put her hand on Margie's shoulder to get her attention. "Can I get out?"

"If you put on your shoes. There'll be cockleburs here." Margie got out and opened the back door.

"Can I play with that little girl?"

"We'll go over and talk to Mrs. Taylor and see if she wants to play. You can take your jump rope or your ball."

Margie tied Anna Marie's shoes, then leaned down to whisper to her.

"You girls are always whispering," Brady complained.

"This is something you don't need to know."

"Yeah, Uncle Brady. You don't need to know."

Later Margie was able to report to Grace and Mona that the outhouses were as clean as could be expected and that generous doses of lime had reduced the odor. Grace informed her that Brady had already asked if she and Mona would keep an eye on Anna Marie while he took Margie out for the evening.

"Go," Grace whispered. "Have a good time. Mona and I will keep an eye on Anna Marie." She tilted her head toward where Brady was talking with Foley. "If I was young and single, I'd be after him like a shot. That is, if I hadn't met Alvin yet." She finished with one of her contagious giggles. "I think we just might invite the other folks over and have a singin' tonight. They seem to be right nice folks. It'll give Rusty a chance to sing his new song."

Excited about the prospect of going out with Brady, Margie left Anna Marie playing happily with the little Taylor girl and climbed into the truck to wash herself thoroughly and dress for her big evening.

"Shit, shit, shit!" Homer pounded on the wheel when he saw that the caravan wasn't going to stop at the crowded public campground. "Now, where the hell are they goin'?" he snarled.

When Homer had caught up with the caravan outside Tucumcari and discovered that two more cars had joined it, he had felt safe with those two cars between him and

Foley Luker. Now one of those cars had taken the lead, and with only one car between him and Luker, Homer backed off.

"Does your arm hurt?" Sugar asked.

"Hell yes, it hurts."

"You should of let me drive more."

"I don't trust ya drivin' in town."

"Well, hell. You trusted me to drive in Tucumcari."

"Tucumcari ain't Albuquerque. Now, shut up!"

Sugar sulked and made no comment when the caravan turned off at the sign that said CAMPGROUND 1 MILE. Homer drove on.

"They'll be easy to find, but first we'll find us a place to spend the night." He looked over at her and grinned. "Ya got to get all gussied up, pretty puss, so we can go huntin' for easy pickin's. I'm down to a hundred bucks."

At the El Rancho Motor Court they parked the car beneath the shelter attached to the cabin. Homer unlocked the door and went inside, leaving Sugar to get the bags out of the rumble seat of the car. She pulled her case out and set it on the ground, then reached in for Homer's cloth bag. She paused. In the far corner she saw a leather belt with a big brass buckle. Chester's belt and buckle.

Had Chester taken the bus back to Oklahoma without his belt and his watch? If so—she almost giggled—what was holding his pants up? Seeing the belt only confirmed her suspicion that Homer had gotten rid of his uncle. Instead of being horrified at the thought, Sugar smiled. Homer knew that she didn't like Chester, and he cared enough for her that he'd gotten rid of him.

The little shit!

Homer was in a better mood after he had rested on the

bed and Sugar had changed the bandage on his arm. After watching her strip and wash, he was aroused and insisted that she do something about it. She was willing to comply.

When they left the cabin to eat, Sugar was dressed as a boy, but later she wore her demure blue dress when they went to scout the hotels and fine eating places for their "easy pickin's."

By midnight they had robbed one gentleman and two drunks, and their take was a hundred and forty dollars. Sugar deemed it enough, but when Homer spotted a pool hall that was closing, he decided they'd wait until all the patrons had left and the door had been locked. After being coached by Homer, Sugar rapped on the door, and when a man came and unlocked it, she acted scared and pointed down the street. Then Homer stepped up and rapped the man smartly on the head with the butt of his gun. He shoved him out of the way and went inside.

While Sugar was bringing the car around, Homer rifled the cash register. On a shelf beneath it he found a bank bag with several days' receipts. It was their most successful take so far, four hundred and sixty dollars all told. Sugar hooted with glee when he told her.

"We're rich! Let's go honky-tonkin'!"

"Not in the town where we're doin' business, little bitch. Frank Barrow, brother of Clyde, told me that. He said, 'Strike quick, lay low and get out.' We're gettin' back to that cabin and that's that."

"Well, hell. What's the good of havin' money if ya can't spend it and have a good time?"

"We'll have us one hell of a time when we get to the next big town. Now, don't go sulkin' on me, little pussy. We're gonna have us a real slam-bang tonight. I've been holdin' back a trick or two that'll set ya to squealin' like a rabbit bein' humped by a six-foot jack."

"Don't you even want to go see where the cowboy is campin'?"

"I got time 'tween here and California to get to the cowboy and that prissy-ass bitch that shot me. What I'm wantin', pretty pussy, is to get ya naked and in bed where we can be *nasty!*"

"I'll swear to goodness you're the horniest little stud I've ever known."

Homer grinned proudly. "Thank ya kindly, little puss."

Chapter 28

AT THE WAGON WHEEL RESTAURANT BRADY placed his hat on a hook beside the door and led Margie to a table at the end of the room. After they were seated, he handed her a menu.

"You look awfully pretty."

"So do you."

"Did you notice that I shaved?" He fingered his chin.

"Uh-huh. Did you notice that I combed my hair and put a ribbon in it?"

"You're pretty without a ribbon."

"Flattery will get you nowhere, Mr. Hoyt. I'm still going to order the most expensive thing on the menu."

Their eyes held. She was the girl of his dreams, even more wonderful than he had imagined. Her hair was the rich color of ripened wheat, her mouth wide and sweet, her eyes like stars.

She stared at him for a long silent moment. She was afraid that if she moved, he would be sure to know how happy she was being here with him. When she finally spoke, her voice caught, then came out in a husky whisper.

"I'll have beef, mashed potatoes and gravy."

"I'm going to have a steak, medium rare. I haven't had a decent one since I left the ranch."

"And I haven't had mashed potatoes since I left home." A smile tilted the corners of her mouth.

Brady chuckled. She was fun, intelligent . . . soft. When he started on this trip, he never dreamed that he would meet a woman like her.

The overweight waitress who came to take their order had eyes only for Brady. She was still looking at him when she walked away. Margie wanted to scratch her eyes out even though she couldn't blame her for looking at him.

While waiting for their order, Margie smiled into the eyes observing her. When his hand moved across the table, hers met it halfway.

"I hated leaving Anna Marie. She was afraid we wouldn't come back."

"She's grown attached to you. She'll have to learn to share you with me, honey." He watched her, and when she tried to pull her hand away, his fingers gripped hers tightly. "This is my time to claim all your attention."

Margie noticed the looks he was getting from two women who had just come in and sat down at a table not far from them. He was an exceedingly attractive man who would radiate confidence if he stood barefoot and ragged. His thick black hair sprang back from his forehead and hung to the collar of his shirt. Deep crinkly grooves marked the corners of his eyes, etched there from squinting at the sun. There were other lines too, which grief and experience had made.

How was it possible that she was here with this wonderful, handsome man? *It was a miracle!*

When the waitress brought their order, she glanced at Margie, then fixed her gaze on Brady again. Brady smiled and thanked her. They had just started to eat when the waitress came back to the table.

"We have one piece of fresh peach pie left. Want me to save it for you?" she asked Brady.

"Do you want it, honey?"

The waitress took her eyes off Brady long enough to glance at Margie.

"No. I'd rather have raisin or custard."

"We have custard." The woman spoke again to Brady.

"We'll each have the custard," he said.

After she had walked away, Margie said, "I thought she was going to sit in your lap."

He smiled broadly. "Jealous? It's a good sign."

When they left the well-lit restaurant, Margie couldn't even feel her feet on the ground. Happiness sang like a bird in her heart. She was proud to be walking beside this tall, broad-shouldered man who said he loved her. She cast a glance up at him and found him smiling down at her, his arm holding her hand tightly to his side.

"What would you like to do? If we go to a movie, we may not get out in time to get back before eleven o'clock, when the man locks the gate."

"We could sit in the car outside the gate all night." A blush covered her face.

Brady laughed. "When we spend our first night together, sweetheart, it will be in a bed where I can love you all night long." He stopped and looked down at her. "Are you blushing?"

"No! Well, yes!"

"Does it excite you to think of spending the night in bed with me?" He started walking again.

"Of course! I've . . . never spent the night—never wanted . . ." Her voice trailed off as embarrassment took control of her tongue.

"Thank God for that!" They reached the car. "Would you like to stop at that place we saw on the way in? We can get something to drink and dance for a while." He held open the door for her.

"All right," she said after he had gone around and slid under the wheel.

"The other time we danced you were so mad at me I thought you'd bite a chunk out of me." The hand at the nape of her neck brought her face toward his, then slipped down to cup her shoulder to allow her to turn away if she chose. "I want to kiss you, right here on the street. If I do, will you bite me?"

"I might. And I might yell too."

"To kiss you would be worth a bite and a hundred punches in the nose by those who come to rescue you." His voice was husky and raw, like his deep, quivering breaths.

She felt the caress of his warm breath on her cheek before his lips, with the utmost tenderness and caution, settled on hers. A warm tide of tingling excitement washed over her. Her heart beat wildly, and her mind whirled giddily. Brady moved his head and placed his cheek against hers. His arm tightened; he was as breathless as if he'd run a mile; he was stunned with happiness.

Finally she stirred and gently moved away from him. People passing on the sidewalk were gawking. She uttered a little laugh so soundless that it was no more than an exhalation of breath.

"We're putting on a show for people passing by."

He laughed intimately, joyously, and started the car.

"I don't care if the whole world is watching. I like kissing you. I'm going to kiss my wife every day for the rest of our lives."

"I'm not very good at it."

"Practice makes perfect. We'll practice some more as soon as I find a place to park the car."

The next morning at sunrise the women gathered around Grace's giant coffeepot. Margie's eyes dwelled on Brady, who was with the other men looking at a map spread out over the hood of Alvin's truck.

Her mind kept going back to the night before, trying to remember each and every word that was said. Their love was so new they had not talked about the future. They both knew that they would be together, and that was enough for now.

Margie was absolutely sure that it had been the most wonderful evening of her life. They had come back to the campground, sat in the car and in between kisses listened to the singing coming from the group gathered at the Putman camp. Rusty had sung his new song, "What I See." One of the verses stuck in Margie's mind.

> *You were there watchin' over me*
> *With gentle touch and sweet sympathy,*

With tender care like a gift so free,
You were there givin' strength to me.

Margie shivered recalling the chorus of the song.

They are blind who will not see.
None so blind as a man like me.

Rusty was so remarkable, so cheerful, loving and kind, she prayed that he had found the happiness with Mona that she had found with Brady.

Brady. The wonderful feeling of belonging to him was so new, so exciting, that at times she was giddy. A thrill spiraled down her spine when she thought of his words last night as he caressed her breasts.

"Soon I'll see them, kiss them. No man will ever touch them but me."

Her daydreaming was interrupted when Alvin folded the map and began talking.

"The man here at the campground says that most of the highway between here and Gallup is under construction. There are many rough spots, and sometimes we'll have to wait for as long as an hour before we can go on. Loaded as we are, we'll be lucky to make seventy-five miles a day for the next couple days. After that the going will be easier. I figure that we're about nine hundred miles from Bakersfield, and unless we have a breakdown, we should be there in about ten days."

"Hallelujah! I'm wantin' to sleep in a real bed and put my feet under a real table," Grace declared.

Alvin smiled at his wife. "There's a campground at Grants. It's one hundred and four miles. If we see we can't make it, we'll camp along the road. That's as much as I know. Anyone got anything to add?"

Harry Wills drank the last of the coffee and tossed the dregs from his tin cup. His main concern was the comfort and safety of his wife, who was pregnant with their first child. They had given up all hope of having a family and had decided to move to California to be near his brother and his family when she became pregnant.

He had wanted to postpone the trip until after the baby was born, but she would not hear of it. It worried him that they were bouncing along on rough, dusty roads prowled by bootleggers and outlaws who would cut your throat for a dime. The pistol in the bib of his overalls was a reassuring weight.

"Ya may have another tagalong," Harry said. "A Ford coupe was about a half mile back all day yesterday. When a car got 'tween us, he'd move up. He coulda passed all of us anytime he wanted to."

"I noticed a coupe back up the road a ways when we stopped before we got to the public campground," Foley said. "A fella was out foolin' around with somethin' in the rumble seat."

"I'm wonderin' if it's the same one that was in the campground back in Amarillo. It looked like a pretty late model." All eyes turned to Mr. Taylor. "Two young fellas was in it. Drove in, set a spell, then pulled out. Wasn't loaded with campin' gear like ya usually see."

"They may be thinkin' it's safer to tag along. I don't know what help they think they'd get from us way back there." Alvin opened the door of his truck and stuck the map inside.

Brady came to Margie, and they went to the truck, where Anna Marie was still sleeping.

"Wake up, honey. Uncle Brady is here to take you to the car." Margie led the sleepy child to the end of the truck, where Brady lifted her out and carried her to his car. She was picking up Anna Marie's clothes when Rusty and Jody arrived to check the tie-down canvases.

"I'll be out of here as soon as I find Anna Marie's shoes."

"Let me give you a hand," Jody said.

"My turn." Rusty held up his hands. Margie put hers on his shoulders, and he lifted her down.

"Thank you. You'll get me in trouble with Mona."

"And with me." Brady appeared, took Margie's hand and pulled her to him. "This woman's mine."

Rusty spoke aside to Jody. "He's gotten selfish lately."

"And grabby." Jody began tying down the canvas.

"Darn right. A man's got to be on his toes when his woman is being manhandled by a couple of young scutters."

"Manhandled? Brady, for goodness' sake," Margie scolded, but her eyes danced and her lips tilted. She pulled a bill out of her pocket. "This should be enough for gas and ten pounds of ice, Jody, if we find a place. That chunk we got yesterday is going down fast. Why don't you fix a jar of ice water for yourself and Rusty?"

"I take it I've got a steady job ridin' with Jody."

"Yeah," Brady retorted. "And your pay is getting to cuddle with Mona all day."

"What more could a man ask for?" Rusty was all smiles as he moved around the truck to the cab.

*   *   *

It had been a week since Sugar Luker left them at Sayre. When he stopped to think about it, Foley was surprised how seldom he thought of the woman he had been with day and night for almost three months. He admitted to having been smitten at first, flattered by the attention of a young, beautiful woman and the sex she offered. After he had married her, it hadn't taken long for him to suspect that her beauty was only skin-deep. Then, when he knew that to be true, he had been too embarrassed to admit that she had made a fool of him.

He was lucky to have two wonderful kids—his and Marion's children. They had stuck with him, endured the rough times when he knew that Sugar was making them perfectly miserable.

For the past two days Mona had ridden with him for half a day and with Rusty and Jody the other half. Foley and his children were now close again, as they had been after they had lost their mother and he his beloved wife. It was as if Sugar had never been there.

His little girl was in love with a man who would forever be blind. At first he had felt keen disappointment. He wanted so much more for her: a strong man to take care of her. Then he thought of when he first met Marion. Would he have loved her had she been blind? Hell yes! He would have loved her if she had been deaf and blind and couldn't move a muscle. If it turned out that Mona and Rusty were truly in love and wanted to be together, he would be there to help them, as would Alvin and Grace.

As soon as they reached their destination, Foley planned to try to get his marriage to Sugar annulled. He was determined to break all ties with her. He suppressed the little nagging fear that he had not seen the last of the woman with the face of an angel and the soul of a wicked witch. She knew he had the money from the sale of his icehouse and was no doubt plotting how she could get it.

The stretch of highway west of Albuquerque was as they had expected. It had been start and stop since they left the campground. A stiff breeze from the south blew the dust that sprayed up from beneath the wheels. Marge pitied the construction workers who had to stand on the north side of the road while a string of cars passed.

Anna Marie was hot and tired. Margie did her best to entertain her by telling stories and teaching her to count on her fingers. The child stayed awake all day, not giving Margie and Brady a chance to talk alone, but Margie was happy just to be with him. By afternoon they'd hit a stretch of newly paved highway and reached Grants in the late evening.

The campground was a large, open field. There were about as many campers as in Tucumcari, but more families than single men. The caravan parked at one end with plenty of space around it. Foley led the other two cars to form a circle with the two trucks and Brady's car. Anna Marie waited eagerly to play with her new friend, Lucy Taylor. As soon as the Taylors stopped, Lucy jumped out and Anna Marie ran to meet her.

"Stay where I can see you, punkin," Margie called. Brady caught her hand when she attempted to follow.

"Wait a minute, honey. I've been thinking—"

Margie turned quickly to look at him. Something about the tone of his voice chilled her. *O Lord. Don't let it be that he's changed his mind!* His next words caused a flood of relief to wash over her.

"I want us to be married as soon as possible. I don't want to wait until we get to California. I want to know that you're mine."

"I . . . am yours."

He brought her hand up and rubbed her knuckles against his lips. "I want to take you home to our ranch as my wife, and Anna Marie as our daughter. You can leave the truck and the rest of Elmer's belongings with Alvin and tell him about where to look for Elmer's wife. Alvin is a good, honest man. He'll see to it that she gets it."

"All right." Tears filled her eyes.

"Darlin' girl. Don't cry about it. You want it too, don't you?"

"You know I do. More than anything."

"Tonight go through Elmer's things and see if you can find the cousin's address. He had to have some idea of where his wife was going."

"He didn't talk to me about anything, but I heard that Goldie's cousin was in a place called Victorville."

"Honey, I need to keep as much of my money as I can to get us to Colorado. If you're not dead set on going on to California, we could be married in Gallup and head home."

"I thought you'd planned on spending some time in California before you left Anna Marie with Opal."

"That was before I had a wife and daughter to take care of. I could have bummed around by myself. Things are different now."

"I'm not dead set on going on to California. I just want to be with you and Anna Marie. If you think Alvin will handle seeing that Goldie gets what was Elmer's, it's all right with me. We'll leave at Gallup, and Jody will drive the truck on to Bakersfield. Let's go through Elmer's things tonight. It would be easier if we could tell Alvin where to find Goldie's cousin."

"We don't have to worry about Alvin and Foley being alone. Wills and Taylor are good, reliable men. They'll be with them for the rest of the trip."

She saw Alvin getting out the kerosene stove. "I'd better go help Grace if we are all going to eat together."

"Go on, sweetheart. We'll talk about it tonight." Brady reluctantly released her hand, and she got out of the car.

"What a dump!" Sugar's patience had almost reached its limit by the time they reached Grants. "Whater we goin' to do in this hick town? We've fiddle-farted along behind that drag-ass outfit and eaten their dust all day. We've not been dancin' or to a picture show. I doubt they even got a place to piss in this shitty burg."

Sugar had complained most of the day and wasn't aware that Homer was getting tired of it.

"Lord, what I wouldn't give for a glass of cold beer. I'm so sick of lukewarm soda pop that I could puke."

"Hush yore bitchin'," Homer shouted. "If ya don't shut up, I'll stop and put ya out. Ya can wiggle yore ass and get a ride with someone else. That clodhopper yo're married to might be sucker enough to take ya back."

Sugar had learned when to retort and when to keep quiet. She realized that she had gone a mite too far and waited for Homer's anger to cool while they cruised the streets of Grants to find a place to stay. The motor court was full. Homer stopped and went into the lobby of what appeared to be the best hotel in town. After standing at the desk waiting for a slick-haired jelly bean to tell him there were no rooms, he came back to the car, let loose a string of obscenities and drove down the street to a third-rate hotel.

"I got a room," he said when he returned to the car. "Keep yore head down and yore hat on. Ya'd be too easy to remember in this town."

Sugar was exhausted by the time she had carried her suitcase to the third-floor room. As soon as the door closed behind them, she snatched off the cap. She was hungry and dirty and tired of wearing the damn cap, but was wary of Homer's temper and kept her mouth shut.

"The bathroom is at the end of the hall. Wear the cap when you go in and have it on when you come out. I'll go out and get us something to eat."

"Can't I go with you?"

"No. I don't want anyone to remember we've been in this town. Hear? I signed in as Tom and Wilbur Smith. Yo're a boy, sugar tit." He grinned and before she could step aside, grabbed her breast and cruelly twisted the nipple. "But I'm mighty glad ya ain't one."

"Shit!" The pain caused Sugar's temper to flare. "When are you goin' to finish up with the cowboy so we can go on?" she blurted angrily.

His mood changed lightning-fast. "When I'm damn good and ready, and if ya don't like it—" He jerked his thumb toward the door. "Make up yore mind while I'm gone. If yo're stayin', be naked by the time I get back."

Sugar glared at the door for a long moment after he went out and she heard the click of the lock. *The stinkin', horny little stud wanted her with him, or he wouldn't have locked the door.*

"All he thinks about is gettin' even with the cowboy and gettin' me naked," she said aloud to the empty room. "If he wasn't so damn good in bed, the little bastard could just kiss my ass good-bye."

Chapter 29

IT WAS DARK BY THE TIME supper was over. Anna Marie, tired from vigorous play with her new friend, was ready for bed as soon as she was washed. Margie sat beside her on the bunk and told her a story about three bears. By the time she was finished, the child was asleep.

She smoothed the dark hair back from the child's face and kissed her chubby cheek. She could hardly wait until she could pick her up, hug her and tell her that she was going to be her little girl and that they would live in Colorado with her Uncle Brady. It still seemed as if this dream of marrying Brady were happening to someone else.

"Is the little tyke asleep?" Brady appeared at the end of the truck.

"Yes. She was tuckered out. Come on in. It will be crowded, but I don't mind if *you* don't."

"It couldn't be too crowded to suit me." Brady stepped up into the truck, bent over so that he could move to the front and sat down on the bunk. "Come here." He pulled her down on his lap.

"Someone will see."

"I don't care if the whole world sees. Put your arms around my neck and kiss me."

A tiny moan trembled from her throat. "Mmm . . ." Her lips moved over his in a sweet caress. His were warm and soft yet firm and insistent. A stubble of beard scraped her chin as his mouth settled on hers. He trembled, and the kiss became deeper. A ribbon of desire unfurled inside Margie. Her body was flooded with the longing that lapped at her senses whenever she was with him.

He backed away slightly. "I'd better stop while I can, sweetheart. One of these nights soon, I won't have to stop."

"Mmmm," she murmured again, kissed him quickly and slid off his lap.

She unlocked the box Elmer had built across the front of the truck and folded back the lid. Brady moved the lantern to hang directly over the box.

"I found the two hundred dollars in the toe of his socks," Margie said, taking out a stack of clothes. "The suit he was buried in was probably the one he was married in." She reached for the Prince Albert can and heard a clinking noise. "I wonder why he put his tobacco in here?" She handed the can to Brady and searched in her pocket for the key to the tin box. "The clock looks familiar. I may keep it. It'll be the only thing I'll have that came from my family."

Brady whistled through his teeth when he opened the Prince Albert can. "Look, honey, two five-dollar gold pieces and all these bills."

"Well, for goodness' sake."

"Ten one-hundred-dollar bills! Lord, that's a thousand dollars."

"My gosh! And there's more in the tin box."

Brady stuffed the bills back in the can while Margie opened the box to view again the strange assortment: a pair of baby shoes, a cameo necklace, a lady's lapel watch and the envelopes tied with string. Sitting on the floor of the truck between Brady's legs, she untied the string.

"The first envelope had four fifty-dollar bills in it. The next five have two one-hundred-dollar bills. That's twelve hundred. With what is in the can, there's over two thousand dollars here. Goldie will think she's hit a gold mine. In the last envelope is a letter to Elmer from . . . I can't make out the postmark, can you?" She handed him the letter addressed to Mr. Elmer Kinnard, Conway, Missouri. He held it close to the lantern.

"Looks like Victorville."

"You read it."

Brady took the sheets from inside the envelope. "It's from Goldie." He scanned the pages, then held them out to Margie.

"You should read this." He reached for the lantern and held it just above her head.

Margie read the letter quickly, then went back and reread it.

Elmer,
    It gives me great joy to write this. At last I will say what I've thought of you since first we met. You are without a doubt the most miserable excuse for a man that has ever lived. At first you were kind and

generous, and I thought to amuse myself with you while I was there. When you thought you had me hooked to do your washing and cooking and to service you once a week in bed, you turned out to be a miserly, hateful, self-centered man. I hated every minute I spent in your bed. It was like having sex with a hog. You gave no thought for anyone's pleasure but your own.

But, Elmer, I will have the last laugh. I used you to have a place to live. I made fun of you behind your back and I took three hundred dollars that you had hidden behind a dresser drawer. A whore would have charged you much more than that for the services I gave you.

I've returned to be with my husband, the love of my life. You see, I was only separated from him, and the marriage that you thought would bind me to you as your unpaid housekeeper and whore was not a marriage at all. Ha ha ha.

Goldie

"My goodness." Margie looked up at Brady. "Did you read all of this?"

"Over your shoulder, honey. It's no wonder he was such a bitter man."

"Why did she marry him when she was already married?"

"Sounds like she wanted a place to live while she was separated from her husband."

"It was mean of her to use him that way." Margie folded the letter and put it back in the envelope.

"She doesn't sound like anyone I'd like to know."

"Brady? If she and Elmer weren't married, she's not entitled to any of this, is she?"

"Not by law."

"Then I don't have to give her anything?"

"I wouldn't think so. If they were not legally married, you're Elmer's next of kin."

"I had a half brother somewhere in California. I don't ever remember seeing him. He lived with his mother's parents. I heard later that he had died, but I don't know for sure."

"I don't think you have to worry about his family coming after the estate."

"This is all mine . . . ours?"

"Yours, sweetheart. After reading this letter no one could dispute it."

"It's a lot of money. I knew he was close with his money, but I had no idea he had so much."

"You've got money now to go to Hollywood, stay as long as you want and see all the movies you want to see." It about killed Brady to say the words, but they had to be said—and said now before he lost his nerve.

She turned to look up at him. "By myself?"

"Sure, honey. It's what you planned to do when you came on this trip, and I've got to get back to the ranch."

"Are you trying to say that now that I have this money and this truck, you don't want me to go home with you to . . . to Colorado?" The words caught in her throat.

"No, honey, I'm not saying that. I'm trying to say that now you have the means to fulfill your dream of seeing Hollywood without having to worry where your next meal will come from."

She got up on her knees between his legs and grasped

his arms. Her eyes were so full of tears her vision was blurred.

"I woke up from that childish dream as soon as I met you. I have another now—the dream of going home, living with you in our cabin, cooking and cleaning for my husband and our little girl, giving you all the love in my heart."

He lifted her chin with his fingers and placed his lips on hers. At first his mouth brushed gently over hers in soft, lingering kisses, then his fingertips stroked the tender skin at the nape of her neck.

"You are my love," he whispered against her mouth. His hand moved down her back, pulling her closer. She could feel the pounding of his heart against her breasts. "I thank God every day that I found you."

"We've not known each other very long."

"I feel like I've known you forever. Do I seem like a stranger to you?"

"You've never seemed like a stranger to me."

"That proves it, sweetheart. You were meant for me."

"If you're going to let this money come between us, I'll . . . I'll give it away. I don't know how to handle this much money. The most I ever had at one time before I took the two hundred dollars out of Elmer's socks was the one hundred and eighteen dollars my granny left me." She wrapped her arms around his neck. "I don't even know how much is here; but if it's really mine, I want to use it for our home, for our children." She pulled away and looked at him. "You wanted me an hour ago when I only had the two hundred dollars. I'm no different now."

"I wanted you then. I want you now!" He buried his

face in the curve of her neck. "I'm trying to be fair to you. All I've wanted to do since I met you was work and take care of you."

"Please, please, Brady." She cupped his face with her palms. "Don't be stiff-necked with pride. Let's think of this as a gift from Goldie. She said the last laugh was on Elmer, but it was on her. If she hadn't written that letter, all this would have been hers. Now it's ours. In a few years we might want to make our house bigger, or build a new one."

Brady hugged her to him and kissed her again and again, the money forgotten while he held this sweet woman in his arms. Her lips parted in a soft sigh. As if it were the signal he'd awaited, Brady captured her lips in a kiss that was rich and deep, a kiss she desperately welcomed.

"Nothing has changed?" she asked fearfully when he released her lips.

"Nothing's changed, sweetheart."

"You'll help me with . . . this?"

"Of course. What do you want me to do?"

"Tell me what to do with the money and the truck."

"Well the first thing we should do is lower the back flap in case someone comes by. Then we search in all the places where he may have squirreled away even more money."

A half hour later they were stunned by what they had found: one-hundred-dollar bills in the back of the clock, in the bib of a pair of rolled-up overalls, behind the wooden back of a framed picture of a farmhouse and in the drip pocket of the leather shield he wore when carrying ice. The snuff tins were full of gold pieces.

Brady counted the bills. "Nine thousand and seven hundred dollars. I don't know the value of the gold coins. It's a fortune, honey. Some men work all their lives and never earn this much. You're rich, honey. Very rich."

"We're rich. I can't imagine him having all this money, although I remember my granny saying that he was from moneyed people. She said his parents owned half of Conway at one time, and he was the only child. He may have inherited some of it. He sold the ice business and his house. With all this money he never once offered to help me when I was working twelve hours a day, in order to have food and a roof over my head. He never, ever bought me a birthday or Christmas present or helped me when Granny died."

"Don't think about it, honey."

"It's ironic, though, isn't it? I think he would hate it if he knew I had his money."

"He would hate it more for Goldie to have it. Now, what do you want to do about the truck?" Brady asked while putting the money in the tin box.

"I don't know. What do you think we should do?"

"We can't take it and my car too. I have a good truck out at the ranch. It might be best if you sell the truck. We'll go home in the car, and later I'll teach you to drive it so that you can go to town when you want to."

"How much is the truck worth?"

"It's worth more than the car. I'd say about three hundred because of the heavy springs, tires and the heavy-duty motor."

"I'd like Jody to have it," she said without hesitation. "We could give it to him, but I'm sure he wouldn't accept it."

"How about if you tell him you'll sell it to him for a hundred dollars, and he can send you monthly payments until it's paid for?"

"That's a good idea. All I want out of here is the clock, my clothes and a box of pictures my granny gave me." She put the tin box in his hands. "What'll we do with this?"

"Put it back for now. It's as safe there as anywhere."

She laid Goldie's letter aside before she locked the tin box. "I want Alvin to see this."

While breakfast was being readied by Grace and Mona, Brady and Margie drew Alvin aside and gave him Goldie's letter to read.

"I can see now what was eating at the man," Alvin said after he had read the letter and put it back in the envelope. "As far as I can tell, you've got a clear title to everything he had, Margie. And I must say that I'm glad. I hated to think of his belongings going to a woman who had run off and left him."

"We're going to be married tomorrow in Gallup and go to Colorado," Brady said. "We wanted you to know before we made the announcement to the others."

"Congratulations to both of you." Alvin held out his hand. "We'll miss you on the rest of the trip."

"From what I've seen of Wills and Taylor, you've got good men with you in case of trouble. I'd not leave you otherwise."

Alvin took off his hat and scratched his head. "Ah . . . do you plan to take the truck?"

Brady looked at Margie. "You tell him, honey."

"We don't need it. I'm going to see if Jody would like to buy it. He can use it in the ice business you and Mr. Luker will start, and he can pay me in installments."

Alvin seemed relieved. "If the Lukers can't see their way clear to buy it, I will and hire Jody to drive it the rest of the way. We were counting on having that truck when we started the business."

Jody was dumbstruck when Margie asked him if he wanted to buy the truck.

"Buy . . . the truck?" he stammered.

"I'm not a bit worried that you won't send the payments."

"Oh, I would. I want to talk to Pa. Back in a minute."

He was back in not much more than a minute with a hundred-dollar bill rolled up in his hand.

"Pa says I can borrow the money from him to pay for it and pay him back five dollars a month when I'm hired to work for him and Alvin." He had a wide grin on his face. "I can't believe that I'm the owner of a truck! I mean me and Pa are the owners until I get it paid for."

"I'm glad you will have it, Jody. Can I give you a kiss?"

"Yes, ma'am!"

"Hey, wait a minute," Brady said. "This is getting out of hand."

After congratulations had been passed around, Alvin led the caravan out of the campground. For Brady and Margie it was the last time. With Anna Marie still asleep on the backseat, Margie sat close to Brady and they talked about the trip.

"So much has happened since we all met. The best part was meeting you and falling in love." Margie turned sideways in the seat and hugged Brady's arm. "The worst part was the storm and Elmer being killed."

"Foley might have thought the worst part was Sugar running off, but I doubt that he thinks so now. He seems a different man than when we started out."

"If not for you, the men up there in Oklahoma would have robbed us and taken Mona. I wonder what happened to them?"

"They're probably still hanging around campgrounds stealing from folks who already are as poor as Job's turkey."

The sixty-three miles between Grants and Gallup went by fast even with one stretch of the highway unfinished. The caravan pulled into a campground at Gallup shortly after noon.

"This is your wedding day, sweetheart," Brady said when he parked the car behind the truck. "Will you mind being married in the courthouse?"

"We'll be just as married as if we said our vows in a great cathedral." She looked at him with tender, loving eyes.

"I told Alvin that I was getting a motor court cabin for our first night together. Grace and Mona will keep Anna Marie, so I'll have you all to myself. Why are you blushing, honey?"

"I . . . I don't know."

Brady laughed and kissed her on the nose. "By the end of the day you will be Mrs. Brady Hoyt."

After Brady had rented a cabin in a court not far from the campground, he left Margie and Mona at a department store and went on to the courthouse to make arrangements for the wedding.

For the first time in her life Margie bought the dress she wanted without first having to consider the cost. The white dress had a full skirt, short puffed sleeves, a round neckline and a wide sash of pink satin. She bought silk stockings and white pumps. Then with Mona giggling and her blushing, she bought a white satin nightgown with a lace bodice.

When Brady picked the girls up outside the store, he'd had a haircut and shave and was wearing a new shirt and britches. His scuffed boots had been polished. The marriage license was in his pocket.

"What did you buy?"

"A dress and shoes."

"Tell him what else," Mona whispered.

"Oh, you blabbermouth."

Grace, Mrs. Taylor and Mrs. Wills were making preparations for the wedding supper when Brady and Margie took Mona back to the campground. Jody and Rusty had found a bakery and bought a cake. The two of them and Mona were going to the courthouse with Margie and Brady to be witnesses.

At the cabin Brady parked at the side and produced a key to unlock the door.

"It's not fancy, sweetheart."

"It's private, and that's wonderful. We'll stay at a fancy place on our anniversary."

"Get ready, honey. I've got one more thing to do. I'll be back in about half an hour. We have to be at the courthouse before six."

Margie ran water in the bathtub for her first full bath since leaving Deke's Garage. She hurriedly bathed, dressed and added a touch of rouge to her cheeks and color to her lips. She wished she'd had time to wash her hair, but had to settle for a vigorous brushing.

She was ready when Brady knocked on the door. She opened it and backed away. He stood looking at her, a proud smile on his face.

"Ah . . . sweetheart. A man never had a prettier bride."

"Thank you. You're . . . kind of pretty yourself."

He came to her, kissed her carefully on the lips, then pulled a tiny box from his pocket, opened it and held up a chain with a small heart hanging from it.

"My gift to you on our wedding day. Turn around, darlin', so I can put it on."

Margie blinked rapidly. "I don't have anything for you."

"You're giving me you. Nothing could top that." He fastened the chain around her neck and kissed the nape.

"Thank you. I'll treasure it always." She turned and kissed his lips.

"Ready to go?" His voice was husky with emotion. "Jody's here. We're going to the courthouse in Foley's car, so I won't have to unload mine."

She gave him her hand, and they went out the door.

"Stay right there," Mona called. She was waiting by the car with a Kodak. "You've got to have a picture taken on your wedding day."

"Smile, honey. We'll have it enlarged and hang it on the wall."

"Wedding pictures are usually of the woman sitting down and the man standing behind her."

"You know why that is, don't you?"

"No. Why?"

"I'll tell you after we're married. Now smile."

Mona took several, then Brady helped Margie into the backseat of the car, where she found a bouquet of white roses.

In the cabin next door Sugar looked over her shoulder to where Homer lay naked on the bed. They had followed the caravan to Gallup. When it stopped so early and when Brady rented a cabin at the motor court, Sugar thought that maybe someone was sick.

"Well, dog my cats. The cowboy and the bitch are getting married, or my name isn't Sugar Wadsworth Corning Hudspeth Williamson Luker. That's why they stopped early."

"What are ya talkin' 'bout?"

"Come look. She's all dolled up in a white dress."

Homer peered out the window. "Well, shit, little pussy. This couldn't be better. When he drove in here, I thought he was just goin' to shack up with her for the night." Homer got up and put his pants on.

"What are you going to do?"

"I'm goin' to shag my ass over there while they're gone and see if the key to our door fits theirs. This is a streak of luck, little puss. I'm goin' to screw his bride while ya hold the gun on him. I want to see his face when I rip into her."

"Are you out of your mind?"

"Jealous, little slut? There'll be plenty left for you."

"They'll recognize you."

"I sure as hell hope so. I want the son of a bitch to know who's screwin' his bride." He came up behind her, reached around and pinched her nipple.

"You're goin' to kill them, aren't you?"

"Sugar tittie, yo're as dumb as dogshit. Almost as dumb as old Chester." He opened the door, looked both ways, then slithered out and around the corner.

Sugar felt a tremor of fear go down her spine. At times her young lover was a cold, vicious little bastard. Even though she knew he could turn on her in a second, she also knew that she was in love for the first time in her life; and when all was said and done, she would do exactly what he told her to do.

Chapter 30

Anna Marie was a bundle of excitement when Margie and Brady returned to the campground after being married. She wore the clean dress Margie had left for her. Grace had brushed her hair and entwined ribbons in her braids.

The wedding cake sat on a cloth-covered makeshift table. Surrounding it were platters of sandwiches. On a keg beside the table was a crock of lemonade, and on the kerosene stove the large coffeepot was sending up a plume of steam. The bride and groom stepped out of the car to a round of applause. Happy to have an excuse to celebrate, other campers had joined those from the caravan to make this a festive occasion for the couple.

Happy tears flooded Margie's eyes. These people were the nearest to a family she had ever known. She glanced up to find her new husband beaming. He knelt down and opened his arms when Anna Marie ran to him.

"Uncle Brady! We're gonna have cake. Aunt Grace made lemonade. See my ribbons?"

Brady laughed, hugged her and set her on her feet. She went directly to Margie.

"Aunt Grace said you're my Aunt Margie now."

"I guess that's right. I married your Uncle Brady."

She pulled Margie down so she could whisper in her ear. "I wanted you to be my mama."

"Oh, honey. You can call me that if you want to. You and I and your Uncle Brady are going to make a home together. Tomorrow we're going to his ranch in Colorado. I'll tell you all about it later."

"Can I tell Lucy?"

"Sure you can."

Mona insisted on taking a picture of the table and one of Margie and Brady standing behind the cake before the sun went down. That done, she talked nonstop about the ceremony in the judge's chamber that made Brady and Margie man and wife and insisted that Margie show the gold band Brady had put on her finger.

Mrs. Wills held Mrs. Taylor's baby while she helped Grace with the table. The nearby campers had been invited, and those who came brought an assortment of food: deviled eggs, potato salad, pickled peaches.

By the time the meal was over and the table cleared, it was near dark. Lanterns were hung, and a place was cleared for dancing. Alvin got out his violin and Rusty his guitar.

"I can't dance in these shoes," Margie whispered to Brady, who had not left her side.

"I'll get your moccasins out of the truck."

When Alvin's voice boomed that the first dance was for the bride and groom, Rusty began to play "I Love You Truly" on the violin. Grace and Alvin sang in perfect harmony. Smiling, Brady took Margie's hand, and they began to dance.

"I love you truly," he whispered in her ear.

"I love you too." Margie floated dreamily in the arms of her new husband.

The dance ended with more applause. When the music started again, Alvin played the violin, and several couples, including Rusty and Mona, began to dance. Later, after Rusty had danced with the bride, his mother and Mona again, he took the fiddle so Alvin could dance with the bride, then with Grace.

Harry Wills, who had brought a pillow and tucked it behind his wife's back, squatted on his heels beside her. His alert eyes swept back and forth around the area. A nagging unease was at the back of his mind, and he was determined to speak to Alvin about it as soon as the festivities were over.

Out of respect for the other campers Alvin put a stop to the party after a couple of hours.

"Many of the campers," he explained, "will be on the road before daylight and need their sleep."

With Margie's hand tucked in his, Brady stood with her beside Alvin.

"My wife and I want to thank you for the reception, for your good wishes and for helping to make our wedding day so festive. Now, as every one of you who has been a bridegroom knows—I want to be alone with my wife!"

Whoops and hollers greeted the statement. Margie hid her face against Brady's arm. Grinning broadly, Brady put his arm around her as they went to say good night to Anna Marie before leaving for the cabin. Mona and Rusty were standing close together at the end of the truck.

"She's already asleep," Mona said.

"Thank you for looking after her tonight. Tell Jody that when we come back in the morning, I'll take my things out of the truck. Rusty, I love your new song. I'll be listening for you on the radio."

"Don't hold your breath. California is probably full of singers."

"Not as good as you."

"It's what I've been telling him," Mona said.

"Is that what you've been doing?" Brady teased. "All this time I thought you were standing over here kissing."

"I notice you've been doing your share," Rusty retorted.

"It's going to be hard to say good-bye in the morning." Margie, suddenly tearful, put an arm around Mona.

"We can keep in touch. Maybe someday Mona and I can come visit."

"Really?" Mona said. Then again, "Really?"

Rusty laughed and pulled Mona to him. "You can never tell. I know one thing: I'm not letting this woman get away from me."

"Oh, I hope you do come see us—together."

"So do I," Mona said, and laid her head on Rusty's shoulder.

"Come on, honey." Brady pulled Margie away. "We'd better go so they can smooch."

"Thanks, Brady," Rusty said. "I knew you'd understand."

"Darn right, I do. I want to smooch with my wife."

Jody, who had struck up an acquaintance with a girl from another camp, had offered to drive them to the cabin. Not wanting to cut short Jody's time with the girl,

Brady and Margie had decided to walk the short distance.

"Are you tired, honey?"

"I'm too keyed up to be tired. It was nice, wasn't it?"

"Yes, it was. Alvin and Grace know how to put on a party."

"I didn't expect to get a ring. I thought maybe sometime later I'd get one."

"That ring tells the world that you're mine. I wish it had a diamond as big as a hen's egg."

"I don't. I'd feel silly trying to do the dishes with a stone as big as a hen's egg on my finger."

When they reached the motor court, Brady noticed that all six cabins were occupied. He unlocked the door to theirs and then swung Margie up in his arms and carried her into the dark room. He kicked the door closed and kissed her before he set her on her feet. She was trembling. Brady held her for a while, then moved away, switched on the light and lowered the window shades.

"You're trembling, honey. Are you scared of me?"

"I'm just . . . excited."

"Go get ready." He pushed her gently toward the bathroom. "Is there anything in here you need?"

She shook her head. "Brady?" she said before she closed the door. "Have you done this many times before?"

"A few, but not with someone I love. That's altogether different. It's the love we share that will make it so special."

Brady began to undress but kept his trousers on. His arousal was embarrassing to him, and he feared for his bride to see it.

Lord, help me to go slow and not rush to completion. This first time for her will set the tone for our mating from now on.

He turned off the light. Standing in the nearly pitch-dark room, the only light coming through the cracks around the bathroom door, Brady felt not only a strong sexual desire for his wife, but a strange fear that he wouldn't be able to make it a pleasant experience for her. He was awed by the responsibility of introducing her to the way a man loved a woman with his body.

The door opened, making a path of light that spread out into the room. Margie came out carrying her dress and draped it over the back of a chair. Brady stood beside the bed.

"Let me look at you." His hands grasped her shoulders, his eyes boldly sweeping over her. He could see the rosy tips of her breasts through the lace bodice of her gown. "Ah . . . honey, no man ever had a prettier or sweeter bride." His voice was low, husky, and trembled with emotion.

He pulled her to him. Her arms encircled him and caressed the smooth skin of his back. He felt so good. His scent was all male, fresh and clean. His chest was warm, and she could feel the heavy beat of his heart. His arms held her tightly before he bent and pulled back the sheet on the bed.

"Get in, darlin'. I'll be right back." Brady used the bathroom, and when he came out, he left the door ajar and went to sit on the side of the bed. He bent down to kiss her. "I want you naked in my arms."

"Did I waste my money on this nightgown?" She giggled happily, wrapped her arms around his neck and pulled his head down until their lips were touching.

The door burst open.

Brady had no time to lift his head or turn before the barrel of a gun was pressed against it. Margie let out a little cry of alarm. In the light coming from the bathroom she saw the menacing figure of a man looming over them and the gun held to Brady's head. Brady threw up an arm. The man with the gun backed away.

"Close the door and turn on the light, little pussy. I want the cowboy and the bitch to see who's come callin'. What we've got here is a bride and groom gettin' ready to do the nasty. I'll just help 'em out a little—show 'em how it's done."

The light came on. Brady blinked once, then fixed his gaze on the woman leaning against the door. Sugar smiled and pursed her lips in the form of a kiss. It took Brady a little longer to recognize the man. When he did, his lips curled in a sneer, but he said nothing.

"Ain't ya got nothin' to say, cowboy?"

"Can't think of anything," Brady said easily.

"You will. Get up, slut. I want to see yore titties, and I just might make you lick my arm where ya shot me."

"Stay where you are, honey."

"I guess ya don't know who has the upper hand here."

"Yeah, I do. A cocky little shithead who thinks he's a man because he's got a gun in his hand."

The barrel of the gun shifted to point down at Margie's face. Homer grinned, showing yellowed teeth.

"Turn around, cowboy, or I'll splatter her brains all over the pillow and screw her corpse."

Sugar stood beside the closed door, her face hard.

Brady turned. His eyes caught Margie's, and he nodded slightly. She got out of bed and took a step toward him.

"Stay back," Homer yelled. "Stay back or I'll shoot him."

Margie stopped, looked at Sugar and, taking a cue from Brady, said calmly, "Hello, Sugar. Nice to see you."

Sugar laughed. "I just bet ya are, Miss Prissy Ass."

"Come here, pussy. Take the gun, and if this big, brave cowboy moves a muscle, shoot him." Homer pulled out a knife with a long thin blade. He jerked Margie to him, wrapped his arm around her waist and placed the blade at her throat. "All right, cowboy, turn around. I want you to enjoy this. Make just one little move, and I'll slit her throat." He pressed the blade to make a small cut. Margie closed her eyes but didn't let out a sound.

"What do you want?" Brady demanded.

"It's payback time, cowboy. Remember the fire stick ya were goin' to shove up my ass? Well, I got somethin' to shove up the ass of the bitch who shot me."

"You followed us all the way from Oklahoma. Slashed my tires and tried to burn my car."

"And a good time I had doin' it—especially since I met a bitch who likes her pussy scratched five times a day and six times on Sunday." He flicked his eyes to Sugar and laughed. "Ain't that right, sweet thin'?"

"Get on with it, Homer. We've not got all day."

"See what I mean?" He bit on Margie's earlobe. "My whore's wantin' her poontang."

Things came to Brady's mind to say, but he choked them back and spoke calmly.

"Let her go. I'm the one you want to get even with."

"And I'm a-doin' it. If ya ain't noticed, I can give her another little nick with this knife."

Brady knew he had to be careful if he and Margie were going to get out of this alive. He had underestimated the disgusting, smart-mouthed robber back at the campground in Oklahoma. He was like a vicious little viper, unpredictable and deadly.

"Get the bitch's stocking and tie his hands behind his back. He ain't goin' to do nothin'. He knows that one swipe of the knife will give his bride a new mouth, right here under her chin." He nicked the skin on Margie's neck again, drawing a trickle of blood.

Sugar yanked the silk stocking off the back of the chair and moved behind Brady. If he'd had a thought that she had been forced into helping Homer against her will, he was soon rid of it. She seemed to take pleasure in tying him as tightly as she could.

His bright eyes on Brady, Homer put his free hand inside the neck of Margie's gown and ripped the lace to expose her breasts. He rubbed a palm over them, pinched and pulled at the nipples.

"She got nice high titties, cowboy. Nipples is good size for suckin'. Take a look. These titties ain't never goin' to get a chance to get flat and ugly."

Margie's eyes pleaded with Brady to say nothing. He clamped his mouth shut on the rage that threatened to burn out of control.

"Have ya busted into her yet, cowboy? I bet ya ain't. Doggie! I got here in time. I figured her as one of them women that's got to have a ring on her finger or she ain't givin' out no pussy."

Brady's rage was so evident Margie feared he would do something that would cause Sugar to shoot him.

"Get somethin' to stuff in her mouth. She's goin' to be yellin' before I'm through with her." Homer, not much taller than Margie, rubbed his erection against her buttocks. "Feel that, bitch? I'm going to shove it up yore ass!"

"Goddamn you!" Brady's shout filled the room. "Get away from her." His control broke, and he took a step forward. "Cut her again and I'll kill you!"

For a second Homer's bravado left him. "Shoot the son of a bitch!" he yelled. "Shoot him!"

Suddenly the door was flung open so hard it bounced against the wall.

Harry Wills stood there with a gun in his hand. Alvin was behind him.

"Let the girl go."

Homer's back was to the door. He turned, dragging Margie with him, and lifted his arm to throw the knife. In the seconds that followed, everything seemed to happen in slow motion. Sugar, seeing the gun pointed at Homer, forgot about the gun in her own hand.

"No!" she shouted, and lunged in front of Homer just as Harry fired. The sound of the shot filled the small room. Blood sprayed, covering her neck and chest. She was thrown back against Homer, then crumpled to the floor.

Homer dropped the knife to grab for the gun when it fell from Sugar's hand. Brady's foot caught him under the chin, sending him crashing against the wall. Then Brady was on him lightning-fast, one foot on his arm, the other on his neck, holding him to the floor, where he squirmed like a poisonous little snake.

Horrified, Margie stood with her hands to her ears, her eyes wide with fear. She came out of her shock when Alvin draped Brady's shirt around her, then knelt on the floor beside Sugar. Her eyes were open and staring. There was no doubt that she was dead.

Harry, as calmly as if this were an everyday occurrence for him, picked up Homer's knife and sawed through the stocking that bound Brady's hands; then he squatted down and put the tip of it in Homer's ear.

"Are ya wantin' to live, or do I shove this knife in and tickle that rotten brain of yores?" Homer blinked his eyes rapidly. "Well, shucks. I was hopin' ya'd be contrary. Put yore hands behind yore back, ya sorry, sneakin' little bastard. Tie him with that other stockin', Alvin. Then yank off his belt and bind his feet."

People from the other cabins who had heard the commotion filled the doorway. They stared at the dead woman on the floor, at the cursing, spitting man being hog-tied and at the barefoot girl in the torn white nightgown.

"Someone call the police." Brady's arms were around Margie. He dabbed at the trickles of blood on her neck with the sleeve of his shirt.

"We already have."

"Are you all right, honey? Oh, God. I've never been so scared in all my life. I wanted to kill that vicious bastard. I wanted to stomp his guts out."

"I'm all . . . right . . . or will be in a minute. Go on and do what you have to do. I'll just sit down here."

"Get a wet cloth." Brady tossed the order over his shoulder, and in moments a wet towel was placed in his hand. He put it gently against the cuts on Margie's neck and eased her down on the edge of the bed.

"I guess I'd better go get Foley." Alvin stood close and spoke quietly to Brady. "She's still his wife. He'll have to bury her."

"I'm sure glad you came in when you did. I was just about to do something that more than likely would have got us both killed."

"Save your thanks for Harry."

Brady glanced down at the dead woman and then at Homer Persy sitting on the floor.

"You slimy piece of no-good shit. You got that woman killed."

"Hell, I didn't pull the trigger. He did." He jerked his head toward Harry, who was squatting on the floor beside him.

Harry looked up at Brady. "He's low-caliber. I been watchin' him behind us for three days. He wasn't even smart enough to hang back when we came into the camp-ground. I figured he was after one of us—thought it was me. I've put away a few of his kind in my day."

"Yeah," Homer sneered. "I might be low-caliber, but I ain't never killed no woman, not even a slut like her."

"The woman saved your miserable life," Brady gritted.

"I never asked her to." He grinned cockily. "She was protectin' her stud. She'd hardly give me time to get my pants down."

"Shut your foul mouth! I'd like to be alone with you for just ten—"

"All right. What happened here?" A man with a star on his chest stepped in through the open door, his voice loud with authority.

Chapter 31

MARGIE WAS ALMOST SURE THAT NO WOMAN ever had or wanted a wedding night like the one she'd had. After she had dressed, she and Brady packed up and left the cabin where they had come so close to losing their lives. He took her back to the campground so that she would be among friends while he and Harry Wills explained to the county and state police what had happened.

Foley had come to claim the body of his wife and, tight-lipped and grim, had sent it away with the funeral director to be prepared for burial. He had been shocked speechless when he saw her and realized that she had taken up with one of the men who would have robbed them in Oklahoma.

It was after midnight when Brady and Harry Wills returned. Harry went first to check on his wife and brought her, wrapped in an old housecoat, to the Putman camp, where they had all gathered and were talking in hushed tones.

The police had received a report that a Ford coupe had

been reported stolen in Oklahoma and was possibly on Route 66 headed for California. A registration inside Homer's car was that of the stolen car.

Empty billfolds and purses in the car, along with nearly five hundred dollars taken from Homer Persy, led the police to believe the couple had been on a robbery spree. Evidence was also found to connect the body found in a ditch outside Amarillo to Homer. He was charged with the murder of his Uncle Chester.

Harry explained that he had been a lawman for fifteen years; but after he had married, his wife worried every time he left the house, and because her peace of mind was important to him, he had turned in his badge. He had been aware for three days that the Ford coupe was following, and when it circled the campground, he noticed that the two inside the car seemed unduly interested in the caravan. Uneasy and suspicious, he nosed around and discovered that the same car was parked next to the cabin Brady had rented for the night.

On a hunch Harry spoke to Alvin, and the two of them had walked down to the motor court. It had not occurred to Harry that whoever was in the car was trailing Brady. He had made many enemies among the lawless and thought he was the one they were following. His intention had been to find out who was pursuing him and why.

It was while Harry and Alvin were standing in front of the cabin, trying to decide if it was safe to look in the car, that they heard Brady shout. Harry's fifteen years of law experience took over, and, with gun in hand, he threw open the door.

"Thank God it wasn't locked," Brady said. "It would

have taken a little time to bust in, and in the meanwhile . . ."

Margie sat on a blanket in the shelter of Brady's arms. Mona sat beside Rusty, her eyes going often to her father. He had not said much since he and Jody returned from the funeral home. The burial would take place at ten o'clock day after tomorrow.

"Thank you for what you did, Mr. Wills," Margie said. "They were going to kill us."

"I'm sorry I shot the woman. I sure didn't intend to hit her. I meant to stop the man from throwing the knife. He would have nailed me if I had hesitated. The woman could have shot me. She had a gun in her hand, but she threw herself in front of that sorry little weasel."

"I understand how it was," Foley said slowly. "I think now that I didn't know her at all."

"It happens like that sometimes." Alvin passed behind Foley and put a reassuring hand on his shoulder.

The next day everyone moved around quietly, except for Anna Marie and Lucy. Totally unaware of the tragic events of the night before, they played happily. When they were not throwing the ball, they were tossing sticks for Blackie to chase.

Brady and Margie removed from the truck what she wanted to take with her. They unloaded Brady's car and repacked it. Brady thought it best to put the tin box containing the money in Margie's suitcase.

"We're going to stay in hotels or motor courts on the way home, and we'll take it inside at night." She nodded in agreement, glad to leave the decisions up to him.

In the late afternoon Brady and Margie left the camp-ground and drove to the downtown area, where Brady registered them at a hotel. He had made arrangements for Mona to take care of Anna Marie one more time, and she was happy to do so.

He carried Margie's suitcase up a wide carpeted stair-way and down a hall to the most luxurious room she had ever seen. The carpet was thick, and a big high bed dom-inated the room. The drapes were a rich wine and matched the bedspread. But best of all, there was a big white bathtub. Her eyes shone when she looked at her husband.

"How did you know that I wanted a bath more than anything?"

"I know you, sweetheart. You want to wash away every reminder of last night."

"Not every one. Some I want to remember as long as I live. This, for instance." She wound her arms around his neck and placed her lips on his.

"Margie, Margie." He said her name twice. "I love you so much. I died a thousand times last night."

"But you kept control." She stroked his cheeks.

"My heart almost stopped when I saw his hands on you, a knife at your throat." He kissed the small red marks made by the knife.

"I left that nightgown at the cabin. I never wanted to see it again."

"We'll buy you a new one."

"I . . . don't think I'll need it."

He laughed happily and hugged her tightly.

"I agree, sweetheart. Go take your bath. I'm going

downstairs and order our dinner sent up. We're going to splurge. We deserve it."

Margie took a long, leisurely bath and washed her hair. When she came out of the bathroom with a towel wrapped around her, Brady was sitting in a chair beside the window.

"I was looking for something to put on, and I think I've found it." She snatched his shirt off the bed and fled to the bathroom.

"That might be all I'll let you wear from now on," he teased later as they ate the meal of roast beef, potatoes and creamed peas.

Margie looked into eyes that shone with pure happiness. Her pulse leaped, bringing color to her face. Her flushed cheeks made her soft brown eyes seem all the warmer.

After he had pushed the dinner cart out into the hallway, it was Brady's turn in the bathroom.

"Sweetheart," he whispered with a catch in his voice. "Be ready for me. I'm going to love you all night long."

When Margie heard the water running in the tub, she closed the window shades, turned down the bed and fluffed the pillows. Then, more daring than she had ever been in her life, she hung Brady's shirt on the back of the chair and looked at her naked body in the long mirror beside the closet door.

Her breasts were high and firm but not very big. She had heard somewhere that men liked big breasts. Her stomach was flat, her hips slightly rounded. She wished that her thighs were not so skinny. Suddenly fearing Brady would come through the door and catch her standing naked before the mirror, she hurried to the bed and slid beneath the smooth, cool sheet.

When Brady came out of the bathroom, he had a bath towel wrapped around his middle. His face was freshly shaven, and his hair was wet. Margie's eyes clung to him. *He was so beautiful.*

He came to sit down on the edge of the bed.

"You smell good," she managed to say.

"It's the shaving lotion."

He moved, flipped off the towel and slid under the sheet. A choking sound came from his throat as he reached for her and clasped her naked length against him.

"You feel so good." She clutched him tightly, her hand biting into the warm, solid flesh of his back.

The feel of his body, the stroking of his hands, the warm moistness of his breath, the love filling and spilling from her heart, brought her mindless pleasure. Being here with him like this was more wonderful than she had ever imagined.

They were feverish in their desire for each other. Blindly, passionately, he kissed her lips, then her breasts, drawing sweetly on the nipple he took in his mouth. With her fingers tangled in his black hair, she held his head to her breasts, never wanting him to stop that glorious torment.

There was no room in her mind for anything but him. He was her universe, vibrating with all the love in the world, and he lifted her to undreamed-of sensual heights. Then he was there, inside her. She was part of him. He was part of her. Her own flesh splintered with an exquisite explosion, sending her into a void where fireworks brightened a blackened sky.

Brady shuddered, clasped her tightly, his mouth devouring hers. After a while he turned onto his back, bringing her with him. He pressed her head to his shoulder; she burrowed into the hollow of his arm, tasting the moisture that dewed his chest. Her whole body pulsated still.

"Oh, Lord. Oh, honey, was I too rough? I wanted to make it last a long time." He trembled and buried his lips in her hair.

"If it had lasted any longer, I might not have made it."

"I wanted you to enjoy what we did together."

"I enjoyed it so much I . . . thought I had died," she whispered.

"Sweetheart, this is the first of many times for us. I love you, want you. I'll have to have you again before the night is over."

"You promised to love me all night long . . ."

He chuckled and kissed her lips again and again.

"Better get some sleep, darlin', 'cause you'll not get any after I get my wind back."

She placed her hand over his thumping heart. "Cross your heart?"

It was on the tip of his tongue to finish the rhyme: *hope to die, cut my throat if I tell a lie.* But it was too soon, the image still too real. He held her to him and smothered a moan. Life wouldn't be worth living without her.

The thought spiraled through his mind that he now had a better understanding of what his twin must have felt for his Becky.

*   *   *

While she lived, Sugar Luker had shown only contempt for the eleven people who stood, out of respect for the husband she had scorned, at the site of her final resting place

Rusty played his guitar and sang "Rock of Ages." A prayer was said by the preacher connected to the funeral home, and the service was over. Sugar would forever be in this small piece of earth alongside the highway to California, where she had connived for so long to go.

The party followed Foley's car back to the campground, where he would hitch his trailer to his car and continue along the highway to the place that held so much hope. Margie and Brady would get Anna Marie, who with Lucy Taylor had stayed with Mrs. Wills, say their good-byes and head for Colorado.

Tears streamed from Margie's eyes as she hugged Grace.

"I'll never forget you. You have been the best friends I've ever had."

"Write, now. Hear? Brady gave us his address. I'll write and let you know as soon as we're settled."

Margie put her arms around Rusty. "I know you're going to be a big star in California. I'm going to be so proud that I know you."

"If it happens, I'll send you my autograph," he teased, his voice husky.

"Alvin, how can I thank you? You are as solid as a rock. If I'd have been able to choose my father, it would have been you."

"Well, now, that's mighty nice to hear. I know that Brady will take good care of you; and if you ever get the

yen to see California, you know where you'll find a welcome."

"Mr. Luker, I never got to know you like I did Alvin.
I'm sorry for the grief you've had to endure on this trip
and wish you the very best from here on. You have two
great kids who are lucky to have you for their father."

"I'm the lucky . . . one," he stammered.

"Jody, I'm going to hug you whether you like it or
not."

"I'll like it a lot even if Brady breaks my head."

"I hope you are happy in California; but if you're not,
come to see us, and Brady will make a cowboy out of
you." Margie kissed him on the cheek.

She shook hands with the Taylors, then moved on to
Harry Wills and his wife.

"If not for you, Mr. Wills, Brady and I might not have
left that cabin alive. I'll always remember what you did."
She looked down at Mrs. Wills seated in her chair and
smiled. "Your husband is almost as wonderful as mine."

Mona was last. "Let me know how things turn out between you and Rusty," Margie whispered. "Oh, I wish I
could be at your wedding like you were at mine. Write to
me . . ."

Margie fled to the car. After the last handshake, Brady
followed. As they left the campground, Margie, tears in
her eyes, waved a last good-bye.

Anna Marie in the backseat stuck her head out the
window. "Bye, Lucy. Bye, Aunt Grace."

Epilogue

Margie drove the sedan along the lane that divided a stand of junipers. When she came out into the open, she could see the mountains, beautiful in their aloof loneliness. She rounded a low hill, crossed a rocky stream only a few inches deep, a few feet wide, the water clear and cold.

She loved this land, this way of life.

Anna Marie had not wanted to come along on this trip. She was enthralled with the new baby of one of the Mexican families who lived on the ranch and was eagerly awaiting the birth of her own little brother or sister.

Margie couldn't wait for Brady to return home to share the letter she had received from Grace. Ramon had gone to town early that morning and had just returned with the mail.

She knew that she would get a scolding from her husband for driving the car out over the rough trail when the time was so near for her to deliver their baby. He was so dear, so afraid something would happen to her or the baby. The scolding would be punctuated with kisses, as was his habit.

The house came into view, and she eased the car up close to the old truck and stopped. It was going to be beautiful with four big rooms downstairs and two beneath the roof that sloped down to cover the wide porch facing the mountains. A large cobblestoned chimney rose from each side of the house: one in the living area, the other in their bedroom.

Brady and a number of workers were on the roof. When she drove in, he started down the ladder. With a worried look on his face he hurried to the car.

"What's happened? Why are you here? Are you having pains?"

Margie got out of the car. "Nothing has happened. I'm here because I got a letter from Grace. No, I don't have any pains."

"Marjorie Hoyt. Someday I'm going to beat your butt—"

"Will you wait until after I have the baby?" She put her arms around his neck and leaned against him.

"I'm all dirty, honey." He rubbed her back and nuzzled his face in the curve of her neck.

"Baby doesn't care." She took Brady's hand and placed it on her protruding stomach. "Feel him kicking? He's wantin' out of there."

"Sweetheart, I wish you'd be careful. I'll be out of my mind by the time he gets here."

"No, you won't. You'll scold and frown and look like

you're mad, but you'll be just as happy as I am. Let's get in the car so you can read Grace's letter."

"We want to finish the roof by tonight. You get in the car and tell me about it."

Margie sat sideways on the seat, her feet on the running board.

"Grace said that the ice business is doing better than they expected. Isn't that great? She said that Jody had been talking about coming out this way, but he met a girl at the radio station where Rusty has his program. Mona and Foley like her and wish that he'd settle down there.

"Foley hasn't yet proposed to the lady he's been keeping company with. I bet he's afraid of being burnt again.

"Rusty's program on the radio is getting to be more popular all the time. His song, 'What I See,' was sung by Woody Guthrie. Grace said that Rusty's records are selling. Oh, I wish we could get one. And . . . guess what?"

He smiled at her enthusiasm, even though he was still bothered because she had driven on the rough trail. Her happy nature never allowed him to stay upset with her for long.

"I'll never guess. Tell me."

"Mona's pregnant. Grace said that Alvin goes around with a grin on his face and that Rusty is walking on clouds."

"I know the feeling."

"She and Alvin will be good grandparents. They are the godparents of the little Wills boy. Who will be the godparents of our little boy?"

"Would you object to Ramon and Claudia?"

"Not at all. She's turned out to be a really good friend."

"Move over. I'm going to drive you home as soon as I tell the men that I'm knocking off for the day. There's only an hour or two of daylight left anyway."

"Can we stop along the way and smooch?"

He leaned into the car and kissed her. "You can bet your boots on it."

References

Oklahoma Route 66, by Jim Ross

Here It Is! Route 66: The Map Series, by Jim Ross and Jerry McClanahan

Route 66 Traveler's Guide, by Tom Snyder

Route 66: The Mother Road, by Michael Wallis

More
Dorothy Garlock!

Please turn this page
for an excerpt
from her new novel
SONG OF THE ROAD
available soon
from Warner Books.

Chapter One

New Mexico, 1935

WHEN THE BUS SLOWED TO TURN off the highway at Cross Roads, Mary Lee was the only passenger awake. Or so she believed. It was hard to tell about the man across from her. He had climbed on at Amarillo, and in the brief time it took him to find a seat, she had seen that he was tall, lean and unsmiling with a level, direct gaze.

Now he sat sprawled in the double seat, his head back, his hat covering his face, awkwardly trying to sleep on a seat designed only for sitting. He seemed vaguely familiar and she wanted to keep looking at him.

Mary Lee's worry for the last hour had been that she might throw up. The lurching, swaying vehicle, and the fumes from the motor were a combination she'd had to endure since she got on the bus in Tulsa. Now, she had a throbbing headache, her back hurt, and her stomach was queasy as well.

Thank God, the journey was almost over.

Before the bus came to a complete stop at the station located in the lobby of Roads Hotel, the cowboy was up and standing at the door. She didn't know why she knew he was a cowboy. Boots and Stetsons were worn by most of the men in New Mexico whether they were bankers, bootleggers, or ranchers. The distinction lay in the quality of the Stetsons and the boots.

The lights came on in the bus and the door folded back. The cowboy bounded down the steps while Mary Lee was gathering up her purse, hat, and a small sack that contained the last of the crackers and cheese she had brought along to munch. She stepped off the bus onto the dark street illuminated only by the street lamp on the corner and the light coming from the hotel lobby. When she looked up and down the street and saw no one, her shoulders slumped. She moved wearily to the side of the bus and waited for the driver to remove her suitcase from the luggage compartment.

"Here ya are, ma'am. It's pretty heavy for ya to be carryin'. Got someone meetin' ya?" The driver had obviously observed her condition.

"No, sir. I was intending to leave it here at the station. I'm going out to the Cross Roads Motor Court. I know I can't carry it that far."

"I'll be goin' right by there. Get back on, ma'am, and I'll stop and let ya off. I ain't supposed to, but ya ain't ort to be walkin' out there this time a night."

"Thank you. I was dreading the walk. It's been a long ride from Tulsa."

The driver set the suitcase inside the bus and went

into the hotel. Mary Lee got back on and sat down on the front seat. She was so tired that her legs were trembling, her nerves were raw, and she feared that given the slightest provocation she would burst into tears. Her mother had surely received the letter saying she would be arriving on the eleven-thirty bus. She had mailed it over a week ago.

It would be strange going home to the motor court and her father not being there. She blinked away the tears that came to her eyes. Six months had passed since she received word that he had died suddenly while shoveling snow, and at times she couldn't believe that he was really gone.

She had not been able to come to the funeral. The little money she made at the five-and-dime had covered the rent with not much left over for food. She couldn't have arrived there on time anyway. He had died on Thursday and her mother had had him buried on Saturday.

Now Bobby was gone. Poor weak Bobby, killed in an alley behind a beer joint. What a waste of a young life. Gambling was his passion. If he thought he had a good hand and had nothing else to bet, he would wager his life. He seldom drank, but the police said that he was drunk when they found him. The police didn't hold out much hope of finding his killer and it wouldn't do her or Bobby any good if they did.

The driver returned and the bus moved up the main street, turned and headed back out toward the highway. It couldn't be much more than half a mile as the crow flies from the center of town to the motor court so only a few minutes later the bus stopped again. The lights came on and the door opened.

As Mary Lee was getting off a voice came from the back of the bus. "Jesus Christ, why are we stoppin' here?"

"Just hold your horses. This'll take only a minute." The driver set the suitcase beside the drive leading to the house.

"Thank you. I appreciate the ride."

"You're welcome. Will someone be down to help you?" He glanced at the lighted house.

"Yes. I'll be fine."

With a nod and tip of his cap, the driver got back into the bus. Mary Lee waited until it went some distance down the highway before she picked up the case. With slow steps and several stops along the way to rest, she finally reached the house. Exhausted, she leaned on a porch post to catch her breath.

The front door was open. Light shone from the kitchen. Voices, both male and female, carried to where she stood. Her heart sank to her toes when she recognized the slurred, giggly laughter coming from inside the house. It was a dreaded sound from her childhood. She felt the old hurt creep around her heart.

Her mother was drunk.

All the way from Tulsa she had hoped against hope that the shock of her daddy's sudden death had caused her mother to stop drinking. She should have known what would happen without her father here to supervise.

Mary Lee sighed. She ached in a hundred different

places. Pushing herself away from the porch post, she opened the screen door and went through the front room to stand in the doorway leading to the kitchen. Her mother, another woman, and two men were playing cards at the kitchen table.

Her mother's back was to her. The man opposite her was grinning and pouring whiskey into her glass from a tall bottle. Mary Lee recognized him at once. He looked up, saw Mary Lee, and the grin left his face. The bottle tipped in his unsteady hand.

"Yummy." Her mother licked the whiskey from her hand, then turned toward the doorway to see what the man was looking at. She gave Mary Lee a blank stare, then stood and held onto the back of the chair. "Hi, hon. When did . . . ya get here?"

"Just now." Mary Lee hated the silly grin on her mother's face.

"That's nice. Didn't know ya was . . . comin'."

"I sent you a letter telling you what time I would be here."

"Ya did? I don't remember it. We was just playin' a little cards. Bobby with ya?"

"Bobby died two months ago, Mama." Mary Lee couldn't keep the irritation out of her voice. "I wrote and told you about it."

"Oh, yeah. I did hear somethin' about that. This is my girl," she said, still looking at Mary Lee. "She's come on a visit."

Mary Lee looked directly at Frank Pierce. His thick black hair was streaked with gray now. He may have been a handsome man long ago, but now dissipation had reddened his eyes and slackened his jaw. His whiskered cheeks were sunken. He had only four lower teeth and a few upper ones were missing.

She had known who he was for most of her life. He was what her father had called a ne'er-do-well, a man who never held a job for very long and always seemed to get by without working. She hadn't liked him when he was the school janitor and she didn't like him now.

"I'm Pearl." The woman who spoke had black penciled eyebrows and thin blond hair looped behind her ears. Her dress was so low in front that you could see the tops of her breasts and probably more when she bent over. The word "trash" came to Mary Lee's mind.

Mary Lee glanced at her and nodded.

"Mama, I'm tired." She was also hungry, but she didn't mention that. "I'll get my suitcase and go to my room."

"Pearl and . . . ah . . . Jim— Pearl's been stayin' with me. You know, I don't like bein' out here on the highway by myself."

"You won't be by yourself now." Mary Lee's eyes scanned the messy kitchen, then back to the four people at the table. "I'm here now."

"You stayin'?" Frank Pierce asked.

Mary Lee ignored him. "Mama, I noticed that there isn't a car parked at Number One. I'll use it tonight. We can make different arrangements in the morning."

"Number One's mine." Frank Pierce spoke again. His voice held a belligerent tone.

"You've rented it for the night?" Mary Lee looked steadily at him.

"For the month," he retorted crisply.

"Are all six cabins full, Mama?"

Dolly's eyes were on the floor. "Number Four is empty, but it's not been cleaned. We . . . ah had a little fire in Number Three."

Mary Lee stepped around the corner to reach the board where the cabin keys were hung. All the hooks were empty.

"Where's the key?"

"It's in the door so it'd not get lost."

Mary Lee turned frosty eyes on Frank Pierce. "I asked Mama."

"And I'm tellin' ya."

She bit back a reply. Something was going on here that she didn't like at all, but there was nothing she could do about it tonight.

"I'll take clean sheets and go to Number Four, Mama."

"I don't have any, hon. I've not washed this week."

"See you in the morning." Mary Lee abruptly turned on her heel and went back through the living room to the porch.

Tired and disappointed, she couldn't hold back the tears that blurred her eyes. She sat down on the steps and wiped her eyes on the hem of her dress. *Her mother had not even noticed that she was pregnant, but Frank Pierce had.* Once when she was looking at him, he had deliberately lowered his eyes to the bulge below her waist.

Knowing that she shouldn't carry the heavy suitcase all the way down to Number Four, she fumbled in her purse for the key, unlocked it and took out a night-gown, two sheets, a towel, and soap. After locking the case she scooted it into the living room.

Scott Finley had built the motor court back in 1929 just before the stock market crashed. At that time Route 66 was just a gravel road and already the main highway through New Mexico and California. With the promise of pavement, Scott was sure that the traffic would increase, and it had. The drought and the dust storms had driven thousands to leave the farms and head for a better life in the fertile fields of California, and the highway had gained another name: America's Mother Road.

The Cross Roads Motor Court was made up of six identical cabins, strung out in a row, with spaces between them for motor cars. The entrance to the road fronting the cabins led to the main house.

On her way down the lane to Number Four cabin, Mary Lee could see weeds in what used to be carefully tended flower beds. Partly hidden in the high grass were sundry items of trash. A mattress with a large burned spot in the middle lay outside the door of Number Three. Seeing the rundown condition of the motor court stirred her to anger.

A car was parked next to Number Five and a truck next to the last cabin where lights shone from the windows.

The key was in the door of Number Four, but the door wasn't locked. Mary Lee went in, turned on the light, shut and locked the door. Why in heaven's name would her mother leave the key in the door? Was a friend of Frank Pierce who would need a bed coming in late?

The odor from cigarette butts and from a coffee can that had been used as a spittoon sent Mary Lee hurrying to open the window on the back and reopen the front door. Anger held her tears at bay as she took the ashtray and coffee can outside. She yanked the soiled sheets from the bed and piled them beside the door. After remaking the bed with her own linen, she washed her face, then turned off the lights before undressing and putting on her nightgown.

Mary Lee would have preferred to leave the door open, but fearing tentative arrangements might have been made for the use of the cabin, she closed and locked it. She wedged the one straight-backed chair beneath the door knob and sank down on the bed.

Lying on her side with her knees drawn up, she rubbed her rounded stomach and let the tears flow. She cried because her back hurt so badly that she felt as if it were being stabbed with a thousand pitch forks. She cried because of the sorry mess she had found at home.

Her mother obviously hadn't been glad to see her. She hadn't even noticed that she was going to have a grandchild. And how had she become tangled up with that sorry, good-for-nothing Frank Pierce? Mary Lee's mind went in a dozen different directions.

"It's going to be hard, baby." Mary Lee had assumed the habit of talking to her unborn child. "Daddy worked hard to build this place. I'm not going to let her run it into the ground. He loved Mama and tried to help her. Even when she came to my high school play so drunk that she staggered, he'd said she couldn't help her craving for alcohol. He had taken her home. I'd had to stay and endure the whispers of my classmates and the pitying glances from their parents.

"I'm not going to let Daddy's motor court go to rack and ruin. The first thing I've got to do is to go see Mr. Morales and find out what authority I have here. You're all I have, baby, now that Daddy's gone. I've got to take care of you and the only way to do it is to make this place pay."

Mary Lee drifted off to sleep thinking that she and her daddy were a lot alike. He had married her mother hoping to cure her drinking habit. She had married Bobby thinking that he needed her, that she could make him face up to his responsibilities. Both of them had failed.

Mary Lee awakened to the sound of a car. Someone was revving the engine. By the time she swung her feet off the bed, a flatbed truck was passing the window.

The person in Number Six was leaving early.

In the light of day, the cabin was ever more filthy than she had noticed from last night. Thankful that her father had bullied the Cross Roads city council members into bringing sewer and gas out to the motor court, Mary Lee used the bathroom, squatting over the toilet because she couldn't bring herself to sit on it.

Feeling better, although she was so hungry she was weak, she washed and dressed, putting her bare feet in her shoes and carefully rolling her hose into a ball to take back to her suitcase. She combed her fingers through her hair and looked at herself in the mirror hanging above the lavatory.

She knew that she was no beauty, but she was passably pretty, or so she had been told numerous times. Her hair, dark-red and curly, came from her daddy; eyes, slate-blue from her mother. She was average height, small boned and slim, except for the rounded abdomen where she carried her baby. She was still able to wear two of her dresses if she didn't belt them.

Leaving the cabin, she locked the door and put the key in her pocket. Walking up to the house, she realized how weak she was. She'd had only crackers and cheese the day before. When they stopped in Amarillo, she had been tempted to buy a hamburger but chose to wait because she was only a few hours from home.

It was broad daylight when she reached the house. Cars were going by on the highway, their tires singing. Her daddy used to call it the song of the road.

Oh, Daddy, you were such a good sweet man. You deserved so much more than you got: a drunken wife, and a daughter who ran off and left you because she was tired of being ashamed of her mother.

The door was open. Mary Lee went to the kitchen thankful that both bedroom doors were closed. A deck of cards, an empty whiskey bottle, and several glasses were still on the kitchen table. She resisted the impulse to crash the whiskey bottle against the sink that overflowed with dirty dishes. Instead she left it where it was and opened the door on the icebox to find only a small chunk of ice. The smell that came from it told her that it hadn't been washed out in weeks. The only things in it that she could use were eggs and butter. She went to the front room and turned the ice card so that when the ice man passed, he would stop and bring in fifty pounds.

After washing a skillet, she buttered two pieces of bread, pan-fried them, then scrambled three eggs.

She felt much better after she had eaten.

Mary Lee had changed her dress in the living room, added a touch of lip color, and was putting on a blue cloth-crowned hat with a stiff brim when her mother came out of the bedroom. She was barefoot and wearing a thin voile nightgown that came down to just past her knees. She cupped her hand over her eyes to shield them from the light.

"You goin'?" she asked on her way to the kitchen.

"Just to town. I'll be back." Mary Lee followed and watched her mother pick up the whiskey bottle then slam it down when she saw that it was empty.

"Son of a bitch!" Completely ignoring her daughter, Dolly Finley pulled open the door to a side cabinet and swore again.

Mary Lee watched her mother search for the whiskey as she had done many times before when her father had hidden it from her.

"Go back to bed, Mama, until you sober up."

"You think I'm drunk? A hell of a lot you know."

"No, I think you're hung over. You'd better get yourself straightened out, because we're going to have a talk as soon as I get back from town."

" 'Bout what?"

"About getting your friends out of my room for one thing."

"Pearl's got nowhere to go."

"Neither have I. That's why I'm here."

"Shit!"

"It wouldn't hurt to tell her to get in here and help you clean up this mess." Mary Lee went to the door. "I'll be back in a little while."

DOROTHY GARLOCK
TOUCHES YOUR HEART AND SOUL

Award-winning, bestselling author Dorothy Garlock brings romance and passion alive as no other author can! You'll love Dorothy Garlock's breathtaking romantic adventures.

"A gifted storyteller." —*Chicago Sun-Times*

- *AFTER THE PARADE* (0-446-60-811-4)
- *ALMOST EDEN* (0-446-36-372-3)
- *ANNIE LASH* (0-446-60-303-1)
- *DREAM RIVER* (0-445-20-676-4)
- *THE EDGE OF TOWN* (0-446-60-812-2)
- *FOREVER VICTORIA* (0-446-36-183-6)
- *A GENTLE GIVING* (0-446-35-990-4)
- *GLORIOUS DAWN* (0-446-36-182-8)
- *HIGH ON A HILL* (0-446-61-209-X)
- *HOMEPLACE* (0-446-35-988-2)
- *LARKSPUR* (0-446-60-253-1)
- *THE LISTENING SKY* (0-446-60-252-3)
- *LONESOME RIVER* (0-445-20-362-5)
- *LOVE AND CHERISH* (0-446-36-524-6)
- *MIDNIGHT BLUE* (0-446-35-522-4)
- *MORE THAN MEMORY* (0-446-60-814-9)
- *NIGHTROSE* (0-446-35-607-7)
- *A PLACE CALLED RAINWATER* (0-446-61-146-8)
- *RESTLESS WIND* (0-445-20-932-1)
- *RIBBON IN THE SKY* (0-446-35-989-0)
- *RIVER OF TOMORROW* (0-445-20-366-8)
- *THE SEARCHING HEARTS* (0-446-36-526-2)
- *SINS OF SUMMER* (0-446-36-414-2)
- *SWEETWATER* (0-446-60-255-8)
- *TENDERNESS* (0-446-36-370-7)
- *THIS LOVING LAND* (0-446-36-525-4)
- *WAYWARD WIND* (0-445-20-214-9)
- *WILD SWEET WILDERNESS* (0-445-20-678-0)
- *WIND OF PROMISE* (0-445-20-368-4)
- *WITH HEART* (0-446-60-589-1)
- *WITH HOPE* (0-446-60-256-6)
- *WITH SONG* (0-445-60-588-3)
- *YESTERYEAR* (0-446-36-371-5)

AVAILABLE AT A BOOKSTORE NEAR YOU FROM WARNER BOOKS

1023-i